Barnabe Riche
His
Farewell to Military Profession

Publications of the Barnabe Riche Society

Volume 1

Medieval & Renaissance Texts & Studies

Volume 91

Barnabe Riche
His
Farewell to Military Profession

Edited with

Introduction and Notes

by

Donald Beecher

Dovehouse Editions Inc.
Ottawa, Canada

Medieval & Renaissance
Texts & Studies
Binghamton, New York

1992

Acknowledgments

This book has been published with the help of a grant from the Canadian Federation for the Humanities, using funds provided by the Social Sciences and Humanities Research Council of Canada.

Canadian Cataloguing in Publication Data
Main entry under title:
    Rich, Barnabe, 1540?–1617
        Farewell to military profession

(Publications of the Barnabe Riche Society ; 1)
Originally publ. under title: Riche his farewell to militarie
profession. London: Imprinted by R. Walley, 1581.
Includes bibliographical references.

ISBN 1-895537-03-7 (bound)
ISBN 1-895537-02-9 (pbk.)

I. Beecher, Donald.   II. Title.   III. Series.

PR2336.R8F3 1991   823′.3   C91-090500-2

©Dovehouse Editions Inc., 1992

Typeset in Canada by the Journal Production Centre, Carleton University

For distribution write to:

Dovehouse Editions Inc.	Medieval & Renaissance Texts & Studies
1890 Fairmeadow Cres.	State University of New York
Ottawa, Canada K1H 7B9	Binghamton, N.Y. 13902-6000

| ISBN 1-895537-03-7 (bound) | ISBN 0-86698-105-5 (bound) |
| ISBN 1-895537-02-9 (pbk.) | ISBN 0-86698-104-7 (pbk.) |

Cover design: Carleton University Graphics

For information on the series write to:
The Barnabe Riche Society
Dept. of English
Carleton University
Ottawa, Canada K1S 5B6

This Book is Lovingly Dedicated to

My Mother and Father

May the length of my days be the proof of

my honor.

Table of Contents

Preface

The publication series of The Barnabe Riche Society has been established to provide scholarly, modern-spelling editions of works of imaginative literature in prose written in English between 1485 and 1660, with a special emphasis on Elizabethan prose fiction. The program allows for works ranging from late medieval fabliaux and Tudor translations of Spanish picaresque tales or ancient Greek romances to seventeenth-century prose pastorals. But the principal goal is to supply much-needed editions of many of the most critically acclaimed works of the period by such authors as Lodge, Greene, Chettle, Riche, and Dekker, and to make them available in formats suitable to libraries, scholars, and students. Editorial policy for the series calls for texts carefully researched in terms of variant sources, and presented in conservatively modernized and repunctuated form in order to remove those obstacles to wide accessibility that arguably do not affect the meaning of the texts in any substantive way. Each edition will provide the editor with an opportunity to write a full essay dealing with the author and the historical circumstances surrounding the creation of the work, as well as its style, themes, conventions, and critical challenges. Each text will also be accompanied by annotations.

The Barnabe Riche Society is based in the English Department of Carleton University in Ottawa, and forms a component of the Carleton Centre for Renaissance Studies and Research. Its activities include colloquia, the awarding of an annual prize for the best new book-length study dealing with English Renaissance prose fiction, and the editorial management of the series, backed by an eleven-member international editorial board. The society invites the informal association of all scholars interested in its goals and activities.

Acknowledgments

Reconstructing all the many phases of transcription, checking, modernizing, correcting and annotating that went into the preparation of the *Farewell* is beyond my powers of recall, but I remember with pleasure and gratitude the many roles in that complex process played by three most able student assistants: Deborah Wills, Andrew Robertson, and Dallas Harrison. Their patience and perseverance in the face of so much fussy detail has been remarkable. I am grateful, at the same time, to the Dean of Arts and to the Department of English through whose offices these assistants were made available. I wish to extend thanks, moreover, to the Social Science and Humanities Research Council for the funds administered through the Dean of Graduate Studies and Research that enabled me to consult the sole surviving copy of the first edition of the *Farewell* in the Bodleian Library. Many friends and colleagues have generously consented to look at the several parts of the edition as they emerged, and I have profited greatly from their comments and insights. Brenda Cantar's reading, informed by her extensive work on Elizabethan prose fiction, was most valuable and appreciated. To Charles Whitworth, a special word of thanks for his careful scrutiny of the text, and for saving me from several potentially embarrassing errors. Thanks also to Wyman Herendeen for his thoughts on the introduction, and to three colleagues and members of the Riche Society editorial committee, Ian Cameron, Faith Gildenhuys, and Douglas Campbell, who examined the completed text with care, who nudged my style into greater clarity, and who generally helped me determine just when the completed text was also a final one.

The typesetting was most ably carried out by Christina Thiele of the Journal Production Centre, and I am also grateful to Alan McLay for his willing part in checking the final proofs.

Finally, I am indebted to the Aid to Scholarly Publications Programme of the Canadian Federation for the Humanities for their subsidy in support of the publication of this book, and to their readers for their useful comments on the manuscript. This organization is invaluable for its role in the furthering of Canadian scholarship in the humanities and deserves our ongoing gratitude and support.

Introduction

The Life of Barnabe Riche

At about the same time that John Lyly was publishing his *Euphues, the Anatomy of Wit*, Stephen Gosson was putting the finishing touches on his *School of Abuse*, and Thomas North on his translation of *Plutarch's Lives of the Noble Grecians and Romans*, at about the same time that Thomas Churchyard's *Misery of Flanders* and Edmund Spenser's *Shepherds' Calendar* appeared, Barnabe Riche, somewhere in Ireland, was "forging" the eight novellas that constitute his *Farewell to Military Profession*. He published the book in London in 1581, but he tells us he completed it before the momentous arrival of James Fitzmaurice of Desmond in July of 1579 on his way to rekindle the Munster rebellion. The *Farewell* was a departure for Riche, a new literary exploit, as is signalled in part by his title. Though he did not in the event abandon his military profession, he was in fact turning his attention as a writer to a new form, the pleasantly playful, teasingly didactic, and highly diversionary story-telling that was thought to appeal to a female audience—or so he pretended in his Epistle Dedicatory to the gentlewomen of England and Ireland. Like many another Elizabethan amateur, he clearly thought that no apprenticeship was necessary for the new task, that following the fashion was enough. That fashion was the Italian novella that came into popularity in the 1570s with William Painter's *Palace of Pleasure*.

In addition to cultivating a fashionable form, he also claims to be cultivating the favor of the "ladies" in offering these literary graces to them in compensation for his self-proclaimed lack of social graces. This clever strategy is entirely to be expected in a man who throughout his career had shown a penchant for striking dramatic postures and assuming purely opportunistic roles. His search for supplemental income from his writing to repair his lifelong penury is, without doubt, one of his motives. That same opportunism is perhaps to be associated with the sense of expediency that caused him to pilfer the works of his contemporaries. Paralleling his career as a writer, for which he claims 26 books, was his career as soldier—but a career that, in keeping with his opportunistic bent of mind, deviated in many directions. He was also a failed profiteer, an unsuccessful litigant, an outspoken military critic, a satiric pamphleteer. Moreover, he was a seeker of royal favor, largely by serving as a spy and informer in Ireland during his postings there. The man who protests as he does to the Privy Council about being more sinned against than sinning, by his insistence undermines much of our sympathy for him as a man. But his life is a fascinating one for having moved through so many echelons of Elizabethan society in a way that few others could boast.[1]

In a publication of 1601 Riche tells us he is fifty-nine years old, and again in 1606 that he is sixty-four, confirming 1542 as the date of his birth—the year old Henry VIII had his fifth wife, Catherine Howard, tried and executed, and the year in which English troops routed the Scots under James V at the battle of Solway Moss. Twenty years and three monarchs later, Riche himself was in military service. That he was part of a contingent from Essex suggests he was an Essex native. One observer, however,

---

[1] The life of Barnabe Riche was the subject of a thorough archival investigation carried out forty years ago by Thomas Cranfill and Dorothy Hart Bruce. Nearly all that follows in this section must in some way be related to their very thorough labors. Cranfill and Bruce were Riche enthusiasts, keen to rescue him from centuries of oblivion and to establish him as at least "a major 'minor Elizabethan'" by dint of the copiousness and variety of his literary efforts and his importance to the age. *Barnaby Rich: A Short Biography* (Austin: University of Texas Press, 1953).

argues that he was from Maldon and another that he was from Witham, while a third claims he was from Lexden, Colchester and that his father was Thomas Riche, yeoman, who acquired arms as a gentleman in 1590.[2] That Riche proudly styled himself a gentleman with his own coat of arms in later years has led some scholars to look for associations in even higher places than the yeomanry, although for a soldier like Riche the status of gentleman is as likely to have been earned as to have been inherited. Whatever the case, if he were judged by the criteria for true blue that he gives in the *Farewell* (status of gentry for at least three generations on both sides) it seems unlikely that he could be categorized as anything but (in his own words) "an upstart, a nightgrown, a mushrump." He often boasted that he was a landowner by the age of twenty-four, although it is clear from later records that if he had property he had no knack for keeping it. In *The Adventures of Brusanus*, he tells us that by 1592 he had been soldiering for thirty years, and that he had spent all his friends had left him, "which was something."[3] Again, in *Faults, Faults, and Nothing Else but Faults* he states that by 1606 it was over forty years since he had owned land, but that he had been haunted by revenue seekers who "hadde it amongst them."[4] Those revenue seekers reappear in his subsequent tales of ill-advised financial ventures that left him in long-standing debt.

Whatever his social status, he had no university education, a fact that on some occasions he took as a serious lack, and on others as a pledge of his integrity as a stylist. In *A Right Excellent and Pleasant Dialogue* (1574), he apologizes for the lack of schooling that accounted for his low and unadorned style, the efforts of a simple soldier that nevertheless, by implication, avoided the excesses of the learned and embellished styles.[5] That lack became

---

[2] *A Short Biography*, p. 14, wherein the matter of several articles is offered in résumé.

[3] *The Adventures of Brusanus Prince of Hungaria* (London, 1592), sig. Di.

[4] *Faultes, Faults, and Nothing Else but Faultes* (London, 1606), sigs. Diii^v–Div.

[5] *A Right Excellent and Pleasaunt Dialogue betwene Mercury and an English Souldier* (London, 1574), sig. Aii^v.

part of his narrator's pose in later works, including the *Farewell*, as the frank and direct reporter, the bluff and honest soldier. Such a posture may well be grounded in a sense of inadequacy, or so a sceptic might think after observing Riche's occasional and unsuccessful attempts to reproduce the euphuistic flourishes of Lyly.

Riche was to know disasters on the battlefields that would send men of less resilience to an asylum. He seems so impervious to the disasters he describes that one is never sure where the courage stops and the bluffing starts. His career began with the ill-fated expedition against Le Havre in 1562–63 that ended for the English troops in a devastating typhus epidemic. Riche served under Captain Darcy and so must have shared in the action of May 1563 that brought in 500 of the enemy captured. He must also have been one of those who lived through the epidemic that broke out on June 7 and reduced the garrison from 5,000 to 1,200 able-bodied men by July 23, when Queen Elizabeth grudgingly gave her permission to retreat.[6] Riche returned home a captain, and the rank may well have fallen to him for his perseverance and valor; even so, the Le Havre campaign was a harsh introduction to the military life.

Riche's next exploit was a privateering venture, the financial repercussions of which would haunt him for the next thirty years. Privateering, a business encouraged by the Crown after the humiliating loss of Calais to the French, was vastly lucrative if one had the luck and skill to make it work. Francis Clarke and John Bryan, two of the Queen's best seadogs, had made fortunes capturing French merchant ships and towing them into Newhaven harbor. Barnabe Riche had a weakness for financially promising fashions even so early in his career. He borrowed money from one Richard Cooke in 1565 to outfit a ship at Maldon, Essex. What he understood as venture capital, however, Cooke understood as a straight loan not attached to the risk of the enterprise. When the ship sank, as indeed it did, Cooke pursued Riche and had him arrested and imprisoned in the Counter in London in 1570. Riche was released on a bond for eighty pounds—four times the origi-

---

[6] J.B. Black, *The Reign of Elizabeth 1558–1603* (Oxford: Clarendon Press (1936), 1969), pp. 61–62.

nal loan. Two years later, upon return from service in Ireland, he
paid twenty pounds and a horse to Cooke's brother in return for
release from the bond, and the sum no doubt represented most
of what he had gained from two years of soldiering. Cooke returned to the matter in 1601, after his brother died. Riche had
lost his document of quittance, and Cooke brought him before
the Court of Common Pleas for the whole debt. Documents from
the two sides paint such contrasting views that right can never
be established with certainty, and the decision of the court does
not survive.

Incidental to this tale of debt and prosecution we find evidence
that Riche served as a soldier in Ireland from 1570 to 1572. Over
the next ten to twelve years he seems to have been constantly on
the move, catapulting through London, back and forth from Ireland to Holland, participating in many of the military campaigns
of Elizabeth's reign, though whether officially or as an adventurer
is never entirely clear. Thomas Churchyard makes use of Riche's
notebooks in his *True Discourse Historical of the Succeeding Governors in the Netherlands and the Civil Wars There* (1602) to
explain the seige of Zutphen in 1572, to recite the names of the
captains involved, and to offer details on the siege of Haarlem.[7]
It seems clear, then, that Riche was off to the Dutch front soon
after he returned from Ireland in 1572, attempting perhaps to
repair his fortunes as well as to fight the good Protestant cause.
His stay was not long, however, for by July 1573 he was bound
for Ireland again, this time aboard the Black Bark of Lord Riche,
who was a member of the Earl of Essex's expedition to colonize
Ulster. Lord Riche was accompanied by his wife's brother, Lord
Darcy, the brother of the Captain Darcy under whom Riche had
served in Le Havre. Riche may have been taking advantage of
old connections in order to improve his fortune, a motive that
seems to have dominated this entire venture. It proved to be another spectacular disaster. In A.L. Rowse's account, it developed
into a grand debacle of insufficient supplies, of plague, of foolish
political conflict with the locals, and of a criminally inept high
command.[8]

---

[7] *A True Discourse Historicall of the Succeeding Gouernours in the
Netherlands and the Civill Warres There* (London, 1602), p. 19.

[8] *The Expansion of Elizabethan England* (New York: Harper and

Three years later, in June of 1576, Riche was back in Holland at the siege of Zieriksee upon which he reported in his *Pathway to Military Practise*. In the *Farewell*, he names cities and fortifications that he could only have seen during that same period. Yet, if the *Farewell* was written in Ireland as he claims, then he must have returned there no later than 1578, for in *The Irish Hubbub* (1617) he relates that he was an officer in the field in Limerick during the 1578 war with the Desmonds. He was apparently still in Ireland in 1579, for Nicholas Malby, Walsingham's commander in Ireland, mentions Riche in a letter he wrote in September of that year, and Riche wrote an epitaph for Sir William Drury, who was killed in action in October.

It was possibly while carrying letters to London in 1580[9] that Riche made arrangements with Robert Walley, the London printer, to publish the *Farewell*. But he would have had little opportunity to examine the galleys or to make any corrections to his book as it went through press, for when he returned to Ireland events took a tragic turn. Throughout the autumn and winter of 1581 Riche was involved in the systematic suppression of the Munster rebellion, a period in which starvation and pestilence took the lives of some 30,000 of the Irish. Then in the autumn of 1581, with the Desmond rebellion in hand, the Queen (as Riche's biographers note) "suffered a fit of what one historian calls 'ill-timed parsimony'" in ordering half of the forces discharged, thereby leaving a vast number of soldiers stranded without means of sustenance in a famine-stricken country.[10] Riche himself endured these terrible conditions until March 1, 1582 when he managed to gain passage, though he had had to wait out contrary winds that blew throughout all of February. He relates many of the details of the harrowing experience in his *True Report of a Late Practise Enterprised by a Papist* (1582).

The True Report was not principally about his privations in Ireland, however, but rather it was a hastily written journalistic account about Elizabeth Orton, who had been induced by a Catholic schoolmaster to see visions. By chance, Riche, newly arrived from Ireland, was among the congregation of Chester

---

Row, 1955), p. 140; see also *A Short Biography*, p. 26.

[9] *A Short Biography*, p. 30.

[10] *A Short Biography*, p. 31.

Cathedral that Sunday morning, March 3, when the young girl of fourteen or fifteen years was made to confess to all present the whole sensational business. Always ready to seize upon something extraordinary for his journalistic ends, Riche took up the story, probably to earn some extra money as an anti-Catholic pamphleteer.

According to *A New Description of Ireland* (1610), Riche was in charge of a garrison of 100 men in Coleraine in 1584 in the far north of Ulster, where he spent the balance of that year and most of the following. He nowhere mentions the abrupt termination of his posting in November, 1585, when his garrison was lured out into the open and almost entirely massacred by the Scots, their alleged allies, while Riche was away in Dublin. The next news of him in a military posting is from the Low Countries where he spent 1586–87. On his way through London, less than two months after the massacre, on January 12, 1586, the captain bachelor, at the age of forty-two or forty-three, took a wife, Katherine Aston, in St. Mary Somerset parish. The affiliation might have been extraordinarily advantageous, in that Katherine was daughter to Sir Edward Aston, knight, whose annual income was over ten thousand pounds, making him one of England's richest men.[11] Her brother, Sir Walter Aston, was the patron of Michael Drayton. Riche was proud to boast her pedigree, and there would be news of her in later years as a staunch defender of the honor of King James. But she can have brought him few material benefits insofar as Riche persisted in later years to complain about their poverty. In 1587 Riche received a life pension from the Queen for his service in Ireland, but it cannot have helped much for it was only two shillings six pence per diem, to be drawn in Irish currency from the Irish treasury, and was often difficult to collect in later years.[12] Nevertheless, Riche may well have dedicated *A Pathway to Military Practise* to the Queen in gratitude for what she had given him. Riche was not to know true financial security for his many years of service, and his want may have quickened his willingness to engage in more dubious and dangerous enterprises, both for reward and for royal favor.

---

[11] *A Short Biography*, p. 38.

[12] *A Short Biography*, p. 39.

His next sojourn in Ireland, which began in March 1598, brought him more hardship, but of a somewhat different kind. He had made remarks in the Orton pamphlet that were critical of certain high Irish officials, although he named no one, and he championed the cause of certain of his friends who were opposed to the same officials. He sent reports on these matters to Whitehall, though it is not known whether he was officially commissioned to do so. He ended up in open conflict with two powerful and ambitious prelates, Adam Loftus, Archbishop of Dublin, and his brother-in-law Thomas Jones, Bishop of Meath. In two private reports to the Queen, the first presented in person in November 1591, the second in the spring of the following year, he exposed their many misdeeds, accusing them principally of nepotism and of embezzling crown money. Loftus in turn lodged complaints with Burghley, describing Riche as a malicious man, a frequenter of papists, a man of gross infirmities.[13] The Privy Council censured and threatened Loftus, but did not remove his powers which he used to harass Riche and his friends.

As Riche tells the tale (and no other source has survived), his friend Legge, the Deputy Remembrancer of Ireland, was abused verbally, his house was sacked, then he was beaten and imprisoned. In June 1592, Riche was assaulted in the streets by the archbishop's henchmen, hit, stabbed, and taken for dead by the hundreds who looked on, until two strangers came to his rescue, deflecting blows from the three assailants, and allowing Riche to regain his feet. He made his escape, he tells us, having never had the chance to draw his sword. Riche attempted to gain satisfaction at law but failed. At that point he saw the wisdom of a hasty departure, and he took ready passage to England with a bodyguard of five or six captains to prevent his murder.[14] Riche was to believe henceforth that such dangers and humiliations had won him a debt with the Crown, and his belief spurred him to undertake a self-righteous campaign for recognition, but his efforts won no sympathy with the Queen or with the Privy Council. If he was indeed one of the Queen's "sworn men," as he claimed, there was a debt owing. But in 1592 the Master of Requests, Sir

---

[13] *A Short Biography*, pp. 59–60.

[14] *A Short Biography*, pp. 79–87.

John Fortescue, was preoccupied and unresponsive, and besides, the Queen was refusing audience to most petitioners, and refusing petitioners from Ireland out of hand.[15] As a result Riche found himself caught up for months in bureaucratic evasions. The two ministers to whom he might have appealed for help, Sir Francis Walsingham and Sir Christopher Hatton, were dead. Banished from Ireland and hence from his meagre pension, Riche began to dwell on what seemed to him a clear case of royal ingratitude. He turned, not surprisingly, to satire: it was the only recourse left, and besides it might pay.

The Adventures of Brusanus (1592) contained "complaint" portraits, such as that of the old soldier Martianus, full of bitterness and melancholy, and many another biographical jibe, for Martianus, like Riche, had served for thirty years in the wars, ending his days a hopeless suitor in an indifferent court. In Riche's next work, *Greene's News Both from Heaven and Hell* (1593), he portrayed Fortescue, barely disguised as St. Peter at the gates, so overburdened by his offices that he could not attend to his proper duties, and Riche mounted scathing attacks upon his old enemies Loftus and Jones. The combination was dangerous, and it led to arrest by warrant of the Star Chamber, the judicial arm of the Privy Council. The warrant has not survived, but since it came six weeks after the publication of *Greene's News*, no doubt it charged Riche with slandering men in high places, a legal matter falling under the jurisdiction of the Star Chamber.[16] Riche suggests as much in *The Honesty of this Age* (1614), where he complains that men who would readily speak out against dishonesty find themselves vulnerable to slander suits.[17]

The vocation Riche was struggling towards was that of journalist, what with his eye-witness accounts of the foreign wars, his story of Elizabeth Orton's visions, his reports of corruption in Ireland, and his censure of bureaucratic insufficiencies and inequities at home. "Honest" Barnabe may well have thought himself an objective observer, with his plain and principled style. But journalistic models were wanting, alien models intruded, and

---

[15] *A Short Biography*, pp. 69–70.

[16] *The Reign of Elizabeth 1558–1603*, pp. 206–12.

[17] *A Short Biography*, p. 19.

he presented his reportage and commentary in the framework of
romance, allegorical complaint, humanist dialogue, anti-Catholic
polemic and satiric diatribe. But the sense of an audience eager for news, exciting news from those exciting times, was clearly
emerging, even if the gathering and venting of news had not yet
freed itself from literary forms that carried with them the rhetorical biases of their original context of polemics, domestic tragedy,
courtly romance, broadside sensationalism or picaresque adventure. The versatility of Riche's style is perhaps less that of a
man without a center than it is that of a born journalist who had
no tradition of journalistic style to work within and insufficient
genius to invent one for himself.

The next we hear of Riche is in 1594, when he was involved
in legal problems again, this time in Chester. He charged one
Alexander Coates with assault and theft for attacking him in a
wagon as he made his way across Warwickshire. In the documents of the case on his side, Riche tells how he fell under the
wagon wheels and narrowly escaped with his life. Why it was
that a man of his military experience never managed to draw his
sword remains unclear, and why Coates, a man of respectable
standing in Chester, would attempt to rob Riche of a fair Cy-
press hat band is even less clear. The plausibility of Riche's case
was not improved when James Persivall, the wagoner and key
witness, failed to confirm the identification of the accused. The
magistrates of Chester were uncooperative. Riche threatened to
take the case before the Lord Chief Justice in London.[18] Lord
Buckhurst wrote to the magistrates and struck enough fear into
them to have Coates jailed for a time, but he managed to escape
to Ireland before Riche received damages. Just what Riche had
hoped for in going to law, if not for damages, is not clear, and
there is no evidence concerning the legal outcome.

During the following decade, Riche was frequently in court,
each case producing evidence of his whereabouts and of his unusual litigiousness. The renewal of his Irish pension in 1597 at the
insistence of the Queen suggests that he was back in the military
service. A stray letter mentions that he was serving in London,
and legal documents of 1601, 1604, 1605, and 1606 supply ev-

----

[18] *A Short Biography*, p. 84.

idence that he was resident at Mile End, Stepney, the military training grounds for new recruits on the outskirts of London.[19] It is probable that he was serving as a training officer, the perfect employment for a soldier of his age who had seen twenty-five years of active service. His friend, Captain Christopher Levens, who was so employed in Middlesex County, wrote a letter to Sir Robert Cecil commending Riche's service during the Essex Rebellion of 1601; all the evidence suggests that he was engaged in active service putting down the rebellion.

The year 1604 saw him once again in legal proceedings, this time seeking the prosecution of a fellow officer, Captain Robert Gosnold, whom he encountered at a dinner party in Shanklin, Isle of Wight. All evening Gosnold had made light of matters touching the King and his domestic relations. It was not Barnabe, but his staunch monarchist wife Katherine, who was the audience to his banter. Nevertheless, in a written deposition sent to Lord Cecil, Riche and his friend Captain Levens brought charges against Gosnold for "unreverend speeches against the prince." One may wonder if his motive was not rather material compensation than the King's honor. The parties were called to London. Riche and Levens were unable to make their case, however, and there were suggestions that influential persons intervened on Gosnold's side. Gosnold turned charges of treason into countercharges of scandal by suggesting that Mrs. Riche, in granting certain kisses and withholding others, had raised the whole tempest herself. Riche was outmaneuvered again. He protested, but to no avail. He ended by looking the fool, rather like a Zeal-Of-The-Land-Busy who could find treason in any dinner party. Being ridiculed before Cecil only rekindled his sense of long-standing grievance. He knew by experience how much the ultimate recourse, printed satire, could cost. Instead he sent a stream of pathetic documents in the government's direction, each containing a request for financial succor. None seems to have succeeded. Perhaps the Riches never fully recovered socially from the terrible *faux pas*. The only good news came in 1605: Adam Loftus was dead and Riche was free to return to Ireland, and so he did sometime before 1608, the registration date in Dublin of his *Room for a Gentleman*.

---

[19] *A Short Biography*, p. 92.

Eleven works emerged from his pen between 1606 and 1617, including several confidential reports on Ireland to King James and to Sir Robert Cecil. He was once again a government intelligencer, and some of his reports, such as *The Anatomy of Ireland* (1615), sent directly to the King, were full of accusations. He was ever on the alert for flirtations with Catholicism, for murmurings against the King, for misappropriation of public money, and for dereliction in the performance of official duties. It can be little wonder that in short order Riche was the object of spite and calumniation from all the ranks of Dublin society down to the tradespeople. Riche complained often in his communiqués of the persecution he bore for the kingdom's sake, the taxing and torture of Dublin tongues, the extortionate prices he was made to pay. Why did he behave as he did? There is little evidence that he was being well paid for his provocative intelligence. Was it simply that he was plucky to a fault, outright foolhardy, zealous by instinct? Or was there another motive?

There is a common denominator in Riche's endless supplications at court and such diverse behaviors as his prosecution of a fellow soldier for slandering the monarch, and his endurance of the notoriety of an informer. It is to be seen also in his dedication of four books to Prince Henry, one to Prince Charles, and another to Princess Elizabeth. Apparently his efforts at last bore fruit, for his last five title pages declare that he was now "servant to the Kinges most excellent Maiestie," and in 1616, the year before his death, the King bestowed upon him as a free gift, 100 pounds, as "the eldest Captain in the Kingdom."[20] He was motivated by nothing less than an *idée fixe*—an old man's persistence not in winning, but in regaining royal favor. In 1581, in the closing pages of the *Farewell*, Riche portrayed a devil, Balthasar, going north from London to Edinburgh in order to possess the King of Scotland. Unfortunately for Riche, the real King of Scotland took notice and registered his displeasure in certain diplomatic documents of 1595. The upshot was that the story was suppressed in the third edition of the *Farewell*, published in 1594, by having the books recalled and mutilated; such seems to have been the case from the evidence to be drawn from the sole surviving copy

---

[20] *A Short Biography*, p. 126.

of this edition. In the fourth and last edition, that offending passage was altered to read "our Grand-seigniour the Turke." In the end, King James seems to have come to appreciate Riche's efforts as his chief ferret in Ireland. But to achieve this result Riche for years stinted no cost or danger to regain the approbation of his monarch.[21] In fact, he had only one year to live to enjoy his royal pension. He died on November 10, 1617 at the relatively advanced age of seventy-five.

As a writer, Riche experimented with the favored forms of his age: short stories, episodic adventures, prose romances, character sketches, pamphlets on contemporary events, and satire. Of the many popular forms of writing, only playwrighting seems not to have tempted him. If number of editions is the mark of popularity and success, the *Farewell* with four, along with *The Honesty of this Age* also with four (if one counts the Scottish printing), was the most successful of his writings. *The Irish Hubbub*, his last work, enjoyed two posthumous re-editions. There was an ongoing interest in the Irish question, a continuing audience for the novella, even when the vogue for writing them had passed, and a sustained concern over military questions such as Riche dealt with in the *Alarm to England* (1578), which was republished as late as 1625 under the title *Vox Militis*. H.J. Webb opined rather generously that Riche's "contributions to military literature [were] historically speaking every bit as important as Shakespeare's to drama."[22] Both Queen Elizabeth and King James had been among his readers, and his works had won the praise of Gabriel Harvey and Thomas Nashe.[23] As a writer of the novella in English, Riche holds an important place; as a military reporter, his testimony has been of great value and interest to historians; and as a satirist his books contain a great deal of information about the age.

In a subsequent section of the introduction there will be an occasion to return to John Leon Lievsay's attack on Riche, made some thirty years ago, in opposition to the efforts of his biog-

---

[21] Thomas Cranfill, "Barnaby Rich and King James," *ELH*, XVI (1949), pp. 65–75.

[22] *A Short Biography*, p. 4.

[23] *A Short Biography*, pp. 6–7.

raphers, Cranfill and Bruce, to restore his reputation. We need not be as impressed as they, he argues, by the number of people Riche knew in high places or with the number of his royal dedications, because "in this respect, a cat might look at a king—and brazenly did."[24] Indeed, it is easy from a modern perspective to see Riche as an opportunist, as an informer, more of a coward than is becoming a military man, as a sycophant, a hack, and a pilferer of other men's works. The evidence for Lievsay was clear that Riche half invented the catastrophes of his personal life, was no great military strategist, was perpetually preoccupied with his own interests and image, and hence lacked the objectivity of a responsible writer. He tended therefore to steal from rather than imitate other authors, was accordingly something of a poseur in his image of the honest soldier and author of twenty-six books, was not outstandingly productive or successful as a writer (some of his contemporaries wrote up to three books in a year, some books running through nine to sixteen editions), was a self-plagiarizer, a satirist who sampled "the breezes blowing from Whitehall"[25] before shaping his own versions of wickedness and vice, and that if we held the count of his books to strictly original ones, "we should leave him as naked as Aesop's jay."[26] But if we take one glance at Riche in his original literary context, such rigorist speculations and judgments tend to dissolve. Riche was friendly with Thomas North the translator, Thomas Lodge, and Lodowick Bryskett the translator of Cinthio. Thomas Churchyard was a lifelong friend, and George Gascoigne fought with him in the Dutch wars. He may well have been acquainted with Spenser through Bryskett, and with other writers through Churchyard and Gascoigne. Would they have tolerated as a literary associate a man of so little talent and integrity as Lievsay suggests? We may not be able to say of Riche what Dryden said of Jonson as a borrower that "he invades authors like a monarch; and what would be theft in other poets is only victory in him,"[27]

---

[24] "A Word about Barnaby Rich," *The Journal of English and German Philology*, LV (1956), p. 382.

[25] "A Word about Barnaby Rich," p. 386.

[26] "A Word about Barnaby Rich," p. 384.

[27] *Essays of John Dryden*, ed. W.P. Ker (Oxford: University Press,

but the comment by Dryden does point up the relativity in assigning such evaluations. Ends here seem to justify methods, so that if Riche can be demonstrated, in the pages to follow, to be an accomplished and original story-teller, his alleged failings may then look rather more victorious.

The *Farewell* and the Italian Novella in England

Something of the challenge of dealing critically with the eight short prose fiction narratives that constitute Riche's *Farewell* becomes apparent when one attempts to select a descriptive term for them. In the pages to follow, such words as story, tale, history, fable and novella will appear as though interchangeable. Nevertheless, given the transitional nature of these stories in a period of emerging forms, no single term is without its partially misleading connotations. The easiest course may be to think of Riche simply as a teller of stories, though the generic term "story" hints at none of the more specific genre-related origins of the storytelling form he practiced. To add "short" before "story" is even more problematic. While few would deny that these are genuine short stories, and even forerunners, in their way, of modern fiction, in more precise historical terms they are neither part of that genre, nor in any causal sense precursors. To be sure, they are brief fictions, they display the requisite relationship between narrative and dialogue, they offer implicit and explicit traces of the narrator's voice, and, with the exception of the first story, they display the development of a simple, coherent fable or intrigue built around a constant and limited group of characters. Moreover, they are fictions concerned with social issues projected onto settings that are, for the most part, both plausible and contemporary, despite the sometimes heavy patina of Renaissance conventions and the ambiance of romance. Yet they cannot be joined to the genre, because the short story is generally recognized as having a continuous history going back only to the earlier nineteenth century. Many literary historians remain convinced that the Elizabethan experiments in short fiction were relatively isolated, and separated by a hiatus of over a century, from the first efforts associated with the rise of modern fiction.

1900), I, 82.

The term "fable" is useful only if it is understood in the modern critical sense to mean a short discourse viewed in terms of its characteristic order of plot or intrigue, and not a moral story often related through the personification of animals or inanimate objects. The word "history" raises obstacles for the modern reader insofar as the term signifies unique events verifiable according to archival documentation; we do not today think of a history as patent fiction that can at best boast of some degree of social truth or fidelity, whether to an anecdote allegedly based on a real event, or to a literary model. Yet the term carried these connotations for sixteenth-century readers; to determine, in fact, precisely what they understood as distinguishing fiction from history amounts to a major critical inquiry. The term must at least preserve a certain technical authority in Riche's case, if only because he himself referred to each of his eight narratives as histories, thereby claiming for his work the truth and validity usually associated with the genre.

But finally, it is the term "novella" that designates most clearly and specifically the origins and nature of Riche's practice; it is a misleading term only insofar as Riche's employment of the genre includes a number of English stylistic features. Otherwise, for both manner and for matter, Riche's stories are created in the image of this Italian genre, and represent an important phase in the naturalization of a southern form for which there was an avid northern readership. The *Farewell* is part of a larger process of adapting an imported literary product to English tastes and to the English moral climate.

At the time of the publication of the *Farewell* in 1581, English prose fiction was still in its infancy. In this period are to be found the first traces of thought about how to write quick-paced stories dealing with contemporary events for the enjoyment of a growing middle- and upper-class readership. Such thought is revealed largely by the trends established through practice and the evolution of styles and modes, although occasionally the critical voice breaks through, as in Riche's first story where he pulls himself up short from a moral digression to remind himself of his duty to the movement of the narrative, as well as to his readers and their pleasure. This is not so much the comment of a theorist as of a commercial writer seeking to assure his readers that he knows what they like, while playfully reminding himself to let the story tell itself. Implicit in the comment, however, is an aesthetic ideal of the story plain and simple, as it is found in the Italian *novellieri*. Such statements are relative by nature and subject to considerable qualification, because the novella was not itself without a great deal of diversity. But in general, it furnished an ambiance and an economy that distinguished it from the sermon exemplum, the fabliau, the chivalric romance, and for this reason it could be used in a dialectic with past traditions of fiction. Vestiges of these earlier forms are still apparent in the stories of the *Farewell*, but Riche's decision to imitate the novella remains the true genesis of his work. That decision is evidence of reflection and of critical decisions.

A brief description of the novella cannot take into consideration the many phases of its development during the almost four-hundred-year period before it migrated to England. Paradoxically, that development included a constant cross-fertilization from those medieval forms with which it is otherwise contrasted: the folk tale, the fabliau, the chivalric romance, to name the most important. But most essential to its development was a certain ethos of the novella that accommodated these "contaminating" genres to its own level of mimetic representation. There was already a generic integrity that allowed the novella to host these "alien" forms without losing its characteristic immediacy, agility of plotting, leanness of commentary, and contemporary social ambiance. The novella, by definition, insisted upon a displacement of materials toward a contemporary realism. No matter how elastic the form was in absorbing more rhetorical, mythic, or episodic modes, the essence remained its anecdotal directness, its secular independence, its emphasis upon the witty intrigue, the bizarre event related as being both true and recent. Its forte was the retailing of polished tricks as news, even to the point of converting myth itself into history. It was this generic sense of the novella, together with its "new" social content, that made it an attractive model for English fiction writers in search of a formula.

The English had at their disposal all of those forms said to have contaminated the paradigmatic novella type, including homiletic and folkloric traditions, as well as the Greek novel and romance. But what they lacked was a fresh vocabulary of tricks, *topoi*, and character types whereby they could devise the efficient and witty social fable in a contemporary domestic setting. Despite the English inclination to remodify in the direction of medieval forms in order to accommodate issues of Tudor interest, there was undoubtedly an appreciation for Italianate concentration, rigor of plotting, and efficient realistic detail that attracted them to the novella as a form worthy of imitation.

One of the heartiest and most accomplished of the sixteenth-century Italian *novellieri* was Matteo Bandello, whose concise and pithy stories, though by no means devoid of the vestiges of experimental borrowing from more elaborate narrative traditions, are nevertheless characterized by a quality of realism and contemporaneousness that represented for his imitators a minimalist model revealing the barest essentials of how to tell an effective story. He published, in 1554, a collection of two hundred such stories modelled upon Boccaccio's *Decameron*. The settings were urban, the characters were drawn often from the mercantile class, the plots reflected modern social values and domestic problems, thereby resisting the intrusion of romance themes and structures. These stories contained bits of conversation conceivably drawn from streets and salons, and they were lightly sprinkled with realistic detail. The intrigues possessed surprising twists and turns for the sake of diversion and entertainment, yet they remained single episodes rather than involved and compound plots. A typical novella related an event in a journalistic, quasi-anecdotal way as something true because it actually happened in some nearby town not long before. Even the most outrageous conduct could be described not only dispassionately, but with a degree of amoral indifference.

There is no need to determine here if these stories were principally social events turned into fiction by the stylizations of the authors, if they were drawn from a repertoire of tales and anecdotes and recast in more familiar settings, or if they were new "realities" shaped entirely by the writer's imagination. The topic has been a favorite among students of the genre, but no definitive answers have emerged. Determining the degree of interplay between imitations of life and borrowings from other fiction is particularly difficult for this period because writers left so incomplete a record of their intentions as makers. The terms novella, *nouvelle* and

novel perpetuate the ambiguity insofar as they suggest both the
narrative that begins as news, and hence as a form of journalistic
enhancement, and the invented fable as something fresh, novel
and original. But whether the story was drawn from an observed
event or from prior fiction, what mattered was not historical truth
but plausibility, and not plausibility as the average or most likely,
but as something strange and noteworthy yet entirely possible, a
story that could be touted as an actual event. With this formula,
fact and craft became part of the single expediency of telling
the most effective story, confirming what C.S. Lewis said of the
genre generally, that "it is story-telling naked and unashamed,
story-telling without roots in legend or supposed history."[28] That
impression of the genre remains paramount, no matter how often scholars produce evidence of literary sources in the narratives
themselves. This mode of story-telling had a marked influence on
the Elizabethan fiction writers during the twenty-five year period
following the publication of William Painter's *Palace of Pleasure*
in 1567. Riche assumes a key position in the transmission of the
mode that continued to dictate literary conventions and attitudes
throughout the 1580s and 1590s.[29]

Insofar as the stories of the *Farewell* represent an aggregate
of Italian sources drawn entirely from Bandello, Straparola, and
Giraldi (known in England as Cinthio), we are not surprised that
they reflect the characteristic proportions of the novella with regard to plot, density of characterization, and quality of dialogue.
Still apparent is the Italian preoccupation with surprising actions
built around coincidences, tricks of fortune, knavish pranks, and
extraordinary shows of virtue or wickedness, to the detriment of
more complete characterizations. Novellas rarely proceeded with
sufficient leisure to permit a full development of the inner lives of
the protagonists. Dialogue could be terse and colloquial as well
as ceremonial, but tended to serve the advancement of an action
rather than the exploration either of ideas or of sentiments. These
same habits, whether deemed to be strengths or weaknesses, came

---

[28] *English Literature in the Sixteenth Century* (Oxford: Clarendon,
(1954), 1965), p. 309.

[29] David Margolies, *Novel and Society in Elizabethan England* (London & Sydney: Croom Helm, 1985), p. 25.

to characterize Elizabethan fiction in the Italian style. If there was an imbalance between the clever intrigue and subservient dialogue, it was to find its rebalance in that age not among the fiction writers, but among the dramatists who were, by the very nature of their medium, compelled to reinterpret many of these intrigues entirely in the form of dialogue that could not but lead to a greater refinement of the inner lives of the interlocutors in the action.

By imitating the *novellieri*, English writers appropriated not only their manner of writing but also their disposition of matter. In principle, the novella was a comprehensive medium, capable of containing nearly any aspect of contemporary social life. In practice, however, the emphasis fell upon love intrigues, erotic passions often sadistic in nature, violent or subtle crimes, deviant or abnormal behavior, presumably because audiences fancied the bizarre and titillating. These, in turn, were perceived as belonging to topical categories: stories of social trickery; stories built upon tests of love or fidelity; tales of unusual domestic situations; tales of jealousy and revenge. Such *topoi* could be used organizationally in larger collections, thereby underscoring both the generic matter of these tales, as well as their diversity. Objection could be made, and indeed was made, that such tales were uncharacteristically cynical and amoral, and that the mores and values they examined belonged to Italy rather than to England. In imitating the novella, the English writers would seem to have foresaken their own national experience. The narrowing of potential subject matter to the topics favored by the *novellieri*, the exclusion of English material, and the promotion of southern vice and affectation were different components of a single question concerning these foreign models. The naturalizing of these novella answered initially to an established fascination among English readers with Italian matter, to the dismay of homespun moralists. Paradoxically, however, there is a sense in which these fictions, despite their foreign settings and hyperbolical events, raise issues entirely relevant to Tudor middle-class interests—questions about the sanctity of the family, about destiny and honor, about chastity and loyalty. Even this alien genre with its lurid events could serve as a forum concerning values proven by time and experience to be the most resistent to the tricks of fortune. Riche's stories not only reveal these underlying value structures, but as imitations rather than translations, they reveal a program of selection and shaping of materials that allows Riche to emphasize themes he wished to communicate to his readers. The reinforcement of points of view from story to story is almost certain proof that Riche's imagination was guided by social concerns.

The potential for an adaptation of the genre in support of conservative moral values was by no means apparent to the early critics of the Anglicized novella. The publication of Painter's *Palace of Pleasure* in 1567 provoked Roger Ascham's well-known outburst in *The Schoolmaster*, where he inveighs against those "bawdie bookes. . .translated out of the *Italian* tonge, whereby ouer many yong willes and wittes allured to wantonnes, do now boldly contemne all seuere bookes that sounde to honestie and godlines."[30] Ascham, as a humanist educator, was concerned with the reading habits of youth, more attracted to the diversions of the south than to good native homiletic treatises. Behind that concern was his distrust of the grand tour that produced not well-rounded Englishmen, but Italianized Englishmen who had learned during their travels only to condemn native traditions of marriage, religion and state. Books, like travel, served up examples of corruption that undermined basic moral and patriotic values. The very success of Painter's formula was, in fact, confirmed by the fear which the appearance of his collection generated in Ascham's mind. The cynicism of Bandello's tales, with their scenes of passionate love and violent crime, was evidence enough of the decadence of Italian civilization. Such a writer was not to be condoned for his integrity of reporting, but condemned as a teacher of vice. Ascham raises in his own terms fundamental questions concerning the uses of literature, questions which no imitator of the Italians was allowed to forget.

In the case of the novella the moralist's view was easy to defend. Comparatively, these stories presented a panorama of crime, corruption at court, jaded self-indulgence and rampant individualism. The neutral style allowed luxuriousness, hedonistic experimentation, scenes of rape and seduction, to stand as sim-

---

[30] Roger Ascham, *English Works*, ed. William Aldis Wright (Cambridge: University Press, 1904), p. 230.

ple facts of life. By degrees, a new ethic insinuates itself wherein vice becomes disguised as wit or cunning. Expediency and survival alone count for wisdom. In sexual matters, only the lurid, absurd, or sublime attracted attention. In due course, every English imitator had to come to terms with the amorality of the sources, and to make concessions to the English moral climate with its new-found Protestant vigor and high humanist ideals. However, such concessions often threatened the most attractive features of the genre, its titillating exploitation of social possibilities, its objective clarity and brevity. English practice hence vacillated between a desire for the racy and exotic, and a desire to offend neither the general reading public nor the censors. The result was a new repertoire of interferences whereby characteristic stories were surrounded by programs of interpretation. The narrator could strike an apologetic pose or dissociate himself from the stories. Stories of vice could be turned into cautionary tales by covering them with a veneer of moral commentary. Moreover, Riche permitted himself to write stories in which the order of comedy in the closures allowed for moral approbation by censuring the forces that had attempted to obstruct that comic outcome. Yet, despite this structural concession to moral order, Riche indicates a certain anxiety in his prefatory statements about the acceptability of his stories. The crisis concerning the value of Italianate fiction was by no means resolved by 1581.

The novella, in its ideal uncontaminated incarnation, may be profiled as a brief and witty tale of social intrigue told with leanness and verve for the sake of the striking and entertaining events themselves. These were watershed characteristics, the imitation of which became a decisive factor in the development of English Renaissance fiction. For the reasons already set out, however, the English imitators rarely allowed the frank and bawdy to stand without comment. Whether by aesthetic predilection, or out of moral necessity, or both, their stories in the novella style were marked by degrees of moralization and stylization. Stories most resembling Italian models were often prefaced by feigned or real regrets for their publication as being but toys and trifles that at worst could inflict no harm upon audiences willing to see them as such. Recent critical observers have been baffled by this strategic detachment of the maker from his creation.

Other writers insulated their books from assault by building a didactic framing structure that offers to interpret each work as a lesson in right conduct. A third means of transforming such stories was through the addition of stylistic embellishments, to the point that intrigue structures became but pretexts for the devising of pretty speeches and the presentation of erudite allusions. Such displays of copiousness became their own *raison d'être* as models for speaking and writing, thereby relegating the stories themselves to secondary importance. Trends toward moralizing and toward stylistic amplification were well-established, and have posed serious problems for modern investigators of Elizabethan prose fiction.

The place given to overt moralizing caused John Carey to declare that Elizabethan fiction was "thoroughly and. . .deservedly dead."[31] Detractors tend to brand this body of writing as superficial, overladen with rhetorical display, marked by a dissociation between incident and diatribe. Therefore, it lacks the true substance of social fiction, and rarely rises above the level of schoolroom exercises. Robert J. Clemens underscores the importance of brevity and wit in the novella, the simplicity of its intrigue, and the economy of the oral tradition it sprang from. Hence, for him, the interpolation of long formal speeches, and the addition of moral and rhetorical displays could only compromise the genre, because "unity and verbosity are mortal enemies."[32] These views do not take into consideration either the exceptions to these trends, or, conversely, the great pleasure which the Elizabethan reader might have derived from these rhetorical displays that we no longer enjoy in the same way today. But in general, they express the very real dangers these Elizabethan habits constituted for the development of an uninhibited, effective, contemporary story-telling style. A study of Riche must include an assessment of his work in relation to these "temptations." There are, in fact, strong traces of all three practices—the trivialization of his tales

---

[31] "Sixteenth and Seventeenth Century Prose," *History of Literature in the English Language*, Vol. II: *English Poetry and Prose, 1540–1674*, e. Christopher Ricks (London: Barrie & Jenkins, 1970), p. 361.

[32] "Anatomy of the Novella," *Comparative Literature Studies*, 9 (March, 1972), p. 11.

in his address to the women readers, occasional didactic intrusions, and heightened stylizations—but there is also a constant awareness on his part of the need to design efficient and engaging intrigues and self-contained fictive worlds that preserve their integrity as artistic creations. In this regard, Riche may well prove to be the most faithful of the Elizabethan imitators of the novella.

Such moralizing and stylistic elaborations were encouraged by the French translators whose free renditions of the Italian texts the English often preferred to the originals. One case in point is the influential *Histoires tragiques* of Pierre Boaistuau and François Belleforest. In this adaptation of Bandello the stories are much embellished. The translators amplify speeches, raise the levels of eloquence and sentiment, and invent long, reflective soliloquies. The characters are made to aim their moral invectives, not against the specific ills that afflict them, but at the general ills of the age. A certain ventriloquism appears as characters mount the pulpits of the translators. Such eloquence had its defenders in those who believed that the end of fiction was to teach and to furnish models of eloquence. The spirit of French humanism made its inroads, just as English habits learned in the grammar schools would intrude upon the writing of fiction. There can be little doubt that such practices were strategies for absorbing a potentially subversive literary form into the elite learned culture of the age. In a sense, each practitioner had to come to terms with the rebellious freedom of the form in opposition to the repressive standards of collective mores. The English would be equally tempted to ease reception by adopting similar strategies.

Perhaps the first English excursion into the novella appeared as early as 1531 with Thomas Elyot's retelling of Boccaccio's tale of Titus and Gissipus (*Decameron*, X. viii) in his *Book of the Governor*. But the first work that signals a serious and sustained interest in the genre was *The Palace of Pleasure*. The parts appearing in 1566 and 1567 together formed a collection of 101 tales drawn from Boccaccio, Bandello, Giraldi, Straparola, Marguerite of Navarre and others. This work had a profound influence on English letters both as a model for English prose fiction and as a source of plot material for the English stage. As Joseph Jacobs has noted, *The Palace* is the largest collection of English prose to appear between Malory and Thomas North's translation of Plutarch's *Lives*. The eight collections of novellas next in importance, including Riche's *Farewell*, neither amount to as many stories nor furnish as many plots for the stage.[33] In many ways, the renaissance of prose fiction in Elizabethan England owes its origins to Painter, simply by dint of the clear break his stories represent with the earlier homily, romance, and fabliau.

One hastens to qualify that Painter also absorbed certain of the practices of his French sources. He too added stylistic embellishments for the sake of copiousness and indulged in his own moral mollifications. That he defends these stories as valuable exempla whereby the reader might learn to imitate virtue and to shun vice, while at the same time passing them off as mere recreations and idle diversions for the refreshment of the mind, hints at the motives behind his modifications. His double position seems to dissociate entirely the didactic from the diversionary in his fiction—the result of advancing two entirely separate rationales for the acceptability of his work. Subsequent writers, including Riche, would perpetuate both formulae. But a reading of Painter—who can still be read with considerable pleasure today—will reveal that his overlay of morals and embellishments do no fundamental damage to his effectiveness as a story teller. That was his principal legacy to an entire generation of writers. With *The Palace* came a vast vocabulary of social motivation and trickery, new styles of greed, revenge, lust, jealousy, anger, as well as idealized devotion and heroic constancy, and an extensive repertoire of intrigue patterns and character types. English society had its moments of drama, but nothing that could give birth to the sustained raciness, passion and cunning of the characters in the novella tradition. The English were clearly fascinated, and Painter seized the opportunity to appropriate this literary experience for his own country. That he was at work in the 1560s sheltered him from subsequent stylistic excesses such as Euphuism with its artificially balanced syntax and endless sententiae. *The Palace* was an imposing anthology of short and vital stories, characterized by schematic intrigue structures and a persistent degree of moral indecisiveness derived from the ambiguity of experience

---

[33] William Painter, *The Palace of Pleasure*, ed. Joseph Jacobs, 3 vols. (New York: Dover 1966 [rpr. of London: Nutt, 1890]), I, xxvii.

itself. Such was the strength of the genre which Painter passed to his contemporaries.

During the fifteen years that separate the publication of *The Palace of Pleasure* from Riche's *Farewell* several collections of novellas appeared. But for our purposes only one requires mention, not only because it was one of the more innovative and popular, but because it was the only other collection by an English writer that Riche used extensively in writing his eight stories. George Pettie's *Petite Palace of Pettie his Pleasure* was first published in 1576 and ran through at least six editions by 1613. It contains some twelve pieces in the style of the novella. But rather than refurbishing contemporary materials, Pettie draws his matter from Ovid, Livy, Hyginus and Tacitus. It was a novel attempt on his part to liven and popularize classical history and fable by transforming them into modern fictions. In a sense, his experiment was a denial of the novella because it was a denial of its characteristic content, while in another sense, it was a way of endorsing the novella style by associating it with the official culture of the grammar schools. To say this is to presume that Pettie had commercial intentions in mind in performing the exercise, which is flatly denied by a certain R.B. who states in his preface that he appropriated the work for publication entirely against Pettie's wishes. Such a device may well have been Pettie's own, however, in order to distance himself from the published work while still claiming authorship. But it should not be ruled out that R.B. pirated the work, and that Riche himself may be a candidate for that office. There is little doubt that Riche studied the attitudes of the author's persona in the collection, and particularly his relationship to his gentlewomen readers. Moreover, he drew much of his proverbial lore from Pettie's pages and echoed many of his words and images. At the same time, Pettie the stylist is an incarnation of much that has been accounted the worst trends in Elizabethan fiction, for he squandered narrative vigor by encrusting his tales with euphuistic flourishes, classical allusions, learned and foreign phrases and some two hundred proverbs. His story-telling is frequently cast into second place by his show of eloquence and recondite lore. In that regard Pettie's work is important not only as a source but as a foil to the *Farewell*, for it represents trends not developed by Riche, or certainly not to the same degree.

Riche complained of the lack of books in Ireland, so that what he had he was compelled to use thoroughly. Almost certainly his manner was to copy out favorite passages and bits of plots into his own notebooks, which he then consulted for ideas and wordings in the composition of his own stories. In that way, a substantial number of echoes and paraphrases were passed from donor to receiver, to the discrediting of his imagination for some, and to the dismay of the editor who seeks to disinter all of his sources. Riche would be astonished to think that a twentieth-century editor might actually assume that task.

A particularly high percentage of those verbal echoes derive from Painter and Pettie. As Thomas Cranfill states, "Painter's *Palace* never failed him when he required help in christening a hero, delineating a character, evolving a plot, or, above all, constructing dialogue and soliloquy."[34] Cranfill, in his annotations to the *Farewell*, traced verbal echoes to some twenty-four tales in the *Palace*. It is noteworthy that allusions to Painter are most abundant in the first story, and thereafter decline, while allusions to Pettie increase, reaching their highest frequency in the last story of the collection. Riche, like Pettie, allows his narrator to break into the stories in order to tease and cajole his gentlewomen readers, and Pettie was the probable model for the modest program of euphuistic devices, antitheses, and isocolons that infrequently grace Riche's pages. In these two authors Riche derived a precedent for imitating the novella as well as a vocabulary of modifications that, through different optics, offered to enhance and to diminish the genre.

To suggest that the meaning of a modern short story is partially captured by a simple statement of its *topos* would be to display an indifference to the complex ways in which such texts communicate. But sixteenth-century story-tellers were given to grouping their tales according to *topoi* that describe a form of conduct, a common theme, or social issue, and in turn the story types that arise from these themes. Such topics should not be

---

[34] *Riche's Farewell to Military Profession 1581*, ed. Thomas Mabry Cranfill (Austin: University of Texas Press, 1959), p. xviii.

taken for what a story purports to teach, for there is a variety of lessons to be drawn from diverse stories under the heading of friendship, let us say, or war and peace. Stories could also feature such subject matter as the loss of wealth, perils overcome by quick wit, sudden changes from bad fortune to good, patience rewarded, unhappy love or generosity in love, cuckoldry, jealousy, mean tricks put upon men by women, or upon women by men, and potentially many more. The final impression, however, is not so much of the infinite variety of experience, in an absolute sense, but of a finite number of generic categories and social transactions that constitute the whole of the social fabric. There is a sense that with a sufficient number of stories one could move from phase to phase of the known social world and in due course cover all of its received components, and that, moreover, through a certain concentration of stories, one could ring a full round of changes within each phase. This allows not only for the organizing of fables according to their dominant subjects in a way that creates dialectical relationships among them, but also for a sense of the entire fictive world as consisting of tales both written and unwritten that correspond to a collective memory through which a people could identify its social experience. Such correspondences between narrative structure and a generating *topos* prevail even in Riche's derivative stories, for by dint of their patterning they continue to function as tales corresponding to such *topoi* as generosity in princes, or extraordinary virtue in women. Identifying these *topoi* offers a kind of perspective upon the range of experience Riche is typically concerned with, and hence an insight into the process of selection whereby he came to offer his eight specific stories to the exclusion of dozens of other candidates.

The operation of such categories is more clearly seen in the *Heptameron* of Marguerite of Navarre who takes, as an overt principle of organization, a number of preselected topics: men who play dirty tricks on women; women who play such tricks on men; the hypocrisy of the clergy; the patience of women in winning their husbands; the prudence of men towards women; women who prefer honor to pleasure; those who receive the opposite of what they sought; and the greatest follies ever committed. The practice creates both a sense of individual discretion in the shaping of a collection, and a sense in which the availability of the stories themselves, with their implicit range of interests, dictates the choice of *topoi*. The dynamics of selection come to common ends however as the profile of a collection provides the illusion of a cross-profile of social experience, to the degree that an author-editor seeking comprehensive representation also seeks to create an anthology of the social wisdom of a nation. Each story in turn serves as a laboratory for exploring some problem, conflict, or insight related to the *topos*. Such an organizational procedure encourages the reader to view meanings in relation to the thematic codes that, like genes, are a defining part of the organism. That is an important dimension of the sixteenth-century novella and a component of its creation.

Insofar as the *Farewell* contains only eight stories, it can hardly be looked upon as an index of the English social experience—and even less so given the Italian origins of its entire contents. But because Riche offers only eight in the context of the hundreds of novellas from which he might have chosen, there is the prospect that his selections were made not only with an eye to developing an entertaining collection, but also to choosing *topoi* of particular relevance to Tudor society. The hypothesis at face value allows that Riche's greatest gesture as a thinker may well have been in fitting his collection to his own national milieu through a process of careful selection and adaptation. Such a prospect is not denied by the fact that a clear demonstration is possible only after carefully assessing these *topoi* in relation to Tudor social issues measured by other standards. Only a few observations in that direction are possible here, though the question will re-emerge during the discussion of the individual stories to follow.

Giambattista Giraldi (Cinthio) published, in 1565, his *Hecatommithi*—a collection of 113 tales. The third, fourth, and sixth stories in the *Farewell* are drawn from this source through initial translations made by a friend in Ireland. We do not know how many more had been translated or made available to Riche for reworking, but it is a striking fact that all three stories deal with defenseless women threatened by seduction, who are, nevertheless, rewarded in each case for their perseverence, wit, and integrity. So particularized a set of common denominators suggests, at the least, a degree of thematic reinforcement in the selection. Assessing the degree and direction of his intentionality is

not a self-evident undertaking. There is first the designated audience of women readers for whom tales of women tried and proven
true could have had a certain appeal. There is, likewise, the
author himself with his own private agenda of psychic and social
preoccupations. Both courses of interpretation are more problematic, however, than the simple assertion that Tudor England was
preoccupied with questions of female chastity and constancy in
political, domestic, and literary contexts, and that authors might
thus be inclined to contribute through their fictions to that broad
area of discourse. Riche's interest in the *topos* of beleaguered vir-
gins is confirmed by the prominence of the theme in fully six of
the eight stories in the collection. There are intimations, at least,
that the *Farewell* is a collection in more than a random sense,
that selection indicates a range of reinforced interests and experiences, and that in making those choices, Riche reveals something
of the social dimensions of his imagination. At the same time, in
adjusting the patterns of fiction to an informing *topos*, the reader
is encouraged to see each story as a laboratory in which values
are tested according to the mediations of wit or fortune, and arbi-
trated by the order of closure. These two hypotheses will inform
much of the critical discussion to follow.

Principal themes in Riche's stories are often to be associated
with what it is we most wish to happen in the working out of
the fable. There is, in effect, a direct correlation between the
matter of a story and its teleological design—that principle of
necessity that directs an action to its one appropriate conclusion. We see, for example, a kind of reinforcement of a brief
for the clemency and generosity of princes insofar as several of
the stories lead to impasses that can be broken only by royal
magnanimity—impasses where all other measures of fortune or
trickery have failed the protagonists whose success in love we
champion. Several stories feature the disintegration of the family, and build teleologically upon the necessity of reunification
as the only tolerable shape of the denouement. The desire for
the cohesion of the family is one of the strongest in the collection, and stands next in importance to our well-wishing for young
lovers seeking union in marriage after their courageous endurance
of trials and separation. Both patterns are presented in relatively
naked fashion, not nearly so removed from the underlying rites

of passage that animate these two archetypal motifs as we would expect to find them in the novella. This archetypal imagination is a product of the movement between the displacements of realistic fiction and the conventions of romance—a subtle dialogue that characterizes the entire collection. These stories depict primal struggles that, in turn, produce codes of conduct insofar as fortune rewards those who manifest bravery, valor, continence, loyalty, patience. Equally reconfirmed is the *telos* of the young male hero who, ignorant of his noble birth, nevertheless manifests a nobility of nature that is equal to the expectations of his birth, and in so doing, prepares for the recovery of his birthright. Riche translates this rite of passage leading from obscurity to identity into the context of the novella without sacrificing its primitive patterns.

Riche's heroines are, with few exceptions, vulnerable but strong, active in their self-defense and, excluding Dorothy in the fifth history, entirely virtuous. Modern readers are adversely sensitive to narratives that focus the full thrust of their desire upon seeing the heroine extricate herself from threats of seduction and the loss of her virtue, especially while the author seems to be entertaining his readers with scenes of assault and narrow escape. The identity of such heroines seems reduced to the measure of their chastity and fidelity, while their struggle for honor appears like an act of reflex conditioning imposed by a patriarchal world order. One merely begs the question, moreover, by asking the reader to read as an Elizabethan. Are these legends of good women? Are they individual manifestations of a received idea that female honor and chastity is the counterpart to male courage and valor? Whatever these patterns are, they run deep in the western psyche and may in fact predate the imperatives of cultural genderization. What is worth underscoring is that Riche's heroines not only have remarkable powers of constancy and perseverence in a transient world, but through their continence they gain both grace and power that enables them to dictate their wills and control their destinies. In each instance these women gain a moral victory over their male aggressors. The politics of chastity in Riche's stories is ultimately the politics of female dominion. The theme appears to come full circle. Hence, for all their apparent recycling of the clichés of romance, Riche's tales may also persist as forums for some of the deepest longings and most abiding problems of the race.

Remarkable too is that at the center of his collection Riche includes a carnival tale featuring a subversive heroine who plays astonishing tricks on men, a tale which has no masculine counterpart. This tale serves to modify the balance of the entire collection. The resonances of Riche's themes vary as they shift between paradigmatic structures of romance and more realistic representations of the so-called battle between the sexes. This double optic, this compounding of registers, is the most critically challenging and engaging aspect of his achievement; it was the product of his efforts to modify the novella through an infusion of romance elements that, in turn, serves to reopen the specific events of social history to the elements of myth.

The novella, as it was first translated and then imitated in England, remained identifiable as a genre only for some two or three decades toward the end of the sixteenth century. Its influence might have been far greater had the entire movement for the development of prose fiction possessed sufficient momentum to see it through the seventeenth century without interruption. It is beyond my purposes to speculate at length on the demise of the Elizabethan novella. The poets and dramatists may have simply overwhelmed it, or perhaps it could not survive the double opposition of the humanists and the Puritans, who could not pardon its amorality and cynicism. Or perhaps the genre, as it was practiced in England, was unable to withstand a certain temperamental inclination on the part of its own practitioners to corrupt the genre from within. But during those few decades, the novella was immensely popular and successful, and served as one of the most decisive influences upon the development of Elizabethan fiction.

Translation, Imitation and Plagiarism

Riche was an unabashed borrower from the works of other writers and on occasion even boasted of the propriety of his pillaging, claiming that he would have taken more had the materials been available. His protest is proof that his methods of composition had come into question in his own day, if only through the accusations of malicious detractors. Nevertheless, his practice was born of the practices of his age, for one of the pillars of a grammar school education was learning the art of imitation through translation and copying until the style of the master became second nature to the pupil, and the wisdom of the ancients became contemporary commonplace. Tradition was a matter of cumulative repetition, preserving the integrity of a borrowed plot structure was a form of social memory, and echoing the phrasing of forebears was a form of their immortalization. In the *Farewell* Riche may be seen touching up or reworking the translations of others, or assembling new configurations of his own from pieces of other stories, freely embellishing them with phrases and occasionally with whole passages taken almost verbatim from some of the best known authors of the age. That Painter, who died in 1594, and Pettie, who died in 1589, were both alive and well in 1581 did not deter Riche from a liberal use of their works, perhaps because neither would have seen anything amiss in the matter. Yet a certain ambiguity remains. The rules of literary ownership and of borrowing were not yet clearly expressed; only opinion served to monitor that fine line between honoring one's predecessors through imitation and citation, and pilfering to make up for one's own dearth of materials and creative powers. There is the problem, too, that detractions asserted in these terms may say more about the writer's character than about his literary integrity—that a gentle Shakespeare may be allowed to borrow and refit, whereas a less savory Riche may only be thought to plunder and forge.

An evaluation of Riche's work in precisely these terms was proposed by John Leon Lievsay, who took umbrage at the efforts of Cranfill to champion Riche as a forgotten Elizabethan who merited a higher status among the writers of that age. "Now Elizabethans," he argues, "though they did not make such sharp distinctions as would nowadays be made in matters of plagiarism, knew perfectly well the difference between that kind of 'imitation' which is legitimate and laudable and that other kind of petty larceny which is exemplified from beginning to end in Rich's works."[35] Quite naturally, an editor of Riche might reveal a cer-

---

[35] "A Word about Barnaby Rich," pp. 391–92.

tain bias in promoting the reputation of an author upon whom
he has expended a great deal of labor, while another, for the
sake of keeping minor authors out of the canon, might attempt
to locate ostensibly absolute standards whereby greatness can be
distinguished from insignificance. In point of fact, Lievsay, given
audience in his own terms, brings a damaging indictment against
Riche, one not easily dispelled, for he can and does demonstrate
the many and often long passages Riche copied without attribu-
tion. Even worse, he points out the many occasions on which
Riche plagiarized himself by refurbishing passages from earlier
works in order to fill out later ones. Only in this way could
he create the twenty-six books (often merely long tracts) he so
proudly credited to himself. Adjusting the ratios of borrowed to
original material in his defense is fruitless. That he was a boaster
is undeniable as well, and for that may deserve lowering by a peg
or two. This view allows the stories in the *Farewell* to be but
brilliant collages confected from borrowed sources and festooned
with bits of dialogue and diction drawn from fellow authors, the
whole a product of a dishonest creative process.

Through a change of optics, however, we see that these stories
have a uniqueness and integrity of their own in the light of the
narrative traditions they serve to perpetuate. That perspective
is made possible simply by conferring a status of legitimacy upon
works of art created in the image of prior texts, and, at the same
time, by granting to those works their rightful degree of auton-
omy and anonymity. What is of enduring importance is not that
a creation is the vehicle of an author's reputation, even if such is
the intention of the creator himself, but rather that the author
is the medium whereby old structures are given new incarnations
and passed on to other imitators. I would even argue that the
single most important characteristic of these stories is the memory of prior structures which they contain—a function of Riche's
particular process of imitation.

Lievsay, in his indictment, is concerned not so much with plagiarism *per se* as with evidence of a paucity of imagination. The
playwrights of that age, as is well known, were involved in the
same larcenous procedures, predators as they were upon other
writers' works both for plots and for stylistic elements. The
medium of drama itself served to rescue them by dint of the neces-

sity they were under to reshape materials from prose to verse and from narrative to dialogue. The novelists were more vulnerable to accusation perhaps because the same degree of transformation of materials was not always necessary. But that is an apology where none may be needed, simply because borrowing was not necessarily the sin of minor talents, but the means whereby receiver and donor texts were intentionally related through a program of allusion and interreferentiality. Imitation was not only a means for creating texts from former texts, but also a vehicle of memory whereby the Elizabethans, for example, could preserve the voices and forms of the novella in their own culture. In the terms of Northrop Frye, what matters for this style of writer is the reflection of genius in "building unities out of units,"[36] in devising new and pleasing artifacts out of inherited parts. In this Riche was a master and may perhaps then be pardoned for extending that creative technique to include occasionally literal expropriations. Lievsay's accusations, for the modern critical mind, will always create a cloud of suspicion, but in the contexts of the stories as unique artifacts transmitting common narrative structures, his accusations are far less relevant.

The first, second, fifth, seventh, and eighth stories in the *Farewell* are more original than the third, fourth, and sixth because they are enhancements or reworkings not of a single source, but of several, ingeniously woven together. That process of interlacing parts of existing intrigues to create new ones still carrying the traces of their diverse sources was the essence of Riche's creativity. He described these stories in his general introduction as "but forged only for delight, neither credible to be believed nor hurtful to be perused." He underscores his desire to delight and to amuse with harmless recreations that make no special claims to credibility because they are "forged." The term might imply that the stories were either entirely fabricated or were somehow fraudulent imitations. But the more probable sense is that of the smith who works his creations by beating the parts together. In this way, Riche also differentiates his composite narratives from his mere translations. It is his figure for showing how the delight-

---

[36] *The Secular Scripture: A Study of the Structure of Romance* (Cambridge & London: Harvard University Press, 1976), p. 36.

ful pastime is created to refresh the spirits, not so much by its
claims to truth or to utility, but through its structural novelties.
The statement is important for understanding Riche's sense of the
creative process—one that is based on an uncanny capacity to see
analogous relationships among prior fictions, to see, as the sculp-
tor sees his statue in an uncut block of marble, how one narrative
order with its defining characteristics and values may be modified
through the superimposition of other narrative structures.

The first story in the collection, *Sappho Duke of Mantona*, has
been particularly challenging for scholars seeking out its sources,
not only because of their large number, but because of Riche's
habits of assimilation and reprocessing. D.T. Starnes carried
out the initial inquiries, and his findings have been verified by
T.M. Cranfill. Both concur that among the two dozen narrative
sources, the principal was Thomas Underdowne's translation of
the *Aethiopica* of Heliodorus, modified and transformed through
narrative motifs drawn from Painter's account of the Duchess of
Amalfi in *The Palace*, diverse versions of the St. Eustace-Placidas
legend, Giraldi's *Cesare Gravina* (*Hecatommithi*, V. viii), as well
as Painter's stories *The Earl of Angiers* and *Ariobarzanes*. To
understand their relationships, each must be read for itself, then
one must search out the features each contributes to the modifications and redoublings of the basic romance design. The exercise
reveals just how much Riche functioned in terms of existing narrative orders with their implicit degrees of truth and authority, and
also how remarkably successful he was in producing from such
variety a finely integrated, well-paced, compound narrative, with
its skillful doubling of themes, characters, and situations, culmi-
nating in a denouement unlike any to be found in his sources.
Nowhere is the forging process more clearly in evidence. To the
above must be added another eighteen or nineteen sources from
which he drew names of characters, details of plot, and dozens
of brief citations. Among these are at least thirteen further tales
from Painter, two or three from Pettie and Gascoigne, as well as
his own earlier translation of Belleforest's *The Lady of Chabry*.
The list may not be exhaustive.

Because the challenge to Riche's originality is related closely to
what I perceive as his virtuosic employment of sources, real proofs
of his talent can only be brought forward by plunging into the

full complexity of the matter. One further example must serve. The fifth tale or history, *Of Two Brethren and Their Wives*, is surely one of Riche's finest and wittiest creations. In Giovanni Straparola's *Le piacevoli notti* he found a number of relatively straightforward anecdotal tales illustrating the charms and trickery of women, as well as their spitefulness and bad tempers. The framing design of his tale concerning two brothers he derives from the story of Silverio and Pisardo (Night VIII, ii); it relates how two brothers marry contrasting wives, the one obedient, the other a shrew. The story turns around the question of how a man may distinguish a good wife from a bad one. Riche turns the pattern to irony, however, by modelling the good wife on Polinesse (Night I, v), who is but ostensibly good and who is finally caught hiding her lover-priest in a clothes hamper. Riche, however, derives the idea of making Dorothy a survivor of her ruses from the tale of Simplicio di Rossi (Night II, v). Simplicio works in collusion with his wife in allowing her to lure her lover to hide himself in a sack which the husband then drags out of the house and beats with a cudgel. This motif is modified by yet another story (Night IV, iv), in which Nerino, the King of Portugal's son, escapes the lodging of Genobbia by having himself removed to his own house in a chest by four porters. A careful reading of Riche's story will reveal just how he employed his several sources, how, in the final analysis, he relied upon none of them for the final design and resolution of his own story, yet could not have begun to create what he did without them.

His reading of Straparola's anthology of tales of light women enables him to produce his one multidimensional story of the wiles and infidelities of the "good" wife. From here, one may again go on to examine dozens of minor sources that added to the parodic and ventriloquistic texture of the tale—one that is at once a mock exemplum, an anti- as well as pro-feminist tract, a story of carnival license, and a trickster fabliau of splendid proportions. Arguably, such works are rarely created from life, but require for their genesis the architectonic possibilities perceived through an amalgamation of prior fictions. The example turns attention once again to questions of imitation, originality, and plagiarism in Renaissance texts, and once again the problem must be submitted to a double perspective. In the *Alarm to England* (1578) Riche's argument against his detractors suggests that he was already under attack for his borrowing, given his retort that had more such materials been available to him he would have used them.[37] But he says perhaps more than he knows in urging that the frequent appearance of the familiar gives an additional pleasure to readers with good memories because it allows them to declare the origins of his work in other works. This was not the subterfuge, but rather the expressed goal, of the mannerist artist whose work rises to the height of its *affetti* only when it is received in relationship to the textual tradition from which it was born. The full pleasure of the text for Riche was not only in believing in the reality of its mimetic fictions, but in establishing its relationships to other fictions. In this way the artist guides the reader by monitoring reception through the self-consciousness of his artistry.

The third, fourth, and sixth stories are the most direct and uncomplex narratives in the collection because they remain translations of individual stories derived through a mediator from the *Hecatommithi* of Giambattista Giraldi that are modified only at the level of style and detail. These three Riche refers to as "Italian histories written likewise for pleasure by master L.B." Although the evidence is largely circumstantial, there is wide agreement that L.B. was Lodowick Bryskett; the identification was first suggested by Edward Malone in the margins of his 1606 edition of the *Farewell*. Cranfill, for the sake of scholarly form, shows reservations, though he treats the matter thereafter as fact. Riche and Bryskett were in Ireland at the same time and in the same places, and "could scarcely have escaped being friends."[38] Bryskett had the right qualifications. He was of Italian descent, the son of a Genoese merchant active in London as far back as the 1520s. Lodowick was born in 1546, educated at Cambridge, and sent to Italy for the family company in 1562. He was there again from 1572–74 as a traveling companion for Philip Sidney. He had been employed by the Sidneys in 1564 or 1565, and had undertaken his first trip to Ireland under Sidney's directions in 1565. After 1575 he was there regularly and became a member of the circle of Edmund Spenser after the latter's arrival in 1580. As a

---

[37] *Allarme to England* (London, 1578), sigs. iii$^{\text{r}-\text{v}}$.

[38] *Riche's Farewell to Military Profession 1581*, p. xxiv.

gentleman's literary exercise, Bryskett had translated a treatise
by Giraldi that bore the title *A Discourse of Civil Life*. According to its modern editor, Thomas E. Wright, the work may have
been done as early as 1567, though additions were made from
Guazzo toward 1582, and the final publication did not appear
until 1606.[39] Hence, that Bryskett should translate at least a
few, and possibly many, of Cinthio's stories is highly credible. A
presumed friendship with Riche does not explain why he would be
willing to release his translations to Riche for such slight credit.
The answer may lie in the fact that Bryskett was not very serious about any of his scholarly enterprises. Bryskett called his
translation of the *Discourse* a "private exercise" that he had no
intentions of printing. Riche undoubtedly offered to polish and
refine a few of his stories for publication, making sufficient stylistic changes to enable him to claim them, after making a modest
acknowledgment of Bryskett. Once again, the ambiguities of literary proprietorship come into play in dealing with the origins of
the *Farewell*. But in the final analysis, they were Bryskett's to
give and Riche's to claim through the fairly extensive reworking
he gave to them.

In the absence, today, of Bryskett's original versions, the only
comparison possible is between Riche and Giraldi. There is reason to think that the distance between these versions is due rather
to Riche than to Bryskett, however, because the latter's translation of the *Discourse* was not only highly accurate, but literal.
Cranfill has remarked the addition of a few factual details (such
as the distance in miles between Savona and Genoa, and a more
complete description of the villas along the shore) that only Bryskett could have known. But otherwise the stylistic amplifications
are entirely of a piece with Riche's work elsewhere, including his
liking for doublets such as "joy and contentation," found in these
stories in the same proportions as they are to be found throughout the collection. The range of alterations indicates that Riche
was not concerned with fidelity to an original, but with telling
a lively and engaging story. To that end the bare style of the

[39] [Giambattista Giraldi], *Lodowick Bryskett* [trans.]: *A Discourse of
Civill Life*, ed. Thomas E. Wright (Northridge, Calif.: San Fernando
Valley State College, 1970), pp. vii–viii.

original undergoes change. Characters are more fully motivated, realistic details are added, the drama is heightened, and levels of emotion are intensified. Cranfill takes these changes for evidence of the "picturesque and the robust" qualities of Riche's style.[40] Riche integrated these stories into his collection by bringing to their retelling what he deemed necessary to mediate them to his English readership. Translation, imitation, word echoes, and allusions were techniques whereby he recreated an Italian genre in England, captured narrative clusters and brought them to new incarnations, and amplified his own style through reference to former styles. Vulnerable as these practices may render him to modern critical judgment, they remain, nevertheless, essential dimensions of the creative process behind the making of the *Farewell*, and for reasons closely related to Riche's purposes as a writer of prose fiction.

Fiction or Truth: An Elizabethan Critical Impasse

Philip Sidney's *Apology for Poetry*, as an argument in defense of imaginative literature, is designed, in large part, to oppose the distrust of fictive creations expressed by the English moralists and pragmatists. Their charges against the makers were often levelled in the name of Plato, who pointed out that fictive writers work merely with secondary and hence less significant and reliable realities. The objections have never been answered to universal satisfaction. In short, poets are little more than liars, or at best, confectioners of harmless fantasies. Truth and fiction were terms of qualitative distinction in a debate over the effect of fabling upon conduct and belief. So stated, the bias toward legitimacy and usefulness was on the side of history, on the side of those events that had actually taken place and that could be documented. In contradistinction the rationale for the purely fictive is that such stories were morally benign, that they taught no vice, and that they were utilitarian in their capacity to furnish recreations for the mind. Riche was willing to adopt both positions in calling his stories histories, as he invariably does, while at the same time describing them as harmless diversions not necessarily to be believed as true or historical. His motives no doubt

---

[40] *Rich's Farewell to Military Profession 1581*, p. xxxv.

had more to do with disarming the censorious than with demonstrating his views on the nature of fiction. Yet his contradictory terminology is a reminder of the debate over the truth of literature in its larger context. Perhaps Riche perceived no particular dichotomy in the parts of the Horatian dictum concerning the pleasure and the usefulness of art, though, in point of fact, there is an implicit sense that such works of fiction must function either as innocent recreational fantasies or as exempla whereby the conduct of daily life could be improved in accordance with what one learns to emulate or to shun through literary models. By one approach, literature distances itself from the real, perhaps even delights in its own inventiveness and artistry in order to release the reader from the quotidian, whereas, by another, literature relies upon its social and historical reality as the basis of its moral utility and authority. Riche vacillates between presenting himself as the confident moralist and the self-effacing entertainer, perhaps not certain whether he stood in greatest security under the one aegis or the other, and perhaps equally uncertain as to which attitude would best serve his purposes.

Riche does not wrestle openly with the question of truth in art, though his collection of stories would have furnished a troublesome case in point for the theorists of the age. Riche might well have extended his rationale to include the many kinds of truths which his stories potentially represent: truth to historical events reported in the novella he imitates; truth to nature through a faithful imitation of manners, language, and mores; truth in the preservation of literary forms and paradigms; truth as demonstrated by the emotions and sympathy experienced by the reader; and truth in the justice of the lessons indicated through the rewards and punishments handed out to characters through the actions of each story. The first is a potential rebuttal to the Platonic assertion, insofar as the narrative claims to be based on an event that actually took place, an event that belongs to a theoretically verifiable moment of social history. That illusion of history is enhanced by references to real places and to alleged times and circumstances, though it is to be admitted that such devices were often no more than conventional gestures of realism that were part of the genre. Riche might have argued that truth to nature generates fiction more real than reality itself because it

captures generic and representative conduct rather than specific
and potentially idiosyncratic behavior, and because it can reveal
insights into the human condition; history could misrepresent in
its specificity, whereas representational fiction could relate general truths. Structures also carry their own inherited truths, the
products of a cumulative literary tradition; even the imitation
of genres is a means of perpetuating the wisdom that generated
and maintained them. One could argue, too, that emotions and
feelings cannot be aroused without genuine stimuli, and that the
mark of a true work could be determined by the authenticity
of the emotions and catharsis it raises. Finally, truth could be
viewed as a function of the moral vision inherent in the work's
design, and in the order of the rewards and punishments awarded
at the end of the action. But, of course, Riche did not offer any
of these arguments. They are merely possible arguments on his
behalf that still do not resolve the more fundamental question of
his own sense of these stories as either social histories bearing the
authority of the truth pertaining to history, or as idle recreations
valuable only for their entertainment. Nor does either position
settle the question of moral utility or truth in relation to history
or literary fable. Riche's stories are apt for study for the evidence they bear relative to each argument for the truth of fiction,
and the counterarguments whereby these claims might be deemed
more specious than relevant.

An impasse concerning this critical vortex is almost assured
when the propositions are cross-examined for coherence and consistency. Writers of the period may well have appreciated that
history represented authority for the elite culture, and that it was
in their interests to capitulate and even to believe that history,
truth, and moral validity were synonymous. Proof appears in the
degree to which writers such as Riche were willing to identify as
histories, narratives recomposed from fragments of other narratives relating the most hyperbolical of events, overlaid with all
of the story-teller's artifice with regard to language, structural
play, conventions of characterization, and genre. One wonders
how the term could be seen to have any relevant application under such circumstances. One wonders too how much they understood the term to imply something antithetical to the story-
teller's art, something antithetical to creative liberty, the quest

for the provocative and subversive, the play of ironies and parodic structures, the self-reflective nature of literary works. One
wonders about the degree to which they were aware that, paradoxically, through these elements of fiction, a moral order could
be shaped and delivered with economy and force—an order that
differed entirely from the sometimes ambiguous and uneconom-
ical course of history. The transparent design, the intensifica-
tion of events, the artificial doublings of character and event, the
employment of disguises and trickery, the pleasing coincidences
and accidents of fortune all contrived to recommend those same
"histories" as the clever inventions of their makers—as pleasing
fictions, that, by the magic of the imagination itself, could remain
improving fictions. Again, Riche makes no such arguments and
does surprisingly little to placate the moralist or to accommodate
the historian. There are sufficient signs to indicate that he was
not indifferent to the problem, but that he chose rather to seek
indulgence simply by diminishing the sense of harm. He was not
inclined to show his moral sincerity by veneering his tales with
moral discourse, but trusted largely to the orders of fiction to
redeem the enterprise in the eyes of readers of good will. At the
same time, beyond the use of the term "history," he does little
to argue for the truth of his stories. Ironically, it was an impasse
neither in his power nor his interest to resolve, simply because
art that still believed in the integrity of its own fictive modes had
to remain faithful to the concerns and procedures of art.

Stories for the Gentlewoman Reader

On the title page of the first edition, Riche asserts that these
"pleasant discourses" were gathered together exclusively for the
pleasure of gentlewomen. That he had only a female clientele in
mind is to be doubted largely because of the fact that following
his first dedicatory epistle to the "gentlewomen both of England
and of Ireland" there appears a second to the "noble soldiers."
This alone would seem to invalidate any notion that Riche had
shaped his content exclusively for the tastes and interests of a
female readership. Thus, the *Farewell* would not seem to qualify as an exception to the assertion that no books were designed

with a female clientele in mind before the eighteenth century.[41]
Nevertheless, Riche strikes a pose in that first epistle that tends
to socialize the relationship between the narrator and his women
readers. His conceit is built upon the formulaic separation between the spheres of Venus and Mars. As a soldier, Riche profiles
the hardships of the fields as compared to the delights of the
boudoir, and asserts the folly of any man who would be a fighter
when he could be received as a lover. By such reasoning, Riches
declares his new "profession"; yet, having none of the social graces
necessary to recommend himself to the liking of the ladies, he
sees little future for himself, unless they would accept his "rough
hewn histories" (though carefully polished in order that nothing
should appear to offend their modesty) as a pledge of his courtly
promise. Willy-nilly, through the device, Riche opens with his
women readers by declaring designs not only upon their minds,
but upon their persons.

Sensitized as we have become of late to genderized attitudes
and maneuvres in literature, we are uncertain whether this pose
should be read as a comfortable figure for the commercial relationship between author and the female reader-consumer. So viewed,
the gesture signifies only that the writer, like the lover, tenders
his gifts, begs for acceptance, asks for indulgence for his inade-
quacies, and risks rejection. One may exaggerate the alternative
by attributing the pose to Riche's frustrated sexual energy. Yet
genderization of the maker and the intended receivers is present
in more than a figurative commercial sense insofar as the writer
styles himself a courtier, and his book as a gift through which he
seeks approbation and favor in untroped terms. To be sure, the
privacy of ownership protects the reader from any direct social
implication, while the amplitude of the press run subdivides the
object of desire into potentially hundreds of anonymous readers.
Yet the device serves to remind the female reader that her favor,
however it is interpreted, has been solicited by the author, and
that she must henceforth read as a woman, bringing to bear in
her relationship to the author and his text all that she would
bring to negotiations with a suitor.

---

[41] Laura Stevenson, *Praise and Paradox: Merchants and Craftsmen
in Elizabethan Popular Literature* (1984), p. 65.

The idea for such a dedication had for its nursery the epistle "To the gentle Gentlewoman Readers" prefacing Pettie's *Petite Palace*. It was the work of a certain R.B., who claims to have published the book against the wishes of the author as a "service to your noble sexe." His assertion that the "fervent affection between men and women" is such that he would risk the displeasure of twenty men to please a single woman is the kind of prating gallantry that Riche could also indulge in.[42] Taken at face value, he makes his piracy of a friend's work the proof of his devotion to the women. It is a claim of dubious merit that threatens to undermine an already transparent device. R.B. realized that his inability to claim authorship of the book weakened his case with the ladies. The question remains moot whether the initials were Barnabe Riche's own in reverse, making him the author of the device that was taken up and expanded in the *Farewell*. But such uncertainty with regard to the identity of R.B. does not discount the relationship between the two texts as representations of a common strategy for involving women readers in a genderized relationship to the text and its maker.

The issue may be extended by asking how far the idea of the male writer preparing a text designed to please the female reader enters into the design of the *Farewell*. From time to time, the narrator breaks into the stories to nudge, tease, or instruct his women readers—again a practice traceable to Pettie—but this does not constitute proof of a pervasive artistic design. One way of defining that sense of organic purpose is to approach the entire collection as a set of moral tales aimed particularly, if not exclusively, at a feminine audience. Paul Jorgensen, in his article "Barnaby Rich: Soldierly Suitor and Honest Critic of Women," takes this didactic role largely at face value.[43] In that way, the game of suitor may be taken merely as a pleasing device, broadly enjoyed, as a way of disguising the pulpit and of rendering the role of the women's advisor more acceptable. This is to suggest that Riche has designed all the stories in the collection to serve as exempla revolving around issues of vital concern to women.

[42] *A Petite Pallace of Pettie His Pleasure*, ed. H. Hartman (New York: Barnes & Noble (1938), 1970), pp. 3–4.

[43] *Shakespeare Quarterly*, VII (1956), pp. 183–88.

Proof of his didactic intent is the preponderance of stories concerned with the expression of maternal instincts, fidelity in love, constancy in adversity, and modest cunning and determination in the winning of husbands. The status of the author as honest critic of women once again suggests a collection specifically designed for women readers. This is not to say that the *Farewell*, *ipso facto*, speaks for women, but it is to say that it is engendered by a man's desire to write for women in a way that he believes will win their approbation and consent, or that, at least, will offer pertinent instruction. Jorgensen defends this view by describing Riche's female audience as a commercial one, made up largely of mature, middle-class, married women, who are satisfied with their roles in marriage and the family, but who also have a sense of wit, and who could enjoy the fanciful flirtations of our bluff but harmless author. It is not clear whether his profile of the audience is based upon an independent sociological appraisal, or whether it is his perception of the readership corresponding to the rhetorical ethos of the book itself. Either way, the precision of his profile of the book's readership seems rather too convenient to his purposes.

On the other side of the ledger, however, is the Riche who, if he is a true teacher of women, manages to be so only by virtue of the social experience implicit in his fables, and not by his intrusions upon the reader's privacy, or by his moral platitudes regarding honor, falling prey to fashions, and the rewards of conjugal obedience. Moreover, the device of the self-denigrating suitor removes much of the authority of his voice. There is something preposterous, if not grotesque, about playing the fool in the salon in order to ingratiate himself with his betters. If Riche addresses himself to gentlewomen in more than a perfunctory way, he is also pretending to a deserving familiarity with the genteel. To appeal to such patronage is but a form of social climbing by a man who could declare himself a gentleman only by the most tolerant of definitions. There is something ludicrous about a patriarchal Barnabe tutoring his social betters with regard to their conduct. The very gesture of personalizing the audience in this way subjects the writer to the reader's scorn on social grounds as readily as it allows the writer to dominate the reader through social leverage. Riche the courtier sets out to write legends of good women that function simultaneously as cautionary tales, while doing his best to humor and cajole his readership in all the ways that print allows.

The socialization of the writer-reader relationship in the sixteenth century may also have been a by-product of the oral culture to which story-telling still partially adhered by form, voice, and disposition, even after it had been transferred to the world of print. That is to say, writers still thought of themselves as creating performances on paper not entirely divorced from the sense of a live audience, or from the reader as auditor. David Margolies claims that much of the self-styling and ventriloquism of Elizabethan prose narrative is due to these residual models of the oral tradition.[44] To address an entire collection of stories to an imagined audience of women readers was a way of focusing the voice and of defining the role of the narrator. Once established through a prologue or an epistle, that manner of address was always subject to reactivation, as when the narrator breaks into the fifth story, in playful fashion, not only to seek the approbation of the women readers for all that the soldier in the story had said on behalf of women, but to assert in general that soldiers were, for their discretion, loyalty, and respect for women's liberty, altogether the most desirable lovers. Barnabe may appear for all the world like a comic squire of dames, but at least he names his game.

Perhaps the most compelling dimension of Riche's open genderization of writer and reader through the courtship device is the frank recognition of the author's awareness of himself as a male setting out to please women readers to whom he accords, nevertheless, the right to read as women sitting in judgment of his work. Moreover, insofar as men are also readers, they are, by implication, invited to read as spectators of this relationship between the male narrator and a female audience. In effect, they must deal imaginatively with stories only incidentally calculated for their pleasure or instruction; they must read as through a mirror by first watching women read. If women are invited to read as women, but also as women watched, as at a social event, then the ethos of the courtly encounter, with all that it implied concerning

---

[44] *Novel and Society in Elizabethan England*, p. 22.

gesture, play, desire, and strategies of personal advantage, is carried into the act of reading. In this way, genderal differentiations become part of the rhetorical design, part of a subtle program of ironies, part of the experience of reading. As issues regarding gender arise in the stories themselves, the same cross-values that create plot and intrigue are carried over into the process of readers watching readers. Hence, reading itself becomes part of the active negotiations between the sexes that lead to an acceptable socialization of sexuality. The whole of the design of the *Farewell* is both stimulus and monitor to those negotiations. Both men and women readers may join in the tussle, each reading for vindication and the confirmation of supremacy, each reading for the ironic hits and favorable ambiguities. The clumsy sport of the opening epistle does not, in fact, live up to the promise of the comic vision of the stories themselves through which an ethic of mutuality attempts to overcome the differences that separate the sexes. But it does abet the sense of the politics of gender that is an integral part of all of the fictive realities constituted by the stories that follow.

The Novella and the Conventions of Romance

In a previous section of the introduction, the *Farewell* is described as a contribution to the vitalization of Elizabethan fiction through a purposeful imitation of the novella. The novella has features that recommend themselves to the modern reader because they represent a move toward greater realism—that dimension which has often been taken as the ultimate mark of progess toward modernity in fiction. Such an impression is only partially true, however. The novella is also an elastic and recidivous genre that allows for the readmission of earlier forms of narrative—a process of recontamination that nevertheless serves as a means to the thematic revitalization of its social content. The process is fully visible in the *Farewell*; in short, Riche harkens back to the structural habits of romance in organizing and patterning his intrigues, and in the process he reincorporates certain themes and motifs that are inherent to romance structures. It is not easy to say whether Riche was induced by former habits, by the narrative models of his age, or by a desire to borrow the "wisdom" of romance in order to extend the forum on social ideas implicit in his stories. Whatever his motivation as an artist, we must nevertheless allow that the stories themselves become "problem" structures insofar as the lower mimetic levels of realism preserve a hermaneutic code in their vestiges of romance. For a critical reading of these stories, this may well be their most engaging feature.

In speaking of romance, such terms as primitive and atavistic are appropriate, although potentially misleading. The novella represents, to use Northrop Frye's term, a "displacement" away from myth. Romance falls about midway in the process; it is the principal genre out of which the novel is born. Moreover, "the more undisplaced the story, the more sharply the design stands out,"[45] which is to say that the closer one approaches myth the more the pattern of narrative is shaped by remembered experience that is captured in ritualistic sequences, while the closer one approaches the novella, the more one has at least the illusion of freedom to create according to that which is observed in random social behavior. The fact is that behavior reduced to narrative is seldom random, and a hidden force sometimes redirects creative talent to align the observed with the remembered, or indeed to recreate it in the image of the remembered. Riche may come to that process by artistic predilection as well as by dint of the process of imitation which is the basis of his creativity. That the most primitive forms of fiction can also be the most revitalizing is due to the transparency of the cultural memory that is carried by their narrative structures. It is for this reason that romance, as a genre, has undergone recent reappraisal, and has been given a new critical lease.[46]

For Riche's stories, the romance elements become a formal

---

[45] *The Secular Scripture*, p. 38.

[46] For Northrop Frye's study, see note 36 above; A.C. Hamilton, "Elizabethan Prose Fiction and Some Trends in Recent Criticism," *Renaissance Quarterly*, 37 (Spring, 1984), pp. 21–33; Paul Salzman, *English Prose Fiction, 1558–1700: A Critical History* (Oxford: Clarendon, 1985); Louise Schleiner, "Ladies and Gentlemen in Two Genres of Elizabethan Fiction," *Studies in English Literature 1500–1900*, 29 (1989): pp. 1–20.

matrix that serves to align his fictions with a select few archetypal stories. My primary purpose in following this analysis is not to confirm theories about genre and cultural memory *per se*, but to illustrate the dynamic tension within the stories themselves, and to characterize the generic qualities of these particular stories as a collection in relation to the salient narrative types that constitute the Tudor literary frame of reference.

In a sense, the stereotyped heroes and heroines of romance, cast in their idealistic and absolute struggles, motivated by their wish-fulfilment desires, and surrounded by marvelous circumstances, have never really gone out of fashion; they have merely disappeared into the more popular forms of fiction, or they have been transplanted into more familiar settings. As a form of popular literature, the romance has never enjoyed much favor with critics. It has been the object of disdain among historians of literature because it is not easily periodized. It lacks historical specificity by its very nature because of its stability as a genre. From the third century B.C. down to the beginning of the seventeenth century its conventions and characteristic materials show little change. The lost child raised by a foster parent featured in Riche's seventh story differs little from the foundlings of the Hellenistic novel. The Silla who is the sole survivor of shipwreck in Riche's second story has many predecessors, and the family separated and reunited years later by the tricks of fortune in Riche's first story is a standard element of the genre. The resistance to change is due to the cultural memory that invests its structures. Meanwhile, textual critics showed little interest in romance as long as they esteemed those texts that featured the ironies, ambiguities, allusions, and symbolism that could only be teased out by close reading. These were the necessarily elite texts. Romance comes into its own only when interest is extended to structural parallels and motifs that relate stories to myths and archetypes. Insofar as the genre is privileged by the deep cultural experience buried in its mythic patterns, it lends itself to investigations of received experience, particularly with regard to relationships between the sexes. Romance is a new territory for gender critics, narratologists, and sociologists of literature. While the romance elements in Riche's stories could only have damaged his reputation formerly, they now enhance his potential critical profile.

Developments in recent criticism have, in effect, created a new intellectual context that should be altogether more receptive to the *Farewell*.

If my hypothesis is correct, these stories of the *Farewell*, to the degree that they feature romance elements, should present the reader with a kind of double optic, a dialogue between the social anecdote and an archetypal motif. That motif will come into relief not only by the recognition invited by the protruding patterns of an underlying myth, but by the reinforcement brought to these patterns through reiteration in stories within the collection, as well as through comparison with stories in other collections. A striking feature of Riche's work is the tendency for his imagination to be attracted to variations on only two or three story types: the beleaguered but rewarded virgin, the reunion of the broken family, the struggle to a desired union in marriage after overcoming great odds, and, to a much lesser extent, the lost hero's recovery of his birthright through valor and good fortune. The first type will serve to illustrate the point. Fully six of the eight tales in the *Farewell* are concerned in whole or in very large part with attempts on feminine honor and chastity by men driven by erotic desire. Each threat leads to a rigorous trial of the woman's continence and fortitude from which she emerges not only safe but, in certain cases, victorious over her male assailant. Each story is told as a single historical event, but the patterning and paralleling tend to make them emblematic at the same time. The conflict of sexual interests is resolved by the performance of a ritual of psychic and moral concentration whereby the woman protagonist gains credit in the moral order sufficient to turn opinion and fortune in her favor. We sense that we are in the presence of a "deep" narrative, a fundamental transaction in which the woman is rewarded for her civilizing role in the management of sexual energy. Riche may have intended these legends of good women to serve in the most transparently moral way as complimentary and cautionary tales for his women readers. But even the most naively intended of fictions continue to encode the underlying rituals implicit in the conduct of the protagonists. For this reason the reader who is committed—through the contract of belief in the reality of the depicted world—to wish for the ful-

filment of the heroine's desires, thereby also participates in the
re-enactment of her myth.

If we look at this "deep" story, not in terms of its social function, but in terms of its structure, it parallels the paradigmatic
story of Persephone, who becomes the epitome of the harassed
virgin. She was taken into the underworld by Dis and there held
captive until her mother, the earth goddess Demeter, negotiated
her release. Her story is easily translated into a ritual of descent into hell and resurrection into the world of light. Such
an experience allowed Persephone, in ancient times, to be honored as a goddess of the twilight, having known the realms of
light and of darkness. Through her resurrection, she becomes an
agent of fertility, and through her periodic re-endorsement of the
darkness she assumes its mysterious forces.[47] Yet, insofar as her
adventure was also a quest to gain victory over lust and mor-
tality through the combination of her sacrificial submissiveness,
her fortitude, and her integrity, her story contains elements easily
translated into lower mimetic levels. Hers is the generic story of
threatened violation, resistance through self-mastery, and social
victory. As a rite of passage coupled to the comic design leading
to marriage, the story served the interests of the social collectiv-
ity, even if the female protagonist is subversive in her ultimate
dominance over the erotic appetites of the male. Not surprisingly,
the myth is at the foundation of the modern bourgeois novel, as
in Samuel Richardson's *Pamela or Virtue Rewarded*. Riche's assaulted heroines preserved this paradigm through the romance
motifs that informed their narratives, and, as stated earlier, such
structures were sure to persist as the implicit subjects of cultural
transmission for as long as imitation and "forging" remained the
primary processes for claiming new fictions out of older ones.

Inevitably, the romance patterns must form a part of any discussion of these stories in terms of their social functions as well.
That such fictions function as miniature social laboratories testing hypotheses about values and conduct is not necessarily a matter of authorial design. They may, in fact, conduct their experi-

---

[47] There is a sensitive account of the story by Arianna Stassinopoulos
in *The Gods of Greece* (Toronto: McClelland and Stewart Ltd., 1983),
pp. 178–85.

ments more creatively where the author does not lay didactic or polemical hands upon the design. What has been argued with regard to the accumulation of experience within romance structures is, of course, yet another condition of the experiment. A sense of the story as a social laboratory arises with the liberty of the maker to create the fictions of his choice, coupled with the belief that narrative orders are assembled in accordance with values, and that rewards and punishments are evaluations of success and failure, if not of right and wrong. Moreover, readers are presumably inclined to read stories in relation to their own social context, especially if they are members of the same age and milieu that produced the story. Later generations of readers are at liberty to attempt a reconstruction of that frame of reception, although we can never hope to read entirely as Elizabethans. In a sense, with our historical hindsight and critical tools, we may even surpass them. Our context for right reception may include a sense of the uses of literature as vehicles of indoctrination for young women concerning matters of honor and chastity. Didacticism is one of the potential functions of art. Such stories may also support the rise of the bourgeois family in Elizabethan England by exemplifying marriage as the sovereign reward for right conduct—an ideal we are perhaps better able to identify, given the advantages of historical perspective, than they.

One could look upon these stories as contributions to the polemic over women that had generated a subgenre of literature in which the battle between the sexes was reduced to generalizations about women as either saints or shrews, with few possibilities between. In that same context, Elizabeth herself offers a variety of models for women from humanist scholar to virgin goddess. The mystique attached to her virginity was a phenomenon of her own lifetime, fostered by poetic blazon and popular superstition— the belief that her virginity carried magic powers capable of protecting her nation and people. Readers are invited to reflect upon whether the mystique of Cynthia and Astrea, names associated with the Queen, is related to the ritual powers of chastity in altering fortune within the stories. As a social laboratory, each story will put beliefs and motivations to the test of experience. Each story will ponder a dimension of the relations between the sexes, of the instability of the world, and each will draw conclusions in accordance with the narrative motifs that direct the intrigue. Reality, experience: these are the words that attempt to signify the compound response that lies between the social context and structural determinism, between the spontaneous relation of an event and myth.

Romance has been a potentially subversive genre to the degree that it has allowed for, even championed, the wish fulfilment of the woman in opposition to a male hegemony. Moreover, it has granted to her, as one of its operational characteristics, the right to use trickery and cunning in order to arrive at her ends; it is hers in compensation for her physical weakness. These factors increase her chances of marrying the suitor of her choice—a prerogative often assumed for her by the genre. In this way she becomes a fair match for the male ego and for male erotic drives. Such advantages are revealed throughout the *Farewell*, and never more clearly than in the fifth story where Dorothy becomes the trickster motivated not merely by self-preservation, but by her own hedonistic drives. The heroines of *Twelfth Night, As You Like It*, and *Alls Well that Ends Well* are full incarnations of the type who practice the schemes, manage the disguises, and orchestrate the deceptions necessary, first to maintain their integrity as women in difficult worlds, and then to wrestle into marriage the men of their choice. In harsher versions, such heroines must pass through a period of threat, suffering, and endurance, must survive the world of the nightmare that anticipates the recovery of reality and pleasure. In the romance of the female heroine, uncontrolled erotic desire is the most conventional destabilizing factor. The fundamental content of the underlying myth involves the control and exploitation of phallic energy. Out of this nexus arises the institutionalization of desire in marriage, while marriage itself is internalized by the feminine psyche as her greatest good. We see this clearly in Spenser's Britomart, who is certainly to be understood as one of the major paradigms of that literary age regarding the heroine of the romance ideal. The woman may be an adventurer on behalf of her chastity, but rarely on behalf of her sexual freedom. The mythos of the female psyche is to be defined, rather, in terms of the nourishing mother and all that is necessary to secure that role. Her method is to gain control over the institution of marriage, and to maintain an unwavering faith in the good marriage, in the ideal of the eternal couple. That is why marriage or the restoration of the foreordained couple is the right conclusion to romance intrigue; that is why Agatha cannot abandon the husband who attempted to poison her in Riche's sixth story and marry the apothecary who adores her, for in regaining her husband she achieves perfect control over the institution of marriage insofar as a single further infraction on the part of Gonsales would mean full intervention by the good magistrate. In romance, the measure of living happily ever after is the assumption of stable conditions for motherhood. The heroine of romance seeks this end through wit, the careful management of her chastity, and a corresponding censorship of the male imagination. The appearance of the romance-styled heroine in Riche's stories requires that the conventions and themes of the genre must form a part of the critical appraisal of these works.

Just as the romance-novella formula seeks a place in the continuum between myth and mimetic realism, so in social terms these stories seek a place in the continuum between the female protagonist marginalized for her unearthly virtue and the female protagonist marginalized for her irreconcilability to domestic tranquility. The two processes are closely interrelated: the former is a matter of the evolution of literary structures and their "vertical" relationships; the latter is a question relating to the Tudor literary context. If these stories value the rites of passage leading to the emancipation or reward of the heroine and to the restoration of the family unit, they do so within a larger literary context that offers both parallel and contrasting narratives. As has been stated, the question of women's natures had already settled into a formal polarized controversy in which virtue was represented by tales of near martyrdom in the preservation of chastity, while vice was revealed through tales of shrews, temptresses, and viragoes, stories of domestic strife, infidelity, and the limits of male tolerance and long-suffering. It was an issue fixed in the Tudor imagination that produced works as diverse as Edward Gosynhill's *Schoolhouse of Women* and Book Three of Spenser's *Faerie Queene*. The anatomization of women through literary exempla was a passionate Tudor pastime, and any collection of stories, no matter how modified in the direction of history, could not escape evaluation in these terms. That women were wholly virtuous or wholly vicious was the least interesting face of the controversy. The more nuanced fictional accounts abandoned the open polemics, and turned instead to a genderized point of view divided between stories of good men distracted or destroyed by passions provoked by temptresses, and stories of good women attempting to control their destinies in a dangerous world. Together, these stories make up by far the most significant part of the Tudor literary creation, and together they form a complex forum on the nature of women, as potential redeemers and as potential destroyers.

Humanist writers, who as educators turned their energies to the formation of an elite corps of statesmen, lawyers, and theologians, took up the brief against woman the temptress through stories exhorting young men to refrain from the destructive pleasures of the flesh—stories generally marred by the transparency of their didacticism. Riche's work stands out in contrast to the episodic *bildungsroman* accounts of the emerging hero whose adventures have to do with the wiles of the deceitful female and the allurements of the passions. The generic story follows the career of a young man of quality, nurtured in a kind of paradise of male bonding, who risks everything through his prodigality. John Lyly was a leading practitioner of the formula in his *Euphues*, and Shakespeare recounts essentially the same story of male friendship interrupted by lust in the sonnets. Warnings about squandered time and mutability take on a primary significance as the adolescent confronts the limitations of his personal resources and the loss of his innocence through his own wantonness. If the protagonist learns in time to steel himself against the effeminate indulgences of courtly love, to refrain from inordinate passion, to cherish male friendships, and to avoid the snares of women, he may be recovered as a kind of returned prodigal. Or he may be lost to unprofitableness, melancholy, obscurity, or death. There is, of course, a strong misogynist undercurrent in these stories, the inevitable by-product of a story-telling tradition linked to the values of mercantile productivity, political stability, and dynastic continuity.

Many of these stories are tales of adventure cast in the mode of social or chivalric romance. Hence, mere distinctions of genre will not serve to distinguish these stories from those dealing with the assaulted virgin. The episodic structuring, the fickleness of

fortune, the wandering protagonists, indeed all the traits of romance are potentially common to both story types. But the *telos*
of each story type is determined differently, the one by the enduring heroine, the other by the hoped-for rescue and return of
the prodigal male. These stories simply cause the reader to long
for different ends. In the male adventure, the protagonist, as a
subject of temptation and repentance, sometimes approximates
the pilgrim of the soul; allegory comes closer to the surface. The
return of a wiser but sadder hero, buffeted by inconstancy, struck
by a sense of the unprofitableness of social enticements, is central
to the type. That Riche also understood and wrote stories of this
nature adds to our sense of the binary relationship between the
tales of tempted males and the tales of beleaguered women.

In his *Strange and Wonderful Adventures of Don Simonides*
(1581 and 1584), the hero emerges into his world an idealistic
defender of women and their virtue. But Clarinda, the Don's
chosen beloved, merely deceives and cruelly rejects him, not for
another worthy suitor, but for an old and ugly man taken only
for his wealth. As Riche tells us in the preface, it is a melancholy
essay for the melancholy and but sober diversion for the merry, an
anatomy of youth misspent in the pursuit of a cold and inconstant
woman. It is no coincidence that one of the Don's adventures is
a detour to Athens to meet Euphues. The protagonist of Riche's
Adventures of Brusanus Prince of Hungaria (ca. 1592) considers
marriage a cure for lechery—a means to avoid fornication—but
concludes ultimately that it is far worse than the disease it cures.
The story is about the taming of a proud and stubborn woman
in an effort to make her fit for marriage. Both romances dwell
on disillusionments regarding the conduct of women; both illustrate the conditions that keep the sexes in a perpetual state of
misunderstanding and conflict. Men are victimized rather than
redeemed by love; women are merely the objects of male weaknesses. That Riche understood in these works the model of the
disillusioning sentimental education so well renders significant the
total absence of the genre in the *Farewell*.

Admittedly, there are many variations within the story type of
the romance heroine and the story type of the tempted hero, but
the two motifs remain distinguishable as structural and thematic
"points of view" throughout the literature of the period. Together

they represent a significant portion of Tudor literary production, and must have corresponded to serious questions about the social expressions of the male and female psyches and the difficulties in the relations between them. It is possible to believe that in moving from one ethos to the other that Riche was, to a considerable degree, aware of the profound contrasts in social and genderal values informing these distinct story types. The total exclusion of the semi-allegorized humanist, male, *bildungsroman* genre of story from the *Farewell* is more than accidental, and for that reason the *Farewell* has a specific place in the broader socio-literary profile of the age.

Much of the critical comment on the individual stories to follow will be concerned with the "polyvocalism" that arises through the reinvestiture of the novella with romance motifs. It is for this reason that meanings emerge up and down the scale that joins representationalism to myth. Relationships among characters remain social, yet they take on emblematic significance. Patterns of action are always what they seem, yet they may contain vestiges of forgotten archetypes. Pyschological motivation is interwoven with the offices of fortune. The tensions created are, in their way, forms of argumentation, insofar as the reader is invited to reflect upon the action at greater and lesser distances and in variously concrete and abstract ways. These stories are vehicles of social analysis that are colored by a tendency toward an "imitation of actions near or at the conceivable limits of desires."[48] A certain hyperbolical dimension is cast over ordinary behavior so that fundamental longings are laid bare. Actions at realistic levels of imitation also vacillate between symbolic attitudes of despair and dreamlike gratification, thereby generating an emblematic quality. Patterns of suffering and escape correspond to desires frustrated and desires fulfilled, creating the comedic movement from anxiety to reward that marks these stories. The symbolic movement of romance clarifies the transitions from captivity to freedom, from loss of identity to recovery of identity, from powerlessness to power. All but one of these stories hints at the transferring of power, through a ritual of suffering and self-

---

[48] Northrop Frye, *Anatomy of Criticism* (New York: Athanaeum [1957], 1967), p. 136.

proving, from the older generation to the younger. In this way, too, the experiences at the "limits of desire" are transferred to lower mimetic forms. In disguise plots where girls become boys, we have preposterous though attractive situations that, nevertheless, answer to a wish-fulfillment sequence, such as the bonding between a prince and a page, in Riche's second story, that allows for the transition to husband and wife. We see the denial and the reclamation of the self, the passage and the return, that is imbued with pure desire. In the seventh story a leper son redeems his birthright by valor, though desire brings him near the nightmare of parricide at the same time. Story and myth interact in the tale of Aramanthus, who is both a man of adventure and a fairy-tale prince.

Introductions to the Stories

Sappho Duke of Mantona

This story is by far the longest in the collection and, as the first, the length suggests that Riche was still uncertain of his new directions as a writer of short fiction. The action is set in a Mediterranean-like world bearing place names that are almost familiar. The drawn-out, episodic action and the conventions of the narrative are redolent of Hellenistic romance. The characters are generalized according to their roles and they are each, in turn, called upon to deal with poignant adversity, albeit as an expected dimension of the sublunary world. Christian patience, stoicism, and chivalric endurance unite into a single ethic. Despite the length, however, there is a lack of leisure in the style, a sense in which Riche sought to manage this compound plot that stretches over two generations with a degree of economy and efficiency. Riche is writing old style, but he seeks a fresh symmetry and grace in the telling and concentrates on pleasing his readers.

The traditional approach to this story has been through its sources, and there is no doubt that such an approach must form at least a part of any critical analysis, given the rich overlay of materials represented. D.T. Starnes, many years ago, laid the groundwork; he traced the central fable, not to a prior novella or

romance, as one might expect, but to a saint's legend.[49] Sappho's
career is based on the life of St. Eustache the martyr who, before
his conversion, was Placidas, a Roman commander under Trajan.
As his initiation into Christianity, Placidas was tested like Job,
first by the loss of his wealth, then by separation from his wife
and children. Fifteen years he toiled as a common laborer before
being recalled to his military post by the emperor. The wars lead
him to the town where his wife is a seamstress. Soldiers from
his army are billeted with her and one of them, by telling his
story, rediscovers his mother. Word of the marvelous reunion is
passed throughout the camp, and Placidas thereby rediscovers
both wife and son. The high incidence of parallel motifs places
the relationship between the two stories beyond doubt. At a
glance, one sees how Christian legend was secularized, and how
the wheel of fortune, first casting men down to lowest despair then
raising them aloft to new happiness and prosperity, takes over as
the organizing principle of the fable. In Riche's version, the Job-
like laments, the outcries against fortune, the medieval fatalism
concerning adversity and prosperity are still in the foreground. In
parallel fashion, the Duchess of Mantona, like Theospita, the wife
of Eustace, works at her needle for a livelihood and withstands the
assaults of unwanted suitors. She is an analogue of the patient
Griselda figure, her woes echoing those of her husband, and a
sister to the beleaguered virgin, now more like Penelope than like
Persephone, who must struggle to remain aloof until her husband
can return. It is the constancy motivated by faith and love that
permits the reconstitution of the family. This is surely one of the
most enduring and emotional themes in western literature.

Riche's genius in his adaptation of the legend is most in evidence in his handling of the parallel destinies of the two children: the lost Aurelianus and the dutiful Phylene. Both reveal
the innate nobility and courage of spirit that was the heritage
of their noble births. Both find worthy partners who are nevertheless forbidden to them by dint of their impoverished circumstances. Both, upon recovering their parents, are able to fulfil

---

[49] "Barnabe Riche's 'Sappho Duke of Mantona': A Study in Elizabethan Story-Making," *Studies in Philology*, 30 (July, 1933), pp. 455-
72.

their desires—Aurelianus (Sylvanus) in gaining approval of his
clandestine marriage to Valeria, Phylene in having permission to
marry Arabianus. Riche came by the material for their interlock-
ing stories in a diversity of sources. For the mechanisms of the
courtship of Sylvanus and Valeria, he turned to Painter's *Duchess
of Malfy* (a story best known today from plays by Webster and
Lope de Vega), in which a widowed duchess courts and secretly
marries her steward. Sylvanus, the presumably low-born orphan,
plays an unwitting prince-in-disguise role in attracting the love of
the princess through his innate qualities. She, like the duchess,
hints at her love, woos the boy, and encourages the clandestine
union. But the tragic thrust of the original story must be interrupted if Riche is to join this story to the happy reunion of the
family.

The plot motifs necessary for making that transition he finds
in the *Aethiopica* of Heliodorus. Paradoxically, in this tale the
hero and heroine, Theagenes and Chariclea, are rescued by dint
of the discovery of their secret marriage, for they had otherwise
been individually singled out for ritual sacrifice. In due course,
it is discovered that the girl is nobly born, and that the boy is
the son of the man designated his executioner. In the face of
such unnaturalness, the crowds call out for remission for the two
lovers. Similarly, the sudden rise in Aurelianus's social status
with the rediscovery of his father alters the anger of the girl's
father, and Sappho is thereby released from the duty of executing his own son. These are the principal sources among the two
dozen or more employed. The dovetailing of the parts is an indication of the processes of Riche's creative imagination. It is
striking that a Hebraic, Job-like tale of suffering and endurance
could be wedded, through romance conventions, to the comedy of
troubled courtship, parental interference, and final union. Riche
finds the means to bring these diverse "myths" to closure in a
single peripeteia.

The story of the Duchess of Amalfi features a tragic denouement; that of Theogenes and Chariclea is shadowed by ritual
sacrifice; the saint's life is a study of the family in distress. The
persistence of structural echoes, of themes and their displaced
variations, provides a surprising degree of resonance, enhanced
by the careful reinforcement of motifs through the structural par-

allels that make mirror images of the brother and sister stories. Ancient religious rites and tragedy are just below the surface. The measured displays of rhetoric in the speeches and the moving circumstances of the characters lend a satisfying texture of language and feeling to the surface, making the story of Sappho one of Riche's best performances.

The story did not go unnoticed in its own time. The anonymous author of *The Weakest Goeth to the Wall* not only borrowed from this work for his plot, but dramatized many of Riche's lines and named one of his minor characters Barnaby. The play was published in 1600 "as it hath bene sundry times plaide by the right honourable Earle of Oxenford, Lord great Chamberlaine of England his seruants," and it has been twice edited earlier this century. Cranfill finds the work sufficiently accomplished as a play to consider it the best, after the plays by Shakespeare, of all those inspired by the *Farewell*.[50]

Of Apolonius and Silla

The second of Riche's stories has received more critical attention than all of the other stories together because of its relationship to Shakespeare's *Twelfth Night*. That association alone has served to keep some memory of Riche alive when most of his other works had fallen into oblivion, though such an interest was rarely to his advantage as a writer worthy of notice in his own right. Even here it would be unthinkable to discuss the story without alluding to the play. The danger for Riche is that the play, because it is so well-known, becomes an inspired norm by comparison with which Riche's story is thought to appear as a kind of corrupted variation. One purpose of the analysis to follow is to establish the independence of Riche's own literary purposes in relation to his own sources. At the same time, because the matter of Shakespeare's debt to the story as a narrative source has been so thoroughly yet so inconclusively sifted by numerous Shakespearean critics, there is little point in reopening that controversy here. What will become clear is that both Shakespeare's and Riche's versions

---

[50] *Rich's Farewell to Military Profession 1581*, p. xxxix; see also T.M. Cranfill, "Barnaby Rich's 'Sappho' and *The Weakest Goeth to the Wall*," *University of Texas Studies in English*, 1945–1946, pp. 142–71.

belong to a larger narrative tradition, and that what Riche does with that tradition is entirely reflective of his talent and interests as a maker, whatever his ultimate influence upon Shakespeare.

The common denominators of that narrative structure were probably first assembled by the anonymous author of *Gl'ingannati*, a play written for performance by the Sienese Academy in 1531. It is instructive to be reminded that the story originated as a play, and that many of its dramatic elements were maintained in the intervening prose fiction versions. Moreover, *Gl'ingannati* had much in common with the *Menaechmi* of Plautus—the play that, by other channels, greatly influenced Shakespeare's *Comedy of Errors*. Significant parts of the Sienese play underwent the modifications necessary to turn theater into novella at the hands of Matteo Bandello, a narrative that became story thirty six of Part II of his *Novelle*—the story of Lattanzio and Nicuola. From there it was taken over and altered according to French tastes by François Belleforest and published in his *Histoires tragiques* (1559). Another version of the story appears as Novel viii, Decade V of Giraldi's *Hecatommithi*, published in 1565, while Niccolò Secchi turned the material back to the theater in his *Gl'inganni* of 1549. Debate will continue as to how many of these sources Shakespeare knew in addition to Riche and their order of importance to his play. Evidence is fairly strong, in Riche's case, however, that he knew only two of them, namely the versions by Belleforest and by Giraldi which he, in turn, modified considerably through appropriations from other stories; notable among them were Giraldi's *Cesare Gravina* (one of Riche's favorites for such purposes), and once again the legend of St. Eustache. In the former he found the model for having a sister accused and imprisoned in her brother's stead for abandoning a lady he had gotten with child; in the latter he found the model for Silla's attempted seduction by the ship's captain. Both are distinguishing episodes in Riche's "re-romanticized" version of the tale; both episodes were subsequently jettisoned by Shakespeare.

Given the origins of the story in a theatrical tradition that featured intense stage traffic and compressed social intrigues, there can be no surprise that its most persistent features include crosswooings, mistaken identities, and ironic situations arising from the use of disguise. Equally unsurprising is that in bringing these narrative configurations back to the theater, Shakespeare abandoned the early episodes of the expanded version in order to concentrate upon the final phases of the story, to the extent of eliminating all references to the cause of Viola's voyage by sea to Illyria. In fact, it was not to his purposes to let his audience know that in the *Farewell* Silla had fallen passionately in love with Apolonius—Orsino's counterpart—during his visit to her father's court, and that her voyage was for no other reason than to pursue her desperate and compulsive attraction to him. Shakespeare's own creative purposes are further highlighted by the fact that the idea of a prior relationship between the lovers goes back to the Sienese play. What is lost sight of in examining the transition to Shakespeare is the process that created the story of Apolonius and Silla, for, in a sense, just as the playwright was bent on shedding those elements of a romance-novella that were unsuited for the stage, or for his "festive" view of the story's events, Riche was intent on reinterpreting the novella version as a miniature romance in such a way that the deeper mythic structures implicit in the tale are able to rise again closer to the surface.

The prototype of the story is relatively complex and not easily characterized. Essential to every version is a prescribed group of four characters that includes a brother and sister who are lookalike twins. The formula allows not only for a new exploitation of the misidentifications relating to twins, but also for amorous misadventures wherein the brother may be mistaken for the sister in a male disguise. Riche's Silla expedites such possibilities by adopting her own brother's name of Silvio, so that when the real Silvio appears he will be called by his own name. In all versions of the fable there is an aristocratic young man beloved by a girl disguised as his male servant—the twin sister. This young man will be in love with an eligible but scornful woman: in Shakespeare she is a virgin lamenting the death of her brother; in Riche she is a widow; in the original play she is the daughter of the old man to whom Lelia, the counterpart to Silla and Viola, has been pledged in marriage by her father.[51] The formula of the prototype calls

---

[51] This is an element of the original story to which we must return when considering the last story in the *Farewell*, *Of Phylotus and Emelia*, because Emelia is also pledged to an old friend of her father's,

for various cross-adventures whereby the twin sister, in male disguise, is sent as a proxy wooer to the lady, and herself becomes the mistaken object of the lady's devotion. The denouement calls for an unmasking of the page under circumstances that permit her to claim her "master" in marriage, and her twin brother the abandoned lady. In all cases, the story is a study of the quirks and impasses of love that can be turned into possible matches only through comic shock, error, and humiliation.

Riche, following his own literary inclinations, extends the story in the direction of romance plotting. He begins well before the shipwreck, at the court of Cyprus, where Apolonius was driven by storm on his way home from the wars. Silla, daughter of the governor of the island, found herself so strongly attracted to the young visitor that she could not resist her passions. Yet Apolonius was entirely unreceptive to her "amorous baits" and only looked for the first wind to continue his voyage home. Unlike Dido of Carthage, Silla decided to follow the man she now considered the object of her destiny, much as Helena went in pursuit of Bertram. Her odyssey was full of danger, a rite of passage in which she hazarded life and honor. That she was hard beset by a lecherous captain during the voyage places her in company with the other assaulted women in the collection, and to an extent, her disguise and her role as wooer to a rival love were continuations of that suffering and testing of her fidelity that she must undergo before fortune would turn to her advantage. Far more than in the case of Viola, it was her cunning, her management of situations, and her shaping of Apolonius's sentiments that enabled her to gain her ends. She was a woman scorned yet determined to wrestle her man to the ground. In that regard she has more in common with Tirso de Molina's Jerónima in *El amor médico* whose strategies as a doctor-in-disguise allowed her to follow and to take into her care the man who had abandoned her and who had fallen lovesick for another woman. Like her, Silla had to

---

and like Lelia runs away in a boy's disguise, just as her twin brother appears, is taken for her by the two old men, and goes through with the marriage disguised as his sister in order to seduce the old man's daughter. In effect, *Gl'ingannati* is broken into two parts, thereby initiating two related story types that will end up on the English stage, both through the offices of Riche.

exercise a tolerance and a patience that in time might "heal" a temperament disinclined to love her. Hence, it is the woman who, through the use of a male disguise, makes the male psyche receptive to her love. Riche tells us that to Julina, Apolonius played the courtier with "fair words, sorrowful sighs, and piteous countenances" accompanied by love letters and gifts; this was the same Apolonius who, while in Cyprus, "had no skill at all in the art of love, although it were more than half proffered unto him." Is there evidence sufficient here to see in Apolonius a man able to act out romatic roles, but unable to come to terms with a flesh-and-blood woman? Did Shakespeare find in this character hints for an Orsino transported by his eroticized and melancholy imagination? Are we to understand that it was the daily contact with the unthreatening page that enabled him to make the transition that would allow him to share that daily life with that same page in her true identity? Sidney's heroine Philoclea in the *Arcadia* was unable to give up Zelmane the Amazon, who was none other than Pyrocles prince of Macedon in disguise, for when the prince threw off his feminine disguise Philoclea was suddenly afraid to be alone with one who had before been her closest friend. Louise Schleiner believes that Riche's story is not only another such study, but that Silla has negotiated the transformation: "Duke Apollonius learns that he can enjoy simple, day-to-day intimacy and affection with a woman too, when she is page-like, just as he always has with boys and men; the intimacy contrasts sharply with the stilted and bookish feelings he had earlier for the beloved of his conventional suit."[52] The denouement of Riche's story has a psychological time frame as well as a narrative frame insofar as the discovery of Silla's identity must correspond to the first moment that Apolonius would be receptive to her as a woman.

The circumstances for this metamorphosis are created by the abject humiliation of Julina, who has not only encountered Silvio and taken him for Silla in disguise but has come to court to accuse Silla before all present of being the father of her unborn child. All that follows by way of threat and recrimination was

---

[52] "Ladies and Gentlemen in Two Genres of Elizabethan Fiction," p. 12.

a product of Riche's interpretation of events by means of a conflation of sources. In this reading, Silla must demonstrate her
innocence to the amazed Julina in the fashion of St. Eugenia,
who exposed her breasts to demonstrate her true sex. To Julina
she recounts her own woes as a woman, her utter distress in the
cause of love. This is far from the ethos of wonder that surrounds
the meeting of Viola and her brother Sebastian. Riche seeks his
highest moment in Apolonius's recognition of Silla's suffering and
fidelity. It was the magnitude of her commitment that earned his
love, a sense of his debt to so much devotion. "O liberality never
heard before! O fact that can never be sufficiently rewarded! O
true love most pure and unfeigned!" These are more than words
of love; they are the words of admiration for a woman whose endurance in adversity had won for her a quasi-divine status. That
same mythological transformation will characterize other stories
in the *Farewell*. Silla answers to the story *topos*: what is the
greatest form of devotion and loyalty a woman can show for a
man? It would seem to be a case of feminine subjection and self-
denial in disguise. But that is to undervalue the intelligence and
subtlety of her stratagem. Her feminine self-mastery and the pre-
calculated discovery of her "true love most pure and unfeigned"
produces the sense of guilt and admiration whereby the female
gains a psychological mastery over the perversely eroticized male.

She has not only begged a place through her extraordinary
devotion and sacrifice, but she has reformed her beloved and indebted him to her. This is a tactic for creating the possibility of
"pair marriage," that ideal institution difficult to achieve where
men relate to women essentially through attitudes of dominance
or ascetic worship. Perhaps she has in a sense merely exchanged
male indifference for worship, but her own odyssey has been a
rite of passage whereby in the defense of her chastity and the
constancy of her affections she has commanded respect and admiration. That psychological victory over the male at least reduces
her state of victimization. There is a poignant counterpart to
Silla's quest for control in love in the person of Julina. She is the
woman who in having the role of nurturing mother forced upon
her without the legitimating presence of a father and husband
must endure not only obloquy but virtual banishment. In her
echo of Dido, "Oh happy and more than right happy had I been

if inconstant fortune had not devised this treason wherein I am surprised and caught," we hear Riche striving after the deepest resonances of a vehement grief. If it is thought that he is not, as a stylist, equal to such occasions, nevertheless we may appreciate what the trauma of her situation signifies for the thematic order of the narrative. Julina is desperate to find the father of her child; her quest for the wayward father becomes a parallel to the quest for the redemption of the wayward lover. Through such structural reinforcement, the manifestations of the legitimizing instincts of the feminine psyche become fully emblematic.

Leo Salingar remarks that Riche builds narrative at a single level, whereas Shakespeare, with his interest in festive comedy, orchestrates a dual perspective through such characters as Feste, who stretches our vision by transporting the present to a kind of nostalgic long ago. Moreover, Shakespeare succeeds in surpassing Riche's thrust toward realism by creating more individualized character traits, stronger and more dramatic loyalties, more dramatically telling coincidences, and a more powerful role for Fortune in resolving the events of the main plot.[53] Undoubtedly all this is true; it is a question of individual talent. But Salingar is writing from the perspective of the festive comedy with its sweet-sour contrasts, and not from the perspective of the polyvocal heritage of romance structures. Riche, in imposing romance patterns on the social fable, has his own techniques for turning anecdote back into myth, and the single level narrative into a vertical or synchronic experience. Concerning the strength of loyalties expressed by the characters, we cannot be so sure, for while Fortune may be on Silla's side, it is her fortitude of mind and her delightful cunning that allow her to master circumstances and to win the marriage that ensures to her a role in the institutions that lead to the succession of generations. Silla is not a child of fortune, but a woman whose loyalties arise in will and desire. That is an interpretation of the narrative cluster defining the story that deserves examination in its own terms.

---

[53] "The Design of Twelfth Night," *Shakespeare Quarterly*, 9 (1958), pp. 117–39.

Of Nicander and Lucilla

The third history deals with another set of stresses and complications that obstruct the marriage of two lovers for whom the author seeks the sympathy of the reader from the very start. It is the first of three translation-adaptations from the *Hecatommithi* of Giraldi, known in England as Cinthio. This is the third novel of the sixth Decade. Riche's approach to his material shares in the patriotic impulse behind many of the translations of his age: the desire to English and hence naturalize a wealth of foreign materials in order to enrich the cultural base of the Tudor literary establishment. That effect is largely realized through the idiosyncratic qualities of Elizabethan English itself, and the translator's penchant for localized description and rhetorical embellishment. Riche added such bits of detail, adjectives, pieces of familiar dialogue, that Cranfill could claim for Riche that he had turned "Cinthio's relatively sedate Italians, Spaniards, and Tunisians into robust Elizabethans."[54] Riche sought his own formula for maintaining the exoticism of setting and event that attracted readers to the novella while examining social values that were of immediate concern.

Despite the primacy of the lovers in the title, the story is, to a large degree, about the obstructing character, Prince Hercules, for it is through his generosity and self-denial that true love achieves its ends. This story could appropriately be grouped with others illustrating the *topos*: outstanding displays of selflessness and of magnanimity. The prince, driven by powerful erotic desires, and abetted in his course of conquest by Lucilla's own mother, is not only brought to relinquish his designs upon the girl, even as he has her in his grasp, but to supply the dowry she needed to marry her beloved Nicander. That gesture is celebrated as a form of princely self-mastery, for being "of that highness of courage and of that constancy of mind" the prince "was able not only to conquer himself, but also to subdue the forces of love." This represents a double victory because princely munificence is proof of the worthiness of a ruler, while a mastery of the passions is tantamount to a victory over the god Cupid, celebrated by poets for his tyrannous command over both men and the gods.

---

[54] *Rich's Farewell to Military Profession 1581*, p. xxxiv.

If we read the conditions of Hercules's attraction to Lucilla in Renaissance terms, that self-conquest becomes even more pronounced. Riche is seldom given to evoking the mechanisms of erotic melancholy in motivating his lovers, but in this story we are assured that Lucilla's comeliness has so imprinted itself upon the prince's imagination that unless he can enjoy her he must surely die. All of the authority of the medical analysis of love as a pathological agent is brought to bear on the situation. That his reason alone should suffice to beat down so fervent a drive constitutes the praiseworthiness of his conduct.

A second center of dramatic interest arises with the decision of a mother, driven by poverty, to offer her daughter for seduction in order to supply the dowry required to attract a suitable marriage. The idealistic innocence of the virgin stands out in sharp contrast to the pragmatic moral relativism of her own mother. Lucilla becomes the assaulted virgin in her own bed as her mother, in the neighboring room, turns a deaf ear to her cries for help. Were it not for the employment of her own wits, Lucilla would have been condemned to harlotry as a precondition for becoming a bride. The story is effective, through its brevity and simplicity, in bringing her trauma into the realm of experience that otherwise, in that age, lacked for descriptive terms.

The focal point of the narrative is the drawn-out negotiation between Lucilla and the prince in which she exercises a sweet persuasiveness in her own defense, while the prince urges her submission. The delicacy of the exchange is symbolized by the gesture of the prince in reaching for her breasts, and her care neither to arouse his anger nor to impugn his sincerity in gently pushing back his hand. No other scene in the *Farewell* so emblematically represents the primal contest between the divergent interests of male and female. The prince solicits but is held in check by courtesy, a measure of empathy, and his princely honor. Lucinda speaks for virginity as the only wealth possessed by poor maidens, and the only dowry whereby she may still hope to recommend herself to an honorable marriage. Just as the encounter permits the male to retreat into the honor of his aristocratic generosity, it permits the young girl to exercise a charming tact and quick-witted sensibility in the defense of her honor. She may be the beleaguered virgin in a more gentle social mode, yet her adventure is no less a trial and a dangerous rite of passage that stands as a precondition to the mythos of comedy—and her union with Nicander.

The texture of Riche's story is surprisingly heterodox in the light of its thematic sobriety. The reader is drawn into a serious combat of wills that answers to our moral expectations, yet the prince's enjoyment in looking upon Lucilla's naked body is sensuous and titillating. Even her tears of fear and shame are stylized as "drops of dew hanging upon roses in a May morning," while the hand, though firmly refused, has been enticed by breasts "like two little balls of ivory." If anything, it is this prettiness of description, together with the ceremonial dialogue, that counterpoints the mythic structures, raising questions about sensibilities stylistically dissociated. Such overtures to the sensual alert us to a mixed response in ourselves regarding desire and censure, and intensify the archetypal tableau of the suppliant male and the defensive female locked in "gentle" combat.

Once this generic motif is clearly identified in the patterning of the narrative, the story is potentially a reminder that nature has incited both genders to seek fulfilment of their physical and psychological natures through sexual union, but that it has at the same time enjoined upon the woman certain risks and responsibilities, while social necessity has enjoined upon the man the need to censor and repress his erotic instincts. Each new social generation must renegotiate the terms of that repression—a negotiation that was for Freud an unavoidable condition of all civilized societies. The story may continue to represent for some the harassment of the woman by the imperious male, but the moral order of the denouement also represents the capitulation of male interests in deference to the social condition of women and the sacredness of marriage. This symbolic action is presumably a reconfirmation of collective values and undoubtedly the representation of a Tudor ideal as Riche understood it. But that such a gesture of generosity should be deemed remarkable in its disinterestedness is a solemn reminder of the fragility of the truce between the sexes, and of the discontent that is seldom far below the surface in any age.

Of Fineo and Fiamma

This story is the second of Bryskett's translations adapted by Riche: the sixth novel of the second Decade of Giraldi's *Hecatommithi*. It is a tale of young love tested and strengthened by parental opposition, the banishment of Fineo, capture by pirates, the incarceration of Fiamma in the seraglio of an African ruler—a fantasy of adversity and escape. The realism of the novella, with its identifiable geography and particularity of detail, ties the story to the possible if improbable, while the stuff of romance furnishes the contents of an adolescent daydream adventure. These are the exercises whereby salad-days love revels in the persecution that quickens the delights of bonding, secrecy, and exclusivity; it is a significant rite of passage that serves to invest pragmatic unions with a measure of the ideal. In the end, the lovers return to Genoa, the land of the quotidian, to receive the long-begrudged blessings of the girl's parents. Readers are lured into sharing the daydream, given that we are compelled to see events through the lovers' eyes, and given that we instinctively side with those who suffer from alienation and who seek community in marriage. The order of nature and the will of God are both on their side; in lending our sympathy to the lovers, we also seek to confirm our association with the side of right. The *telos* of the story is never in doubt—we know that the lovers will prevail—thereby freeing the writer's fancy to design such hyperbolical obstacles as to surpass even the cunning of young lovers. The story surprises us not by furnishing the protagonists with one last unexpected ruse, but by liberating us from our bastion mentality by having the final reunion and escape depend upon the clemency and generosity of a pagan prince.

The relationship of this story to that of Romeo and Juliet appears to be accidental, although the common elements reveal how easily and naturally the vocabulary of events in one story may belong, in the final analysis, to a finite repertory of structural and social possibilities. The hero, against opposition, refuses to relinquish his claim to a forbidden girl, a girl who is defended against this intruder by her kinsmen. An angered brother provokes the reticent Fineo to a duel. Although no deaths ensue, a slight wound received by the brother is sufficient to have Fineo sentenced to death by the magistrates—a sentence allegedly softened by having Fineo bound and set adrift on the high seas in a small boat. Fiamma, with the courage of a Juliet, seeks to share her lover's fate by inflicting upon herself a similar death. On several occasions during the adventures to follow, despair causes the lovers to mingle threats of suicide with pledges of eternal love, thereby acting out a rhetoric in which the strength of the love bond is measured in terms of ultimate sacrifices. The conventional language of love-death, overworked by the sonneteers, seeks renewal in the experience of romance. A similar vocabulary of adolescent love, stolen pleasures, and suicidal commitment pertains to the entire tradition of the Verona lovers from Luigi da Porto to Shakespeare.

The story of Fineo and Fiamma reads like an opera libretto without the arias. One might argue that the absence of extended expressions of passion is a merciful reprieve for the reader rather than a fault in the design. Riche was equal to the task of halting his action to indulge in the long formal complaints of pastoral and chivalric romance, yet in this story he chooses not to linger over the inner feelings of the lovers on more than one or two occasions. But then, what could Fineo say that he has not already said as Fiamma awaits her turn in the seraglio to be presented to the King of Tunis for his pleasure? Eighteen months the lovers lived in anticipation of that dreaded moment, and during that time Fiamma utters scarce a word. One senses that Riche worked intuitively to keep his story moving forward to its conclusion without overtaxing his readers with rhetorical interruptions. He must have recognized that such vast islands of feeling tend to obscure plots and, in turn, the deeper symbolic order of events. The strength of this narrative lies not in the characterizations, but in the conversion of the sacrifice of two attractive adolescents into a celebration of their union. It is as though we witness over again a deeper story of the substitution by marriage rituals of the rituals of blood sacrifice.

And yet the story does have its characterological and psychological implications. It does not begin with the discovery of true love, but with the circumstantial alienation of that love from its natural social context and the separation of the two lovers from each other. The plot carries a double closure: the long awaited marriage, and the return from a period of exile. Pre-nuptial psychology has been projected into the narrative order of enforced quest and return, joining the peregrinations of the psychic life to the patterns of ritual. Even with the absence of inward reflection, we are aware of an inward experience. Interference has made adolescent love frantic and irrational, and yet interference alone forces the lovers to distinguish between permanence in love and passing fancy. Such adventures build up histories around commitment and deepen desire by delaying its gratification. Values are exemplified by bringing young lovers into situations of secret communication and collusion that at the same time necessitate abstinence, for such situations induce the commitment, collaboration, and mutuality that strengthen bonds and secure the nascent family. Once again, Riche's narrative order assumes thematic overtones that open upon mythic possibilities.

There is yet another sense in which the roles of the hero and heroine remain true to the order of myth. Fiamma takes an active part in pursuing her lover in life as well as in death, but she is also a figure of passive endurance in the twilight zone of the seraglio. Only the assistance and cunning of the fairy-tale hero can rescue her from the prison of her virginity, while at the same time he rescues her from a kind of ritual sacrifice to a pagan king. Fiamma is a projection of the beleaguered virgin; Fineo is a St. George figure whose prowess is invested in a complex strategy of escape. The focal center drifts, however, when the fraud of the lovers is insufficient to defeat fortune and the designs of the king. Their ship was driven back upon the Tunisian shores and live burial was their prescribed punishment. Yet convention dictates that such a fate will never come to pass. The prospects of intrigue have, nevertheless, come to an end; the comedy of deception is to be completed by a comedy of princely clemency, resembling the *telos* of the preceding story. Where trickery could not thwart the King, the lovers' only hope was to arouse his sympathy through the revelation of their secret love and prolonged misfortune. Echoes of the *Aethiopica* are still in evidence.

The story carries a remote memory of bride rights, or of the privileges of a fertility-god ruler among the temple prostitutes in conflict with the sanctity of household marriage. Simultaneously, it carries forward the declaration of secret love that rescues two attractive individuals from the ritual sacrifice of burial. The King of Tunis holds the power of life and death in his hands, and he is not to be deprived of that power by the intrigue strategies generally redolent of erudite comedy. In this story of blocking characters overcome, civilization marks its progress not by deviancy, but by conversion, though deviancy may serve those ends. In the final analysis, the happy closure is the gift of a forgiving patriarch, the ersatz father, who accepts the remarkable adventures of the hero and the remarkable endurance of the heroine as pledges of a favorable destiny in marriage. It is he who gives Fiamma in marriage, as though she were his own daughter; it is he who bestows the ruby ring and feasts the newly-weds while urging them to keep their promised vows. Marriage is not a pleasure stolen by craft but something earned through mental continence, as well as something received from the passing generation which alone can bless and sanctify. Such archetypal transactions are easily translated into the context of Elizabethan society where the ideal of the bourgeois marriage based on freedom of choice among the marriage partners was constantly challenged by constraints and arrangements imposed by the family as embodied in the figure of the father.

Of Two Brethren and Their Wives

This is one of Riche's most attractive and engaging tales, one of his most accessible yet one of his most provocative. A first glance reveals an integration of diverse rhetorical and thematic motifs in the embellishment of a witty intrigue; a second uncovers ambiguities raised by those same polyvocal procedures. The multiplicity of voices is a product of the genre, itself, which offers to host such divergent materials, both as a means for extending ranges of expression and as a way of compounding the nature of experience. In the hands of an accomplished maker, such polyvocalism becomes the essence of the artistry and not merely the by-product of a struggling new form. Such is Riche's achievement in this story, for it is one thing for him to have written merely a racy tale of license and self-indulgence framed in by a dull moral about the goodness and badness of wives, but quite another that he managed to turn such moralizing into an element of play. Ostensibly a conventional voice offers a pair of tales as exempla of contrasting behaviors in women. But the promise of an alignment between contrasting narratives and a moral order is bankrupted by the vitality of Dorothy, the life force trickster of the first tale, who rallies with her own counter ethic. In effect, she holds collective values to ransom by means of her individualism and bravura. The polyvocalism achieves its comic effect as various orders of discourse intrude upon the construct, each seeking to interpret the relationship between the sexes according to its own conventions. But in the end everything pompous and moral is cancelled out, leaving the logic of carnival as the only defining principle of order.

A principal cause of this multiple voicing in Riche's story— as it was in the shaping of the best early novels generally—was the process of imitation whereby stories are devised interreferentially with other texts. Those habits remain visible in such novels as Fielding's *Joseph Andrews*, in which the author foregrounds a composite genesis consisting of a parody of Richardson's *Pamela*, a quixotic parson modelled after Cervantes's Don, an episodic structure patterned after the picaresque novel, stylistic and structural echoes of ancient epic, all of which he calls an epic in prose, sometimes reshaped according to the designs of comedy, sometimes of tragedy. That manner of composing, carried out on a smaller scale by Riche, began with the conflation of four stories consulted in *Le piacevoli notti* of Giovanni Straparola. This conflation of marriageable narrative parts was, in turn, modified by details drawn from stories by Giraldi, Belleforest, six or seven more by Painter, and embellished with stylistic echoes found in Gascoigne, Lyly, and Udall. But it was ultimately the binary relationship of the two tales told as one that brings this story to its full measure of play.

The sport begins with a conundrum, whether it is better to be married to a "wise harlot, or to a foolish overthwart and brawling woman." The reader is promised an answer as a reward for reading a pair of tales in which the experiences of two brothers are brought to résumé in a simple moral: the good wife is she who, though a harlot, manages her extramarital affairs in secrecy and protects her husband's peace of mind; the evil wife is she who, for all her wealth and honesty, plays the termagant and never gives a moment's respite from her shrewish tongue. Attaching such dubious choices to a structure of good and evil is only the beginning of the joke, for Riche also devotes nine-tenths of the telling to the tale of the "good" harlot who is so robust and subversive as to deflate the framing device altogether. Reception of the story is further complicated by the open employment of rhetoric derived from both sides of the formal Tudor controversy over women. The values and language of the debate inform many of the speeches of the three suitors, who both defend and castigate Dorothy, and through her, all womankind. Each identifiable mode arouses its own expectations, thereby creating an involvement at the level of discourse itself.

In the midst of all this play of language and ideology, Riche further capitalizes on the genderized relationship he had created with his readers, first as the suppliant soldier who offers his stories to gentlewomen as a gesture of courtship, and then as the soldier within the story who there demonstrates his discretion as a lover by reeling off an eloquent defense of Dorothy's honor in full defiance of the most compromising facts. At this juncture, the story's reception involves a multiplicity of audiences viewing one another through the mirrors created by the events of the narrative. There is complexity enough for the male reader attempting to read through female eyes the experience of the beleaguered virgin represented in other stories in the collection. Therein the male encounters both a sense of his own inadequacy in the assault upon the woman, and of his own defeat by her moral integrity— this in the heart of an age still defining itself in patriarchal and chivalric terms. How much more complex to think of a male readership contemplating those same women readers and their potentially sympathetic interest in Dorothy, whose working ethic was quite simply that what she owed to her husband was her debt to pay, and that what she had in reversion was hers to bestow upon whomsoever she would. Moreover, all were to see that such conduct was granted the full approbation of the soldier lover, a barely disguised projection of Barnabe the narrator and Barnabe the spokesman for soldiers. Readers can now lose themselves in the debate between the sexes, a debate brought to a mirror examination through readers watching readers, both gazing upon the narrative that separates and unites them. They can also reflect upon the irony that Dorothy has been granted the sexual freedom that, in the interests of pair marriage and social continuity, has been denied to the eroticized male—a curious double standard for a writer like Riche.

At such a juncture readers are further than ever from knowing whether Dorothy is the good wife or the bad, if not, in fact, a creature entirely beyond good and evil. It would take a dull observer not to notice that the choice, in conventional terms, is limited to an unfaithful wife and a shrew. Male readers may relish the joke, while women may find themselves offended. But the story of Dorothy pursues its course. The doctor and the lawyer possess and then abandon her, only because each cannot have her for his exclusive enjoyment. Dorothy is in quest of liberation from the constraints of marriage and not in search of the adolescent bonding that characterizes pre-marital engagements. At the height of her liberty she is, nevertheless, celebrated for her sanctity, for her chosen status as one created not of the dirt, as Adam was, but of the best purified metal of men. And in the end, that chosen status is confirmed by her return from a natural prodigality to a necessary monogamy. Dorothy is both pragmatist and survivor in a fallen world.

The ultimate sport is the degree to which moral structures fail to define the heroine, despite the offer of the framing structure to do so. Dorothy is guided by a natural ethic, that if one lover is good, several must be better, and that limits to her pleasure are determined only by her own ability to maintain secrecy. This was a function of her social cunning and her capacity to slip out of restricting situations. As a pragmatist, she makes certain concessions to the male ego, but her first duty is to nature, and to her own avowedly polygamous desires. She is so open and guileless in her pursuit of pleasure that sin and guilt lose their meaning. As a manipulator of social realities, she is a kind of trickster, more careful of her freedom than of her honor. She is a manifestation of the trickster type in her exploitation of rhetoric by which she holds men off or brings them on at will. She is the consummate trickster in the stratagem whereby a third lover is employed to drive out the first two and beat them into the bargain. These are the bumptious tactics of the fabliau brought into the novella. She represents the type in her capacity to play the moral outlaw, and to make others fall blindly into her carefully prepared snares. In this way, she becomes not only an embodiment of the pleasures answering to the natural appetites, but also the confectioner of a carnival world where topsy-turveydom holds sway over social norms. Dorothy must be seen as an affront to collective mores who is nevertheless redeemed by her spirit of play. She is, after all, an honest expression of the erotic in human nature. In creating her own story by designing its intrigue from within, she produces a narrative order with its own sense of an ending in which the success of her intrigue alone can produce the desired results. The contract of belief sides with the trickster, and with the order of carnival escape that comes to a complete fulfilment before the return to a state of normalcy. We can be doubly sure of Riche's creative bent when we discover that the heroine in his principal narrative source was murdered for her infidelity. Dorothy's tale may be classed among those that describe the successful tricks which women have played upon men. But in the context of the *Farewell*, she also stands out stoutly in contrast to all those surrounding models of patience, loyalty, and subservience. That she does so with so much gusto is all the more remarkable.

Dorothy proves, in her own way, that there is nothing in the nature of things that declares women must be victims. For her lack of physical strength, nature has compensated her with a cunning that baffles her adversaries. By such means she seeks the control of her destiny, for whatever ends, in choosing her lovers, and in manipulating the conditions of courtship. Opposite Persephone is Penelope, with Medea standing well beyond—Penelope, who matched her husband for cunning in holding off her suitors. Brute force succumbs to trickery, a role taken up by Dorothy not out of necessity, but out of exuberance and a love for the game.

Dorothy's quest turns inside out the alienation-and-loss-of-identity model that characterizes the other tales of the collection, save the last. Her adventure is a parodic escape from marriage, an escape grounded in the drive to satisfy erotic instincts. Her infidelity assumes a structural expression that reverses the descent into darkness and the return to light, the movement from the disintegration to the reintegration of the protagonist. It corresponds, instead, to an expression of aberrant appetites that are vicariously released by such fiction into the order of the carnivalesque. Parodies of romance serve simultaneously to break down and define collective standards. The exclusivity of marriage is both denied and resented as an unnatural constraint upon instincts for freedom and variety. The escape into deviancy may itself be a form of reconciliation to the repressions of civilization. It is also a way of testing the margins of society and of toying with the sacred. The laughter of carnival may be the ultimate common denominator between readers peering at readers over the gender gap.

Of Gonsales and His Virtuous Wife Agatha

This is a story of unbridled lust, attempted murder, a graveyard courtship, and a last-moment reprieve from the gallows, a pleasing array of domestic atrocities just right for a theater audience that relished such business on the stage. The first playwright to help himself to the material was the author of *How a Man May Choose a Good Wife from a Bad*. Thomas Heywood is the leading candidate for its authorship, and the year assigned is 1602.[55] The play enjoyed instant success and exercised a certain influence on subsequent plays of the period. Thus, through the offices of Bryskett and Riche, Giraldi's fifth novel of the third Decade nourished the Elizabethan theater. Middleton, Rowley and Massinger took up the material again for the subplot of *The Old Law*.[56] These plays and their source could serve as the basis for a study of the transfer from narrative to dialogue, and from novella to play. Riche's plots may have attracted playwrights in part because they contain so many dramatic situations, and because their dialogue so readily suggests elaboration in the theater. In this story, Gonsales and Alonso the apothecary negotiate the use of a lethal poison for the murder of Agatha in a highly nuanced and hypothetical exchange. A similar dramatic moment arises when Alonso meets the awakening Agatha in the tomb to explain the circumstances of her arrival there, and to press his love suit. The dramatist had only to extend what Riche had already begun.

The story is remarkable for the extreme commitments of the

---

[55] *Rich's Farewell to Military Profession 1581*, p. xxxix.

[56] Charles R. Baskervill, "Source and Analogues of *How a Man May Choose a Good Wife from a Bad*," *PMLA*, 24 (December, 1909), pp. 711–30.

characters: a husband so blinded by the charms of a courtesan that he is prepared to poison his fair young wife; an apothecary so in love with Agatha that he is willing to prepare, in the guise of poison, a sleeping potion, the better to court her after her "death"; and a wife, so devoted to her husband that she would employ her return from the grave only to rescue him from the gallows. It is the formula of the homicidal philanderer, the devoted lover, and the dutiful wife. If there is a psycho-drama, it is in the values implicit in the intrigue, one that has a curiously persuasive power over the imagination.

At the center of this bitter-sweet scenario is a woman who, in waking up from the sleeping potion, has the chance to escape the husband who would have killed her and to share a reciprocal love with a man who had risked much to save her life. Yet she remains true to an ideal—preferring real death to a betrayal of her marriage. We recognize a new incarnation of the chaste woman trapped in a zone of darkness and death, who is beset by a persistent lover whose advances she is constrained by every means to resist. We recognize the integrity of her will and the strength of her endurance, which ultimately gain for her powers sufficient to rescue her former husband from hanging. If there is tension in our response, it is because Agatha lives out the order of a redemption myth that appears, to our social logic, to be but half warranted. Agatha stays true to the original myth of the goddess abducted into the underworld who yet struggles to emerge with the redemptive force of her resurrection from the darkness back into the light. But what she is to do with a half-repentant husband baffles our social understanding. By convention, the orders given to Gonsales by the magistrate—that a slight infraction against so divine a woman in the future would mean death—must stand as security for the appropriateness of the denouement. It is the story's genius that in spite of these social improbabilities the order of myth continues to function. Experience for the reader expresses itself as a tension between freedom and duty, between social realism and mythic order.

Yet there may be other value transactions and social leverages involved at different mimetic levels. The principle of marital loyalty seems to be the only reason that Agatha would so persist in her love for Gonsales. To that extent the story answers aptly to the question: what is the most remarkable example of a woman's constancy, or of a woman's sacrifice for her husband? Yet if Agatha's loyalty exceeds all measure of expectation—indeed becomes remarkable by its singularity of devotion—it is not without a logic almost as perverse as it is noble, for in her constancy she has also gained a mastery, a veritable tyranny over the soul of her condemned and eternally indebted husband. His very life is now in her hands. Agatha has been a guardian saint; she has also provided her own desperate solution to the discontents of civilization by strangling the polygamous male with his own guilt. The stability of monogamy may be built on mutuality and trust, but it is also built on debts, political power, and guilt. In the preceding story, the heroine has secured a polygamous liberty. In this story, she has denied it to the polygamous male. These are the social dynamics of civilization. The readers are still watching readers reading, while the narrator negotiates with his feminine readership for their satisfaction.

A second contest of debts and credits arises between Agatha and Alonso; we could almost wish there had been a longer hesitation on the part of the wife in weighing her obligations to her persistent and dutiful lover. He is the courtly element in a household marriage society, and hence the destabilizing threat. In fact, Agatha rebukes and rebuffs the young man's advances, diplomatically but unflinchingly. Yet the courtly perspective remains present, for just as Agatha had suffered to win the freedom to rechoose her own husband, so the young Alonso had long kept faith with love in order to hold at last some influence over Agatha's affections. Lovers also toil and endure in order to store up debts and obligations from the beloved. That she refused to gratify one who had saved her life was for him the culmination of her ingratitude, but it was for her the supreme moment of victory over herself. Two psychological imperatives come directly into conflict. In such circumstances the woman is compelled to exercise every resource to command that degree of admiration and respect from the assailant that is needed to bring his erotic desire under control. Agatha begins as a moralist by urging Alonso to bridle his unlawful and sensual appetites; she finishes as a eulogist by praising his act as "the most virtuous and worthy of honor and fame. . .since the world began." Just as Gonsales must live

under the threat of feminine control in exchange for his life, so
Alonso must content himself with admiring from afar what he
cannot enjoy: "in a manner to worship her as a divine creature
for the excellency of her virtue." The courtly ethos must face
a sacrificial ethos, as it often did in the stories of the age, leaving nothing but resistance and consolation to be shared between
the lovers. Escape from such rejection, from the sorrows of un-
requited passion, is made possible through the idealization and
spiritualization of the beloved object; Alonso's quest must end in
madness or sublimation. All that remains to him of the beloved is
the enjoyment of the mental image which his esteem for Agatha
has at last converted into that of a saint. Adoration of the sacred
object is a civilized response to the denial of the lady committed
by prior circumstances to the principle of the eternal marriage.
In this emblematic world, Agatha is both the faithful wife and
the unconquerable beloved standing in opposition to the harlot.
The courtesan gains her control over Eros through gratification,
the saint through its refusal. The story is instructive with regard to the foundation of such stereotypes according to the roles
assumed variously by women in the management of male desire.
Still under discussion is whether such roles liberate or enslave
women.

Of Aramanthus Born a Leper

The seventh story is particulary rich in so-called "deep" motifs,
despite the usual degree of refitting in the direction of history
and social realism. Nothing prevents the reader from enjoying
this narrative as a tale of adventure featuring possible if improbable circumstances mediated by the combined conventions
of the novella and the romance. Nevertheless, the ethos of wish-
fulfilment that characterizes the fairy tale permeates the major
events. True to the genre, Aramanthus begins his quest in obscurity as a leper raised by a humble foster parent. Innate qualities
enable him to recover his true identity and good fortune rewards
him for the adversity he has endured. He has heroic deeds to
perform to prove himself valiant and worthy, but he must also
sometimes resort to the cunning of the trickster, as he does in devising the ruse whereby the Turks gain entry into the enemy city.
Mere brawn is not enough; the victor must first answer a riddle,

or reason his way through a labyrinth that leads to the hand of the princess—in this story, Florella, the beautiful daughter of the great Turk. The career of Aramanthus spells out hints of initiation rites, of game combats whereby suitors are eliminated and a succession crisis is averted by trials of valor and wit.

Parallel motifs add complexity to the narrative. Aramanthus grows up in exile from his parents; hence, he is unaware of his own identity. According to the conventions of the genre, this identity must first be regained before the comic solution of marriage can be entertained. An anagnorisis must take place through which the son is reunited to his mother and father. Obstacles to that reunion are posed both by the fraudulent practices of his uncle, and by the fact that the Turks, in whose service Aramanthus has risen to power, are at war with the Christian West. Aramanthus takes charge of the capture of his native city and, in effect, must slay his own father as a precondition to winning the cherished bride. Only the fortuitous unfolding of destiny permits him to discover in time his relationship to the King of Tolosia, thereby bringing him face to face with his dilemma as a would-be patricide. The recognition produces in him feelings of self-loathing and despair. This is his moment of greatest crisis; no narrative projection of psychic conflict could hold deeper echoes.

Once again, completion of the romance closure depends upon the magnanimity of the ascendant prince—in this instance, the great Turk. Not only does he relinquish his hold upon the city by right of conquest, but he allows the marriage of his daughter to a Christian and adds his own conversion to the completion of the festivities. There is a sense in which suffering, alienation, imprisonment, and banishment become redemptive forces, thereby enabling the King of Tolosia, upon recovering his wife and son, to declare, "O happy evil, which bringeth in the end so great a good." The closure features not only the reunion of the family, but the creation of a new society. The mantle of power passes to a younger, uncorrupted generation, and the enmity of Turks and Christians is now at an end, bringing hints of the golden age restored to accompany the union of the two young people.

The banishment of the Queen of Tolosia contributes to the wasteland motif, just as her restoration contributes to the romance closure. She is the nurturing mother treacherously maligned and banished. She is made to endure exile because through her fertility she obstructed the imperial ambitions of the king's brother, the Duke of Caria. Although pregnant with the king's child, she is falsely accused of infidelity and is forced to take up lodging among charitable outlaws and bandits where she suckles her newborn daughter. The story has analogues far and near (Greene's *Pandosto*; Shakespeare's *The Winter's Tale*). Like Agatha in the preceding story, she keeps faith with the husband who had spurned her and returns to rescue him from certain death. It is an important echo and reinforcement of the motif. Isabel the queen, disguised as a poor servant, enters the prison where the king is held captive and, in the manner of the Roman charity, suckles him through the bars of his cell. Her story adds to the legends of good women featured throughout the collection. She is a figure of fertility, a Persephone in exile who wins her way back through virtue and endurance. This is the final exemplification of that mythic structure in the *Farewell*. The return of the nurturing mother adds symbolic confirmation to the comic mythos of the closure.

There are courses not taken in the resolution of this story. Aramanthus is not called upon to deal with the wicked uncle, enemy to his rights and cause of his exile, perhaps because the wicked uncle is not interested in his mother as a future mate. Aramanthus narrowly escapes killing his own father, and concentrates on the conditions for winning the bride prize, which is the key to his future power. That is, of course, the path not taken by Hamlet, whereby his uncle could perhaps have been overwhelmed into submission. This story, in many ways, represents the survival solution to a nexus of events belonging naturally to blood revenge. If youth, beauty, and forgiveness prevail, it is only the force of the comic structure that can invest them with such optimism. Yet the comic imperative does not obscure the underlying conditions of family rivalries and ambitions. Such a generic construction of events readily yields up its relationship to former incarnations of the conflict going as far back as the mythic struggle of the seasons, and the war between the realms of darkness and death and those of light and fertility.

If the story is a narrative palimpsest with its half-erased echoes of prior themes and structures making for a vertical reading, i is nevertheless an accomplished fiction extended in present time, with its own present world of persons and events. Isabel may be sent in storybook fashion to live among the gentle thieves, but she is held in a contemporary world by the language. Emblematic though the structures may be, the telling is uncomplicated and full of immediate detail as when Isabel, in the prison with the king, "something the better to amend his cheer, she would lean herself close to the grate, and thrusting in her teat between the irons, the king learned again to suck, and thus she dieted him a long season." This is a solid vision, punctuated by the verbal substance of "cheer," "thrusting," and "long season." The pleasure is in the juxtaposing of a king learning to suck again as a child with cheer being brought out of season. In maintaining that equilibrium between novella and the structures of romance, the story preserves a biaxial design: an engaging realism and deeper intimations of half-forgotten experience.

Of Phylotus and Emelia

Northrop Frye has assured us that we take delight in the complications of comedy, even the most absurd.[57] The artisan of cross-intrigues, multiple disguises, dense stage traffic, and highly artificial circumstances must subscribe to this credo. Such brinkmanship in the crafting offers situations answering to our desire for the extraordinary, and it invites admiration for the witty maker who is able to bring so much business to satisfactory closure. If these be the measures of excellence, this last story is Riche's most virtuosic performance.

If one of the components of this happy complexity is a conflation of parts drawn from ancillary fictions, Riche's work also begins as a brilliant pastiche. Source critics itemize those works essential to the design of the plot as Belleforest's tale of Nicole, Cinthio's *Cesare Gravina*, and Straparola's tale of Silverio and Pisarda, as well as pieces of Ovid, and Gascoigne's translation of the *Supposes* of Ariosto. These are, in fact, all the sources traditionally assigned, and it is conceivable that Riche built his carnival caper of young love and baffled old men out of these alone. In one way or another they "remember" enough to have enabled

---

[57] *Anatomy of Criticism*, p. 170.

him to reconstruct the tale of the twin brother and sister who unwittingly change places through transvestite disguises, thereby enabling the brother to take the unwanted marriage partner assigned to the sister. Nevertheless, the common elements with the Sienese play *Gl'ingannati* come to mind, suggesting that it was a kind of general catalyst to the plot type. Certain elements of the play not used in the story *Of Apolonius and Silla* are drawn upon here. Silla goes in search of the man she loves, assumes the disguise of a page, and finds herself involved in the proxy wooing of Julina. In the play her counterpart, Lelia, flies to her lover in disguise in order to avoid an unwanted marriage to an old man and friend to her father. Her lover has meanwhile fallen in love with the old man's daughter Isabella, whom Lelia as a page woos on his behalf, and it is her twin brother Fabrizio who returns to break the impasse caused by misaligned loves and mistaken identities. Both of Riche's stories introduce important variations upon the original, and each elaborates only certain parts of the play. It is as though the play had been subdivided into two separate story traditions, each of them developing along independent lines. *Of Phylotus and Emelia* draws upon the feature of the two fathers, the one promising his daughter in marriage to the other, and continues to work out the action in terms of the old man's daughter eventually won through the deceptions of the twin brother of the girl he was destined to marry.

In Riche's story, Emelia does not engage in proxy wooing, although she does steal away to her lover in disguise while Phylerno, her brother, under extraordinary circumstances, assumes his sister's appearance, marries the old man for a joke, beats him into submission on the wedding night, puts him to bed with a prostitute, then settles in with the old man's daughter after performing a feigned sex change on himself in order to hide from Brisilla the device put upon her father. It is high farce, full of verve and theatricality. Machiavelli, the author of the *Mandragola*, would have terminated the story there, in a phase of endless deception of both father and daughter. But by other rules of comedy, stasis arrives only when knowledge and truth are made common, so that yet another reversal is necessary in order to bring the older generation into a full understanding of all that has passed. In the end, Emelia, as played by the brother, must meet Emelia the sister, and the younger generation must complete the celebration of its triumph over the old ones by bringing them to full knowledge of their follies.

The battle scene on the wedding night between an old man licking his chops and a young man in disguise playing the shrewish bride turns the war for mastery between the sexes into slapstick. Here is punishment for the *geron* who has violated nature in presuming sexually upon a young girl, as well as a pitiless parody of the wives who beat their husbands and who withhold sexual favors to gain the upper hand. They are featured regularly in continental farces and shrovetide plays. Here is April beating old January, and warmth driving out cold in the form of a domestic spat. There is comic mirth here for both genders insofar as the gender identifications usually drawn up in the battle are baffled by the role-playing of the young man in disguise who carries out the offices of the shrew. No one escapes, but the multifaceting of the mirror turns the fight into a farcical show.

The hoax put upon Brisilla by this same sporting young man in convincing her that by his prayers to Venus he has become a male and apt for her desires is splendidly preposterous. There is delight in letting ourselves believe that Brisilla could be duped by the ceremony. After all, had not Phylerno taken for his scripture Ovid's account of Iphis, the Cretan girl who was turned into a boy on her wedding day so that his love for Ianthé could be consummated? Had not Virgil and Aulus Gellius told of Caeneus's transformation into a man? Had not Ausonius reported such changes in his *Epigrams*, and had not many of the great physicians of the sixteenth century—Amatus Lusitanus, Jean Liébault, André Dulaurens—described such changes in their treatises?[58] Phylerno knew how to apply such lore in his dealings to the degree necessary to achieve his ends. The goal is opportune seduction, though he stands by his conquest in the end. No girl has been more outrageously seduced.

If the fisticuffs between old Phylotus and young Phylerno is a battle between generations, a burlesque of the battle between the sexes, an echo of the seasonal agon, it remains the stuff of comic

---

[58] Jacques Ferrand, *A Treatise on Lovesickness*, eds. D.A. Beecher & Massimo Ciavolella (Syracuse: University Press, 1990), pp. 380–83.

fiction moved forward to the novella. The narrator, in fact, takes a special delight in recommending so much mimetic and social improbability as a social verity, an event that happened in Rome only a short time ago. Moreover, such uncommon events are attributed to that most common of causes: the unruly desires of the erotic appetites. Riche takes a long moment to explain how the reasoning faculties are baffled by the intrusions of desire, how men thereby come to dote upon women considered ugly by the unafflicted. He reveals how the fancy itself gains in the conspiracy of eros by thrusting the image of the beloved continually before the mind's eye. Where such doting is met by a lack of reciprocity, the victim can be driven to fury and madness. This is the imperious passion in old and young that raises comic strife and that is quelled by comic laughter. Comedy supplies its generic order as mediator between the uncontrollable exuberance of adolescent desire and superannuated erotic pretensions.

Carnival is a period of license, a celebration of the fancy seeking gratification for its wishes, and comedy, in its release from collective mores, can go far to create the projected world of indulgence. But the comedy that turns toward marriage or the ridiculing of blocking characters performs its own inherited values. Comedy holds up the aberrant desires to ridicule, or expels those whose behavior is an affront to nature. Comedy in these stories is the art form of marriage, but of marriage between partners of equal age and social status. Hence, the drives that threaten with their rage for disorder come under the drive of the art form itself for comic order. This final story is perhaps not as carnivalesque as the fifth, *Of Two Brethren and Their Wives*, but it is the apogee of the comic vision in the *Farewell*.

Given the speed of the narrative, the variety of actions, the wittiness of the conception, the integration of the episodes, there should be little surprise that this story enjoyed the favor of the playwrights of the age. It was the principal source of the anonymous play *Phylotus*, first mentioned in 1603, of James Shirley's *Love Tricks*, licensed in 1625, and of Shakerley Marmion's *A Fine Companion* of 1633. It offers everything an increasingly mannerist theater might call for: a transsexual disguise plot; the deceiving of an old lover; a putative sex change; and the subplot of the demonic double, woven together into a single intrigue.

Conclusion

Riche avowed his intent to please as a popular writer by following the literary fashions of his age. That his stories should feature wish-fulfilment closures of the most transparent variety may suggest a classification among the idle amusements for unsophisticated readers. But these stories are never escapist; rather, they generate thought on practically all levels of critical response. The attainment of popular approbation as an importer of Italian wares implied careful thought about the right formula for fiction, simply because Riche was not content to represent the new realism without investing it with certain of the conventions of romance; his reasons for doing so invite our speculation. As popular literature, these stories may appear to have classed themselves more or less opposite the elite literatures that have commanded the greatest critical interest. If those questions of classification are replaced with questions concerning myth and genre, however, critical inquiry will prove more gratifying. The pitch for popularity may, in fact, be more camouflage than credo with regard to the methodologies of the maker. Taken on their own, these stories offer little evidence for differentiating them, whether for matter or for manner, from works enjoying a more privileged critical status. My point is but a modestly polemical one, in that these stories do not rise to the level of the best literature of that era; Riche had steep competition in writers of extraordinary talent. But it is reasonable to ask if his stories have heretofore been overlooked with just cause, for it has always been true that we value literature in relation to the questions we ask of it. In the past we have learned to revalue works fallen into oblivion simply by asking of them more pertinent questions, or rather by taking an interest in the kinds of questions that those works, all along, were best suited to answer. My point is that as critical perspectives change, we may now be asking the kinds of questions that foreground the concerns and the artistry represented in these stories—questions about myth, narrative, gender, the social dimensions of literature, the conventions of romance, and the habits of readers. I posit my case for the possible recentralizing of Riche's stories on those grounds.

All eight of these stories own something of comedy, for in each there is a requisite degree of craft or luck necessary to carry the protagonists to the wished-for ends. The generalized movement of the collection is toward closures allowing for the recovery of lost identity, the restoration of the family, marriage among mutually chosen partners, and social and political empowerment for those proven worthy by their courage and integrity. A vision emerges simply through the reinforcement of this generic pattern. The authority behind such comedy is not moral rectitude alone, or wish-fulfilment, but nature herself—a natural order of which the comic vision is but an agent in the social world. More particularly, in the six non-carnival stories, patience, endurance, and continence are the virtues, especially in women, that earn for them, as if by magic coercion, the protection of fortune. The progress of comedy is coupled to the rites whereby passage is marked from trial to integration to dominance. There is movement throughout the collection toward redemption and renewal, largely through the grace accumulated through the fortitude and purity of the women protagonists. More may be transpiring here than meets the eye. These stories, as social comedies, function in a broad band of myth—myth that allows for a degree of carnival laughter, but that otherwise interferes with literary escapism on the one hand, and with satiric diatribe on the other.

At the same time, these stories speak the language of romance and reflect many of its conventions. For this reason, the terms of resistance and obstruction reflect the circumstances of more paradigmatic and ritualistic story types: long imprisonment, exile, foster parents, direct assault under strained and threatening conditions. Despite their displacement toward modern settings and social milieux, they continue to tell of the son nearly slain in ritual fashion by his father, and of the father nearly killed by his son; they tell of the girl in disguise falsely accused of a capital crime, and of the pregnant queen exiled among thieves. Yet these extremities of expression and of circumstance serve to crystallize the psychic conflicts and agonistic motifs behind each fable. Social and psychological realities have not been left behind—they have merely been realigned with their mythic substructures. The point is that these patterns run deep in the story-telling tradition because they run deep in cultural memory. The consistency of the recall in these stories, and the reinforcement of motifs, is testimony to the perdurability of experience itself and the constant desire to reconstruct these archetypal motifs up and down the echelons separating myth from mimetic representationalism.

For those disinclined to read for polyvocal resonances and archetypal structures, the social fable remains undiminished. Riche does not cultivate imitation at the level of manners only, but at the level of social values. His stories are not brilliant reflections of the individual mind in action, but the situations they project form adequate laboratories for examining and testing a variety of key social issues: the family in distress, social trust, bonding and friendship, the idealization of women, the management of sexual desire, the importance of marriage, behavior in magistrates, poverty and dowries, false appearances and hypocrisy. With the motivation of character comes cause, and with cause comes values. The order of fiction tests and judges. This remains entirely in the abstract, however. We also struggle to relate literary experience to assumptions about social reality. By analogy we increase what we know about desire, ambition, drives, temperaments. These stories tease us with their apparent relevance to Tudor society as well. Did they, in fact, encode the salient social issues of the age? Was Riche entirely in control of a creative process that would allow him to profile a social present through the adaptations of a narrative past? Can one begin with the premise that Riche was above all a social thinker, and that his program in the *Farewell* is a carefully considered confirmation of some of the most cherished values of the age?

Modern readers may also find themselves interested in Riche's analysis of sexual differences. First impressions may suggest genderization by cliché and commonplace. His comic order merely confirms a mutuality in marriage that is thought to be the uninteresting by-product of the agon between the sexes foregrounded in tales of tortured courtship. Yet Riche's persistent interest in eroticism as a principal cause of social destabilization makes him something of a theoretician of desire. His stories run to exaggerated proportions in their manifestations of erotic intent. Women are profiled largely as objects of such desire, and their social ascendancies are determined by their capacities to control that desire. If the book was truly conceived with a female readership in mind, it becomes a kind of grammar in sexual management.

Julina, in the second story, is mocked for her indiscretion, though it was through no real fault of her own, and the shrew of story five is treated as psychopathic or quasi-demonic, while Dorothy, in that same story, is allowed to triumph as a hedonist. But the rest of Riche's women protagonists are virtuous, strong, active in their pursuit of happiness, remarkable for their judgment and, where necessary, able to endure and suffer. As agents of values, they represent fidelity, nurturing instincts, and potential redemption. Their rightful movement is toward integration, justification, and reward within the circumference of tolerated liberties. In contradistinction, the men who find themselves in conflict with feminine self-determinacy are reproved, made to heel to codes of honor, or are brought into subjection through dominance or worship. Repeatedly, these stories turn around questions of desire, the tyranny of the appetites, and their social repercussions. Civilization works its progress in these stories through the negotiations between the sexes that permit the desired exclusivity, mutuality, and permanence in male-female unions, upon which societies depend.

Riche's stories command a certain attention because they are among the best of those inspired by the Italian novella. His imitation of the form involved a formula whereby Italian matter was drawn back slightly toward the conventions of romance. The result was a fiction that was realistic by the standards of the age, yet marked by conventions opening it up to myth. At the same time, the novella, with its plain social content, allowed for openings in the direction of festive as well as subversive comedy. Riche had sound instincts as a story-teller despite his occasional lapses into moralizing or stylistic indulgence. As a stylist, Riche was often faulty; even his grip on basic grammar was none of the best. Sentences sometimes drift from unit to unit in defiance of the logic of syntax. Yet even those concatenations possess a pleasing cachet and produce an extended diversity within his groupings— and in any case his intentions are rarely if ever obscure. Above all, Riche excels at building new plots out of the pieces of prior fictions, and he understands the mechanics of the balanced and energetic narrative. Such creations of text out of text are pleasingly mannerist, and they remind us how much these stories are also to be enjoyed not only as feigned realities, but as artifacts created in relation to other works of art.

A Short History of
the Text and Editorial Procedures

By comparison with many another Elizabethan text, establishing
an authoritative source for an edition of the *Farewell* poses no
complex theoretical challenges, although it does entail an examination of all of the editions published in Riche's lifetime for their
potential value. The *Farewell* was published four times during a
span of twenty-five years, first in 1581, then in 1583, 1594 and
1606; they have been assigned letters from A to D. The first publisher was Robart Walley, who, also in 1581, issued the first part of
The Strange and Wonderful Adventures of Don Simonides. Walley must have found Riche's books good for business, for he was
to undertake the production of some eight of them. The actual
printer, however, was John Kingston, whose ornamental border
featuring King David playing the harp and Moses holding the
tablets of the law graced not only the title pages of the first two
editions of the *Farewell*, but, with the positions of the characters
reversed, the title page of *Don Simonides* as well.[1]

Of this first edition only one copy survives, once the property
of Thomas Tanner, bishop of St. Asaph, but housed today in
the Bodleian Library, Oxford. The Tanner collection, or at least
those books in his collection that were selected by the Bodleian
curators, was given to the library following Tanner's death in
1734. It was the fate of those 900 volumes, presumably including the *Farewell*, to spend some twenty hours submerged at the

---

[1] R.B. McKerrow and F.S. Ferguson, *Title-Page Borders Used in
England & Scotland 1485–1640* (London, 1932), p. 102.

bottom of a lock near Wallingford, where the barge transporting the books from Norwich sank; miraculously the *Farewell* seems to have sustained little damage from the mishap.[2]

The excellent condition of this copy is perhaps also due to the fact that the good bishop did not subject the collection to hard use. It is blemished only by two damaged pages in the fourth story (Pi^{r-v}), by a considerable amount of ink that has bled through the pages and has interfered with the clarity of the print, especially in the sixth and seventh stories, and by an ink blot affecting six pages (Cci^{r}–iii^{v}) in the eighth story. But the text is essentially complete and legible even in the form of a printout from microfilm, although I have taken the final precaution of examining this text at first hand in the Bodleian.

Riche wrote these stories in Ireland in the late 1570s, and may have taken them to press in London on one of his trips as a military courier late in 1580, although in the address "To the Readers in General" he states that he was "forced to *send* them all to the press." No original manuscripts of the *Farewell* have been located by which the fidelity of the printed version can be measured, but a comparison of stylistic features in the *Farewell* with similar features in extant manuscripts of other works suggests that the compositor for this book, for better or for worse, honored Riche's written intentions—for the book reflects his usual forms of spelling, his habit of leaving participial phrases standing free, and his casualness in the matter of agreement between nouns and verbs. Scholars, then, are generally agreed that this sole surviving copy of the A text is not only as close as we can come to what Riche wrote, but also quite faithful to what he wrote. These many factors relating to completeness, relative clarity, and accuracy made Cranfill's choice of the A text for his facsimile edition the obvious one, not only on scholarly grounds, but on practical grounds as well, because none of the five copies from the three subsequent editions is so complete and presentable. Nevertheless, those editions together contain a substantial number of variants, and because they were published during the author's lifetime, the

---

[2] *Rich's Farewell to Military Profession 1581*, p. lxiii; using information derived from W.P. Courteney, "Thomas Tanner," *Dictionary of National Biography*.

possibility that these variants are the results of Riche's second thoughts must be examined.

The B text was published by the same publisher two years after A, in 1583. Two rather imperfect copies survive, both housed in the Folger Shakespeare Library. Fortunately, damaged areas do not coincide, so that it would be possible to reconstruct a complete B were one so inclined. In point of fact, B follows A so closely that many pages are identical; only 63 minor variants differentiate them. Some of these are errors in the type, while others do appear to be stylistic adjustments, no doubt interpolated by the compositor on a fairly random basis, for they represent nothing like a serious reconsideration of Riche's homespun grammar. The more substantial changes seem not to have any consistent purpose: where "courage" replaces "outrage" the force is lost; where "life" replaces "wife" the sense is lost; "lives at this" is an improvement over "lives this"; while "in the same city" for "in the said city" is a matter of indifference. "Fall so conjuring" is emended as a typographical error, no doubt in the course of the typesetting. Since Riche is so cavalier about grammar in general, one does not imagine him concerning himself with these minor adjustments. Because many of the changes, moreover, were introduced into passages that in the A text offer comprehensible meanings, there is no reason to give them preference merely as readings, unless they are corrections of demonstrably erroneous typesetting.

Yet, with its close affiliation to A, B clearly has a great value to an editor concerned with restoring and completing a text. The second of the Folger copies lacks all the pages down to Cii^r, and thereafter, for several pages, portions of the print are displaced by wear. Only small fragments survive of the last page of the seventh story, the first of the eighth, and the final page. Yet the print of B is generally legible and clear, even in a printout from the microfilm, and hence serviceable, not only in supplying those passages missing or undecipherable in A, but in confirming readings throughout the text. Once the 63 variants have been duly noted, the texts may be consulted almost interchangeably. Under these circumstances, A should always be given precedence over B, except in the restoration of passages that cannot be recovered in A, a process that may be carried out silently, because there are no editorial alternatives available.

The C text does, however, demand a moment's attention. The rights to the *Farewell* were sold on Oct. 12, 1591 to Thomas Adams, who in turn either hired a reviser, or gave *carte blanche* to his compositor to make relatively extensive corrections—this time quite pointedly directed at cleaning up Riche's stylistic infelicities: free-standing participial phrases, noun-verb disagreements, missing or non-idiomatic prepositions, false parallels, and misplaced modifiers. The work was not thorough in that many such infractions remain, but in the passages altered there is a kind of legalistic precision imposed by the added prepositions and pronouns. Cranfill studied these revisions closely and concluded that whoever was responsible "may be indicted for aimlessness, inconsistency, capriciousness, poor judgment, perverseness, and pedantry."[3] I would not go so far, although I agree that a certain insouciance, a rustic cachet is lost in the altered passages. Nevertheless, a few of the readings are improvements by any standard and worth adopting in order to bring a desirable clarity to the original. Those affecting the meaning have been acknowledged among the glosses found at the bottoms of the pages or, where comment was in order, among the textual annotations.

The evaluation by touchstone methods does not solve the problem of authorship and authority, however; it only demonstrates that changes in the C text are inconsistent with the stylistic spirit of the A text generally. Yet a kind of argument begins to emerge with another intuitive impression, namely that such tampering with the grammar would be entirely uncharacteristic of Riche himself, who shows no interest in the refinements of grammar elsewhere in his writing. Obviously Cranfill, in referring to the reviser as the "culprit who laid a heavy, impertinent hand on Riche's text,"[4] does not for a moment think that it was the work of the author. Riche often declared himself to be a faulty stylist— indeed went so far as to mock himself in his Dedication to Hatton

---

[3] *Rich's Farewell to Military Profession 1581*, p. lxix.

[4] *Rich's Farewell to Military Profession 1581*, p. lxix. See also Thomas Mabry Cranfill, "Barnaby Rich: An Elizabethan Reviser at Work," *Studies in Philology*, 46 (July, 1949), pp. 411–18.

in the *Alarm to England* (1578) as a man who "would take in hand to write before he could spell." These revisions appear to be neither authorial, nor in keeping stylistically with the unaltered passages of the text. Moreover, the corresponding passages in the A text, though sometimes a bit clumsy, seldom fail to convey their meanings. The authority of the C text may finally be questioned by the probability that Riche was involved in making revisions to the fourth edition or D text, and that when he did so, he used a copy of A. Surely had Riche given his blessing to the C text, he would have insisted that compositors continue in their use of the C text from which they had begun their typesetting. The story is worth a moment's detour.

Evidence points strongly to the likelihood that Riche was called in to make some last minute revisions to his *Farewell* before it went to press again in 1606. Because the only surviving copy of C is missing the whole of the conclusion relating the story of Balthasar-the-devil and the king of Scotland, there is reason to think that a complaint made by James in 1595 may have resulted in a recall and mutilation of all available copies. That remains conjectural, but far more certain is that with James on the English throne after 1603, there was no question of republishing a book containing unflattering allusions to the Scots. One could argue that any publishing house hack could have excised the phrase "the Scottes by custome" from the list of England's traditional military enemies in the "Epistle to the Soldiers," and have substituted "our Grandseigniour the Turke" for the king of Scotland at the appropriate places in the story of Balthasar. But three bits of evidence point to Riche himself: he was then living in London and available for the job; the copy of A in which the revisions were made was more likely to have been owned by Riche than by the publishing house that had already started setting the type for D from a copy of C; and the Turks were a favorite enemy in other Riche stories, including three in the *Farewell*. This is by no means conclusive, but it does stand to reason that where an entire section needed revamping, and the author was nearby, that a publisher would be inclined to call upon him. Presuming this to be the case, the typesetting from C was halted at sig. Bi, three pages before the first correction, and resumed from a copy of A.

Hence, an editor, in the final analysis, is reduced to examining the differences between A and D, and to asking whether these variants are authoritative. But again, their absolutely random and inconsequential nature suggests that, true to form, Riche had no further interest in the revisions beyond the passages touching the Scots, and that we are again confronted by the accidents of a compositor of no particular inspiration. The basis for a modern edition must remain, then, a transcription of A, supplemented only where necessary from B, and emended only in a few clearly defective passages from C where the C reading is deemed the most reasonable possible reconstruction. D need not be consulted insofar as the Scots are preferred to the Turks as Riche's first thought.

Scholars interested in the variants differentiating the first five editions (including Collier's *Eight Novels Employed by English Dramatic Poets of the Reign of Queen Elizabeth* edited for The Shakespeare Association in 1846) may consult the tables, pp. 213–24, in the Cranfill facsimile edition of the *Farewell*. In my close comparison of the A and B texts I found no lacunae in his list, and must conclude that it is equally accurate for the other three editions. Given the availability of this apparatus—the entries being typically of the order of "to" for "unto" and "stolne" for "stole"—it seemed supererogatory to replicate a partial list in this edition.

The editorial processing of these stories involved several interrelated steps, namely a transcription and modernization of the A text, a consideration of all the substantive variations in B and C, a careful reconsideration of Riche's punctuation, a final check against the original in the Bodleian, and finally the preparation of glosses and annotations. Some elements of the editorial process are reflected in both the bottom-of-the-page glosses and in the annotations, but these annotations have been held to a minimum. This is possible because in the modernization of the spelling almost all of the anomalies of a typographical nature are automatically eliminated.

There are only two or three words to be found in the whole of the *Farewell* that cannot be located in the unabridged *Oxford International Dictionary* (1957). One example of such a word is "romer," a nautical term twice used in the *Farewell*, and by all indications unique to Riche.[5] But normally the absence of a word in this dictionary was a strong indicator that it was either a variant of a more conventional spelling, or an outright typographical error. Context and common sense confirm, for example, that "complixitions" is a (corrupt) form of "complexions" and should be so emended. By contrast, "in ure," an archaic form of "in use," was kept and glossed. The intention behind the modernization of the spelling was to remove orthographical obstacles to a spontaneous reading of the text, but never to alter meanings. Hence, "woundyng" has become "wounding," but never "wounded" as in C to eliminate an awkward participle, and "wright" has not been changed to "written" as in C, or to "write" as in D, because Riche could have intended overtones of craft or artistry in choosing this spelling. Riche's common spelling for "travel" and "travail" has been sorted out according to the context.

Place names such as Mantona, Cayre and Tolosia suggest modern equivalents in Mantua, Cairo and Toulouse, and the temptation to modernize is increased by the presence of such indisputably real places as Naples, Ferrara, Constantinople and Seville. Nevertheless, the intermixture of such fictive names as Tariffa, Cherona and Vasconia is a reminder that these stories may intend to vacillate between geographical possibility and complete fantasy. Furthermore, that a brief mention is made of Tolosia's position on the sea coast, while Toulouse is inland, underscores the danger. Riche's spellings have accordingly been retained.

Bottom-of-the-page glosses have been created principally to define words that are no longer current, or that now carry altered meanings. Riche's vocabulary poses few of the problems that must be addressed by the editor of Shakespeare or Donne. His diction is homespun and not highly troped, although it sometimes manifests an archaic texture, while a word here and there has been troped or otherwise used in a way idiosyncratic to Riche. Hence, the glosses are offered as readers' aids in dealing with the immediate text, not as etymological studies. Dual significations are signalled by a semicolon. Often Riche's difficult terms appear in doublings glossed, as it were, by the other word in the pair, as in

---

[5] Donald C. Sampson, "Rich's Farewell to Military Profession," *The Explicator*, Vol. 34, No. 1 (Sept., 1975), Item 1.

"joy and contentation," "snarring and grudging," or "affected and manifest argument." A reader who is alert to the context could conceivably, I think, read these stories with pleasure without once drifting to the bottom of the page. Rarely does Riche's general meaning slip from view as a result of the diction.

There are, in addition to Riche's overtly archaic terms, some two dozen common, if not overworked, words that deceive by their apparent familiarity, since they too carry special obsolete meanings—such words as "quick" for "alive," "let" for "hindrance," and "list" for "desire." Each has been glossed on its first appearance, and often again on first appearances in subsequent stories, but the frequency of several of them precluded a regular reglossing.

The glosses have also been extended very selectively to perform a related function. Parentheses have been introduced to signal readings taken from C, interesting or possibly ambiguous original spellings, and words in A omitted from the transcription. These indications enter the area of textual commentary, but they are so few and diverse as to obviate the need for a separate apparatus. In this way, too, the textual annotations can be reserved almost exclusively for annotations upon the content: historical allusions, proper names, and ideas.

The correction of typographical errors has been at once a product of the completion of the transcription and of the preparation of the glosses. Final distinctions had to be established between pairs of possible readings, which were silently emended to their most probable forms. There were not so many instances of outright error, and those such as "cceipt" for "conceit" do not seem problematic. Even the phrase "the first thing that was to be considered in marriage was the dowry, and the woman" suggests readily enough the need for "and then the woman," which Cranfill took the trouble to confirm in Giraldi's "e poi la donna."[6] Such changes as these are not recorded, most of them having received detailed attention in the annotations to the facsimile of 1959.

One may concede to the textual purists that the modernization both of spelling and of punctuation are forms of compromise in the interests of promoting early texts for a modern readership.

---

[6] *Rich's Farewell to Military Profession 1581*, p. 276.

But I would argue that such modernization, conservatively handled, is by no means a form of betrayal. Words may lose a certain Elizabethan patina, but meanings do not alter with the loss of the cachet of Elizabethan orthography. One could contend that to remove the original pointing and to impose modern conventions of punctuation and capitalization is to remove a precious record of the text as phrased in the author's mind, or as a text shaped for auditory reception, even while being read. It is an attractive argument, but not a conclusive one, because it is often in spite of, and not because of, the punctuation that the texts "perform" well. Others look to the printers in order to lay the blame for erratic punctuation, although that may be to absolve the authors rather too quickly. Finally, where punctuation follows neither a program of coherent breathing and phrasing, nor supports the logic of the syntax, one can then divide the responsibility between the two. Still others have thought that Elizabethan pointing has less to do with phrasing and thought *per se* and more to do with the crabbed legacy of grammar school training. The point of debate is whether, nevertheless, this eccentric punctuation should remain intact as a reflection of the Elizabethan literary mind, and a part of the experience of knowing them as they were. This is to endorse as part of the duty of the reader a constant struggle with the conflicts between sentence aesthetics and sentence logic, for whether the pointing of the age was due to ideas of expressiveness, to unformulated standards, or to residual latinisms, it remains an obstacle to meeting the Elizabethan mind.

Out of the confusion arises a different kind of argument, at least as far as these stories are concerned. Whatever the punctuation does in shaping the reception of the syntax, a certain fundamental narrative coherence must be reconstructed in the reader's mind that permits the story to work. I would contend that the process of finding that story line syntactically, unit by unit, could have differed little then from now, with the difference, perhaps, that the Elizabethan reader was more familiar with the conventions of Elizabethan punctuation and hence more experienced in recreating her or his own mental performance of the story as the story line demands. To be sure, the modern editor, in a sense, imposes a performance in trying to eliminate obstacles, thereby removing other possible readings involving the original pointing. But I would suggest that in the case of Riche, who was a story-teller and not the cultivator of literary ambiguities and textual play, the performance teased out by the editor is going to be very nearly the same performance that must be recovered by a reader in any age.

As a partial test of my hypothesis that the same sentence logic will be recovered by different readers, regardless of the punctuation of the original, I have selected for comparison with my own version two other modernized versions of the second story (one which has often been modernized and anthologized as a Shakespeare source), the first by T.J.B. Spencer in *Elizabethan Love Stories*, the second by Alice Griffin in *The Sources of Ten Shakespearean Plays*.[7] My comparison was based on the paragraph of 18 lines beginning, "In this manner she travelled to Constantinople. . . ." It was revealing that all three editors subdivided Riche's one long sentence into five, at precisely the same places, and in precisely the same way, the fourth becoming a question. In essence, all agreed that Riche had run on five free-standing units, the fourth of which implied a question buried within his syntactical agglomeration. Griffin's reading differed from Spencer's only by two commas in the place of Spencer's stronger semicolons, together with two additional commas in Spencer. My reading differs from Griffin's only by two commas, one in hers, one in mine. The high level of coincidence is demonstrative of the way in which three modern readers worked across and around Riche's often misleading punctuation to find essentially the same groupings of words and pauses in order to make sense of what is, after all, a straightforward narrative intention. If my hypothesis is valid, the case for retaining original punctuation, particularly in the case of a story-teller like Riche, appears less convincing.

In pragmatic terms, such modernization has called for joining Riche's numerous sentence fragments, wherever possible, to neighboring main clauses, and breaking down many of his long run-on units into separate sentences, occasionally allowing a cap-

---

[7]T.J.B. Spencer, ed., *Elizabethan Love Stories* (Harmondsworth: Penguin Books, 1968), pp. 103–04; Alice Griffin, ed., *The Sources of Ten Shakespearean Plays* (New York: Thomas Crowell Co., 1966), pp. 114–15.

italized "and" to begin the new sentence. All of the emphatic colons have been dropped, often replaced by nothing at all. Their use remains a controversial point, and their presence is a certain stumbling block for the uninitiated reader. I have used semicolons only sparingly as a weaker form of full stop. The usual strategy for associating subjects separated from their predicates by long intervening clauses has been to suppress as much punctuation within those clauses as possible. There were a very few passages in which clauses were suspended between units equally modifiable by the clause in question. Where a reasonable choice was possible, the clause was assigned. Where doubt remained, the sequence was allowed to stand. In general, I have eliminated superfluous commas in order to avoid literally hundreds of deceptive pauses, and to quicken the movement of the stories. On the whole, my inclination has been to keep the sentences as lean as possible.

At the same time, Riche's lavish use of capital letters has been reduced to comply with modern practice; they are reserved for proper names, and for such concepts as nature and fortune when they are clearly functioning as personifications.

Editorial additions to the text were permitted where an additional word or two could bring meaning to an otherwise obscure or misleading passage. These are used sparingly and appear in brackets in the text.

Direct discourse has been identified and enclosed within quotation marks. The lengthier speeches have been set off in separate paragraphs. There were a few passages in which indirect discourse suddenly turned into direct—often signalled by the telltale "quoth." In keeping with convention, new indentations appear with each change of interlocutor.

The modernizing editor must look for the ideal balance between mediating a text to a readership unfamiliar with Elizabethan conventions and typefaces, and maintaining a scholar's debt to the author, the integrity of his text, and the spirit of the past. Editing is both an act of appropriation for a new audience, and an act of cultural memory. Riche, above all, wanted to please his audiences by telling them stories they could enjoy without interference, even from himself as a potentially tedious moralizer. He may sometimes baffle us with his clumsy procedures, but his intentions never tend toward the obscure. The editor's task is to mediate these narratives in a way that may allow them to become a literary fashion of our age as they were in their own.

Selected Critical Bibliography

Beachcroft, Thomas Owen. *The Modest Art: A Survey of the Short Story in English*. London: Oxford University Press, 1968.

Bluestone, Max. *From Story to Stage: The Dramatic Adaptation of Prose Fiction in the Period of Shakespeare and His Contemporaries. Studies in English Literatue*, 70. The Hague: Mouton, 1974.

Carey, John. "Sixteenth- and Seventeenth-Century Prose." In *English Poetry and Prose, 1540–1674*. Ed. Christopher Ricks. Vol. 2 of *The New History of Literature*. New York: Bedrick, 1987, pp. 329–411.

Clements, Robert J. "Anatomy of the Novella." *Comparative Literature Studies*, 9 (March, 1972), pp. 3–16.

Cranfill, Thomas Mabry. "Barnaby Rich: An Elizabethan Reviser at Work." *Studies in Philology*, 46 (July, 1949), pp. 411–18.

——— . "Barnaby Rich and King James." *Journal of English Literary History*, 16 (March, 1949), pp. 65–75.

——— . "Barnaby Rich's 'Sappho' and *The Weakest Goeth to the Wall*." *University of Texas Studies in English*, 1945–1946, pp. 142–71.

——— , and Dorothy Hart Bruce. *Barnaby Rich: A Short Biography*. Austin: University of Texas Press, 1953.

Davis, Walter Richardson. *Idea and Act in Elizabethan Fiction*. Princeton: Princeton University Press, 1969.

Hamilton, A.C. "Elizabethan Prose Fiction and Some Trends in Recent Criticism." *Renaissance Quarterly*, 37 (Spring, 1984), pp. 21–33.

Helgerson, Richard. *The Elizabethan Prodigals*. Berkeley: University of California Press, 1976.

Hutson, Lorna. *Thomas Nashe in Context*. Oxford: Clarendon Press, 1989.

Jorgensen, Paul A. "Barnaby Rich: Soldierly Suitor and Honest Critic of Women." *Shakespeare Quarterly*, 7 (Spring, 1956), pp. 183–88.

Kinney, Arthur F. *Humanist Poetics: Thought, Rhetoric, and Fiction in Sixteenth-Century England*. Amherst: University of Massachusetts Press, 1986.

Lievsay, John Leon. "A Word about Barnaby Rich." *Journal of English and German Philology*, 55, no. 3 (1956), pp. 381–92.

McKeon, Michael. *The Origins of the English Novel 1600–1740*. Baltimore: The Johns Hopkins University Press, 1987.

Margolies, David. *Novel and Society in Elizabethan England*. London & Sydney: Croom Helm Ltd., 1985.

Painter, William. *The Palace of Pleasure*. Ed. Joseph Jacobs. 3 vols. London: D. Nutt, 1890; rpt. New York: Dover, 1966.

Patterson, Annabel. *Censorship and Interpretation: The Conditions of Writing and Reading in Early Modern England*. Madison: University of Wisconsin Press, 1984.

Pettie, George. *A Petite Pallace of Pettie His Pleasure*. Ed. Herbert Hartman. Oxford: Oxford University Press, 1938; rpt. New York: Barnes & Noble, 1970.

Plomer, Henry R., and Tom Peete Cross. *The Life and Correspondence of Lodowick Bryskett*. Chicago: University of Chicago Press, 1927.

Pruvost, René. *Matteo Bandello and Elizabethan Fiction*. Bibliothéque de la Revue de Littérature Comparée, 113. Paris: H. Champion, 1937.

Rich, Barnaby. *Rich's Farewell to Military Profession 1581*. Ed. Thomas Mabry Cranfill. Austin: University of Texas Press, 1959.

——. "Of Gonsales and His Vertuous Wife Agatha." In *How a Man May Chuse a Good Wife from a Bad*. Ed. A.E.H. Swaen. Materialien zur Kunde des Älteren Dramas, 35. Louvain: A. Uystpruyst, 1912.

——. "Phylotus and Emelia." In *Philotus: A Comedy*. Ed. John Whiteford Mackenzie. Bannatyne Club Publications, 50. Edinburgh: Ballantyne, 1835.

Rodax, Yvonne R. *The Real and the Ideal in the Novella of Italy, France, and England: Four Centuries of Change in the Boccaccian Tale*. University of North Carolina Studies in Comparative Literature, 44. Chapel Hill: University of North Carolina Press, 1968.

Salinger, Leo. "The Design of *Twelfth Night*." In *Dramatic Form in Shakespeare and the Jacobeans*. Cambridge: Cambridge University Press, 1986.

Salzman, Paul. *English Prose Fiction, 1558–1700: A Critical History.* Oxford: Clarendon Press, 1985.

Schlauch, Margaret. *Antecedents of the English Novel, 1400–1600* (from Chaucer to Deloney). London: Oxford University Press, 1963.

———. "English Short Fiction in the 15th and 16th Centuries." *Studies in Short Fiction*, 3 (Summer, 1966), pp. 393–434.

Schleiner, Louise. "Ladies and Gentlemen in Two Genres of Elizabethan Fiction." *Studies in English Literature 1500–1900*, 29 (1989), pp. 1–20.

Starnes, D.T. "Barnabe Riche's 'Sappho Duke of Mantona': A Study in Elizabethan Story-Making." *Studies in Philology*, 30 (July, 1933), pp. 455–72.

Waller, Gary F. "British Short Fiction in the Sixteenth and Seventeenth Centuries." In *Critical Survey of Short Fiction.* Vol. 2. Ed. Frank N. Magill. Englewood Cliffs, N.J.: Salem Press, 1981, pp. 483–504.

White, Harold Ogden. *Plagiarism and Imitation during the English Renaissance.* Cambridge, Mass.: Harvard University Press, 1935; rpt. New York: Octagon Books, 1965.

Wolf, Melvin H. "Introduction." In *Faultes Faults and Nothing Else but Faultes* (1606). By Barnaby Rich. Gainesville, Florida: Scholars' Facsimiles & Reprints, 1965, pp. 9–76.

Woodbridge, Linda. *Women and the English Renaissance: Literature and the Nature of Womankind, 1540–1620.* Urbana: University of Illinois Press, 1984.

Riche his Farewell

to

Military Profession

containing very pleasant discourses fit
for a peaceable time: gathered together
for the only delight of the courteous
gentlewomen, both of England and Ireland,
for whose only pleasure they were collected
together, and unto whom they are directly
dedicated by Barnabe Riche, Gentleman.

Malui me divitem esse quam vocari.

Imprinted at London
by Robart Walley
1581

[*First Dedicatory Epistle*]

To the Right Courteous Gentlewomen, both of England and Ireland, Barnabe Riche Wisheth All Things They Should Have Appertaining to Their Honor, Estimation, and All Other Their Honest Delights.

Gentlewomen, I am sure there are many—but especially of such as best know me—that will not a little wonder to see such alteration in me, that, having spent my younger days in the wars among men and vowed myself only unto Mars, should now, in my riper years, desire to live in peace amongst women and to consecrate myself wholly unto Venus. But yet the wiser sort can very well consider that the older we wax the riper our wit, and the longer we live the better we can conceive of things appertaining to our own profits. Though harebrained youth overhaled° me for a time that I knew not bale° from bliss, yet wisdom now has warned me that I well know cheese from chalk; I see now it is less painful to follow a fiddle in a gentlewoman's chamber than to march after a drum in the field, and more sound sleeping under a silken canopy close by a friend than under a bush in the open field within a mile of our foe, and nothing so dangerous to be wounded with the luring look of our beloved mistress as with the cruel shot of our hateful enemy: the one possessed with a pitiful heart to help where she hath hurt, the other with a deadly hate to kill where they might save.

overhaled overwhelmed, confused.   **bale** evil.

Experience now hath taught me that to be of Mars his crew there is nothing but pain, travail, turmoil, disquiet, cold, hunger, thirst, penury, bad lodging, worse fare, unquiet sleep, with a number of other calamities that haps I know not how. And when a soldier hath thus served in many a bloody broil, a flap with a foxtail° shall be his best reward, for I see no better recompense that any of them can get. Now contrary, to be of Venus' band there is pleasure, sport, joy, solace, mirth, peace, quiet rest, dainty fare, with a thousand other delights such as I cannot rehearse; and a man having served but a reasonable time may sometimes take a taste at his mistress' lips for his better recompense.

But now, gentlewomen, as I have vowed myself to be at your dispositions, so I know not how to frame myself to your contentations.° When I consider with how many commendable qualities he ought to be endowed that should be welcomed into your blessed companies, I find in myself no one manner of exercise that might give me the least hope to win your good likings.

As first for dancing, although I like the measures° very well, yet I could never tread them aright, nor to use measure in anything that I went about, although I desired to perform all things by line and by level whatsoever I took in hand. Our galliards° are so curious that they are not for my dancing, for they are so full of tricks and turns° that he which hath no more but the plain cinquepace° is no better accounted of than a very bungler, and, for my part, they might as soon teach me to make a capricornus° as a caper in the right kind that it should be. For a jig° my heels are too heavy, and these brawls° are so busy that I love not to beat my brains about them. A round° is too giddy a dance for my diet, for let the dancers run about with as much speed as

flap with a foxtail proverbial for a small reward or contemptuous dismissal.   **contentations** pleasure.   **measures** a grave or stately dance.   **galliards** a quick and lively triple time dance. **tricks and turns** specific gestures pertaining to formal dancing, the trick and the caper being leaping figures.   **cinquepace** a lively dance resembling the galliard, based on a five step pattern.   **capricornus** capriole, the frisky leap of a goat.   **jig** a rapid springy kind of dance.   **brawls** a kind of early French dance, often spelled *braule.*   **round** any one of a number of popular circle or ring dances.

they may, yet are they never a whit the nigher to the end of their course, unless with often turning they hap to catch a fall, and so they end the dance with shame that was begun but in sport. These hornpipes° I have hated from my very youth, and I know there are many other that loves them as evil as I. Thus you may perceive that there is no dance but either I like not of them, or they like not of me, so that I can dance neither.[1]

There resteth, then, if I could play of any instrument, or that I had any sight in song whereby I might delight your dainty ears, gentlewomen, by sweet playing or feigning° some pretty ditties. But to the first, my fingers would never be brought in frame; for the second, my mouth is so unpleasant, either to sing or to feign, as would rather breed your loathing than your liking.

Why yet if I could discourse pleasantly to drive away the time with amorous devices, or that my conceit would serve me either to propone° pretty questions or to give ready answers, with a number of other delights too long to be rehearsed, there were some comfort that I might be allowed of amongst you. But my capacity is so gross, my wits be so blunt, and all my other senses are so dull that I am sure you would sooner condemn me for a dunce than confirm me for a disciple fit to whisper a tale in a gentlewoman's ears.

But yet I trust, gentlewomen, when you shall perceive the zeal that I bear to my new profession, although you will not presently admit me to the pulpit, yet you will not deny me to be one of your parish, where, if it please you but to place me in the body of the church, you shall find my devotion as much as he that kneels next the chancel door.

And here, gentlewomen, the better to manifest the further regard of my duty, I have presented you with a few rough-hewn histories. Yet, I dare undertake, [they are] so warely polished° that there is nothing let slip that might breed offence to your modest minds.

hornpipes wind instruments made of horn, used to accompany a dance by that name, popular with sailors, often danced alone.   feigning singing softly and with due regard to the accidentals.   propone set forth.   warely polished carefully revised in order not to offend morals or sensibilities.

I have made bold to publish them under your safe-conduct,[◊] and I trust it shall nothing at all offend you. My last request is that at your pleasures you will peruse them, and with your favors you will defend them, which if I may perceive not to be misliked among you, my encouragement will be such that I trust within a very short space you shall see me grow from a young puny[◊] to a sufficient scholar. And thus, gentlewomen, wishing to you all what yourselves do best like of,

I humbly take my leave.

Yours in the way of honesty,[2]

Barnabe Riche.

---

safe-conduct (orig. savecundites), Riche seeks their protection of his book by dedicating it to them.   **puny** (from puisne), a novice.

[*Second Dedicatory Epistle*]

To the Noble Soldiers both of England and Ireland,
Barnabe Riche Wisheth as to Himself.

There is an old proverb, noble soldiers, and thus it followeth: "it
is better to be happy than wise." But what it is to be happy
how should I decipher, who never in my life could yet attain to
any hap◊ at all that was good. And yet I have had soldier's luck
and speed as well as the rest of my profession. And with wisdom
I will not meddle—I never came where it grew—but this I dare
boldly affirm, and the experience of the present time doth make
daily proof, that wit stands by in a threadbare coat where folly
sometimes sits in a velvet gown. And how often is it seen that
vice shall be advanced where virtue is little or not at all regarded;
small desert shall highly be preferred where well-doing shall go
unrewarded; and flattery shall be welcomed for a guest of great
account where plain Tom-tell-troth shall be thrust out of doors
by the shoulders; and to speak a plain truth indeed, do ye not
see pipers, parasites, fiddlers, dancers, players, jesters, and such
others, better esteemed and made of, and greater benevolence
used toward them, than to any others that endeavor themselves
to the most commendable qualities?

Then seeing the abuse of this present age is such that follies are
better esteemed than matters of greater weight, I have stepped

hap fortune.

onto the stage amongst the rest, contented to play a part, and have gathered together this small volume of histories, all treating, sir reverence of you,◊ of love.

I remember that in my last book entitled the *Alarm to England*[3] I promised to take in hand some other thing, but believe me it was not this that I meant, for I pretended then to have followed on, and where I ended with the decay of martial disciplines, so I meant to have begun again with the disciplines of war, and withal to have set forth the orders of sundry battles, and the manner of skirmishes, with many plots◊ of fortification, but especially those of the low countries, as Delft, Delftshaven, Rotterdam, Leyden, the Brielle, both the head◊ and the town, Gorcum, Gouldsluice, Maaslandsluce, the Krimpen, with diverse others worth the perusing for such as have not seen them.[4] But I see the time serves not for any such thing to be accounted of, and therefore to fit the time better, I have put forth these loving histories, the which I did write in Ireland at a vacant time before the coming over of James Fitzmaurice.[5] And it pleased me the better to do it only to keep myself from idleness—and yet they say it were better to be idle than ill occupied. But I trust I shall please gentlewomen, and that is all the gain that I look for. And herein I do but follow the course of the world, for many nowadays go about by a great device as may be how they might become women themselves. How many gentlemen shall you see at this present date that, I dare undertake, in the wearing of their apparel, in the setting of their ruffs and the frizzling of their hair, are more newfangled and foolish than any courtesan of Venice.

And I beseech you, gentlemen, give me leave to tell you a tale that comes even now in my mind: the matter is not worth the hearing, but yet very strange unto me at the first. It was my fortune, at my last being at London, to walk through the Strand towards Westminster, where I met one came riding towards me on a footcloth nag,◊ appareled in a French ruff, a French cloak,

---

sir reverence of you in all due respect.   **plots** (A. plattes; C.D. plots), the chart or diagram of a building.   **head** headland or promentory; bank or dam for holding back water.   **footcloth nag** a horse bearing a saddle blanket long enough on each side to protect the feet of the rider—an object of affluence.

a French hose, and in his hand a great fan of feathers, bearing them up very womanly against the side of his face. And for that◇ I had never seen any man wear them before that day, I began to think it impossible that there might a man be found so foolish as to make himself a scorn to the world to wear so womanish a toy, but rather thought it had been some shameless woman that had disguised herself like a man in our hose and our cloaks—for our doublets, gowns, caps, and hats they had got long ago. But by this time he was come something near me and I might see he had a beard, whereby I was assured that he should have been a man, whereat I began to muse with myself whether his simplicity were more to be pitied, or his folly more to be laughed at. For in mine opinion, it is as fond◇ a sight to see a man with such a bauble◇ in his hands as to see a woman ride through the streets with a lance in hers. And as he passed me, I saw three following that were his men, and taking the hindermost by the arm I asked him what gentlewoman his master was. But the fellow, not understanding my meaning, told me his master's name and so departed.

I began then to muse with myself to what end that fan of feathers served, for it could not be to defend◇ the sun from the burning of his beauty, for it was in the beginning of February when the heat of the sun may be very well endured.

Now if it were to defend the wind or the coldness of the air, methinks a French hood had been a great deal better, for that had been both gentlewoman-like and, being close pinned down about the ears, would have kept his head a great deal warmer. And then a French hood on his head, a French ruff about his neck, a French cloak on his back, and a pair of French hose on his legs had been right à la mode de France—and this had been something suitable to his wit.[6]

But I think he did it rather to please gentlewomen, and, the better to show what honor he bore them, would wear one of the greatest vanities that long◇ to their sex. And to this end, gentlemen, I have told you my tale that you might perceive the sundry means we use, and all to please women. I see it is the path that all desire to pace, and sure I would wish my friends to tread

for that because.   **fond** foolish.   **bauble** toy; fool's wand.
defend prevent.   **long** belong.

the same trace. For what is he that is wise which desires to be a soldier? Mars his court is full of bale, Venus' is full of bliss. And, my good companions and fellow soldiers, if you will follow mine advice, lay aside your weapons, hang up your armor by the walls and learn an other while, for your better advancements, to pipe, to fiddle, to sing, to dance, to lie, to forge, to flatter, to carry tales, to set ruff° or to do anything that your appetites best serve unto, and that is better fitting for the time. This is the only means that is best for a man to bring himself credit. Otherwise I know not which way a man might bend himself either to get gain or good report.

For first, the military profession, by means whereof men were advanced to the greatest renown, is now become of so slender estimation that there is no account neither made of it, nor any that shall profess it.

To become a courtier there is as little gain to be gotten, for Liberality, who was wont to be a principal officer as well in the court as in the country, by whose means well-doing could never go unrewarded, is turned Jack-out-of-office° and others appointed to have the custody of him to hold him short, that he range no more abroad so that no man can speak with him. And they say the poor gentleman is so fleeced, from time to time, by those that be his keepers that he hath nothing to give that is good but it falls to their shares.

To become a student in the law, there are such a number of them already that methinks it is not possible that one of them should honestly thrive by another. And some will say that one lawyer and one goshawk were enough in one shire. But of my conscience, there are more lawyers in some one shire in England, with attorneys, solicitors—or as they are termed, brokers of causes or pettifoggers—than there are goshawks in all Norway.

To become a merchant, traffic is so dead by means of these foreign broils° that unless a man would be a thief to his country to steal out prohibited wares,°⁷ there were small gains to be gotten.

to set ruff a former card-game; the act of trumping at cards; or possibly to swagger and bluster.   Jack-out-of-office (orig. Jack-out-to-office), a proverbial expression for a person dismissed from a position. broils wars.   steal out prohibited wares the illegal exportation of domestic goods for profit.

To become a farmer, lands be so racked° at such a rate that a man should but toil all the days of his life to pay his landlord's rent.

But what occupation or handicraft might a man then follow to make himself rich, when every science depends upon newfangled fashions? For he that today is accounted for the finest workman, within one month some new-found fellow comes out with some new-found fashion, and then he bears the prize, and the first accounted but a bungler. And within another month after, the second shall be served with the same sauce, and thus there is no artificer° that can hold his credit long.

Such is the miserable condition of this our present time; this is the course of the world, but especially here in England, where there is no man thought to be wise but he that is wealthy, where no man is thought to speak a truth but such as can lie, flatter, and dissemble, where there is no advice allowed for good but such as tendeth more for gain than for glory. And what pinching for a penny that should be spent in our country's defence?[8] How prodigal for a pound to be spent upon vanities and idle devices? What small recompence to soldiers that fight with foes for their country's quiet? How liberal to lawyers that set friends at defiance and disquiet a whole commonwealth? What fawning upon him whom fortune doth advance? What frowning upon him whom she hath brought low? What little care of the poor and such as be in want? What feasting of the rich, and such as be wealthy? What sumptuous houses built by men of mean estate? What little hospitality kept from high and low degree?

And here I cannot but speak of the bounty of that noble gentleman, Sir Christopher Hatton,[9] my very good master and upholder who, having builded a house in Northamptonshire called by the name of Holdenby,[10] which house for the bravery of the buildings, for the stateliness of the chambers, for the rich furniture of the lodgings, for the conveyance° of the offices, and for all other necessaries appurtenant to a palace of pleasure, is thought by those that have judgment to be incomparable, and to have no fellow in England that is out of her majesty's hands.[11] And

---

racked leased; rack-rent.   **artificer** craftsman.   **conveyance** skillful management.

although this house is not yet fully finished and is but a new erection,[12] yet it differeth far from the works that are used nowadays in many places, I mean where the houses are built with a great number of chimneys and yet the smoke comes forth but at one only tunnel. This house is not built on that manner, for as it hath sundry chimneys so they cast forth several smokes.[13] And such worthy port and daily hospitality [are] kept that, although the owner himself useth not to come there once in two years, yet I dare undertake there is daily provision to be found convenient to entertain any nobleman with his whole train that should hap to call in of a sudden. And how many gentlemen and strangers that come but to see the house are there daily welcomed, feasted, and well lodged. From whence should he come, be he rich, be he poor, that should not there be entertained if it please him to call in. To be short, Holdenby giveth daily relief to such as be in want for the space of six or seven miles' compass.[14]

Peradventure those that be envious will think this tale nothing appurtenant to the matter that I was in hand withal, but I trust my offence is the less, considering I have spoken but a truth, and do wish that every other man were able to say as much for his master, and so an end.

And now where I left off, I was telling what pride, what covetousness, what whoredom, what gluttony, what blasphemy, what riot, what excess, what drunkenness, what swearing, what bribery, what extortion, what usury, what oppression, what deceit, what forgery, what vice in general is daily entertained and practiced in England. And although it hath pleased God by wonderful signs[15] and miracles to forewarn us of his wrath and call us to repentance, yet you see the world runneth forward and keepeth his wonted course without any remorse of conscience, neither making sign nor proffer to amend. But like as we say, an old sore, being once overrun,° will not be cured with any moderate medicine, but must be eaten with corrosives till it comes to the quick,° and like as we say, one poison must be a means to expel another, so what should we otherwise think of ourselves, but if we be grown to such extremity as no gentle admonition will serve to reclaim

overrun overgrown by scab or scar tissue, thereby hiding the sore underneath? quick the living part.

us, what other thing should we look for but a mischief to be the medicine? God will not suffer that vice shall always flourish; He will surely root it out at the last. And how long hath He already borne with us in our wickedness? And what reformation is there had amongst us, unless it be to go from evil to worse? But if we did duly consider how mercifully He hath still dealt with us, how favorably He hath preferred us, and how wonderfully He hath defended us, I think we should not be altogether so unthankful as we show ourselves to be. For who knoweth not what an eyesore this little isle of England hath been to the whole world, and how long we have lived, as it were, in contempt of such countries as be our next neighbors, who, still envying° our quiet and happy government, have practiced by as many devices as they could to bring us into their own predicament, had it not been only the providence of God that preserved us? Or what friendship might we yet hope to find at any of their hands if their opportunity would serve them to be revenged of the despite which long ago they had conceived against us? First the French hath ever been our enemies by nature, the Scots by custom,[16] the Spaniards for religion, the Dutch, although we have stood them in great stead and helped them at many a pinch, yet I could buy as much friendship as they do all owe° us for a barrel of English beer. If we should go any further, then we come to the Pope, the Turks, and the Devil, and what friendship they bear us I think everyone can imagine.

And here we might consider how wonderfully God hath wrought on our behalves, and with all humbleness of heart give Him daily thanks for his benefits bestowed upon us—but most of all, and especially, for our most gracious and sovereign lady, Queen Elizabeth, who from time to time He hath so mightily preserved to be the very instrument of His mercy and loving kindness towards us, and for whose sake, no doubt, He hath forborne us in His displeasure, as many times He did the children of Israel at the request of His servant Moses.

First, how was she assaulted in her sister's time by those ravening wolves that daily sought her death, for they all stood in doubt that she should be that Judith which should cut off proud

envying (orig. enueighyng), suggesting inveighing against as a possible reading.   **owe** bear, profess to.

Holofernes his head.[17] And it pleased God to bring it even so
to pass, not only defending her from their cruelty and rage, but
raised her up, indeed, to the utter subversion of those bloody
butchers, and to the great comfort of us all that were in bondage
and subject to tyranny, not only setting us free from those detestable enormities that so corrosived° our consciences, but made
open way and passage for the word of God freely to be published,
I think, to our own destruction that so unworthily receive it.
Upon this, how many mighty enemies protested against her, and
what harm have any of them been able to do her? And how
many treasons and privy conspiracies since that time hath been
practiced by our own pelting° papists against her? But God hath
revealed and brought them to light. Let us therefore pray unto
God that he would so lengthen her days that we might still enjoy so gracious a princess long to govern and reign over us, and
that from time to time He would so direct her noble council in
all their meetings and consultations as may redound to His glory,
to the benefit of their country, and to their own immortal fame.
Let us likewise pray that God would root such covetous hearts
out of England that, for the sparing of a penny for the present
time, care not to let slip such matter as may cost many a pound
hereafter this.

Now lastly, and as mariners use to sing at the sea, "God save
my mate and me also": God send all soldiers that hath honestly
served their country better consideration than of long time they
have had.

And thus, noble soldiers and gentlemen all, I have held you
with a long sermon, neither can I tell how my preaching will be
allowed of; I crave no more, but wish you all better fortune that
I know the present time will afford you, and so will rest at your
disposition.

Barnabe Riche

corrosived consumed; corrupted.   **pelting** angry, passionate.

To the Readers in General

I assure thee, gentle reader, when I first took in hand to write these discourses, I meant nothing less than to put° them in print, but wrote[18] them at the request of some of my dearest friends, sometimes for their disport, to serve their private use. And now again, by great importunity, I am forced to send them all to the printer.[19] The histories, altogether, are eight in number, whereof the first, the second, the fifth, the seventh and eighth are tales that are but forged[20] only for delight, neither credible to be believed nor hurtful to be perused.[21] The third, the fourth, and the sixth are Italian histories written likewise for pleasure by master L.B.[22] And here, gentle reader, I must instantly entreat thee that if thou findest any words or terms seeming more indecent than peradventure thou wilt like of, think that I have set them down as more appropriate to express the matter they entreat of than either for want of judgment or good manners. Trusting that as I have written them in jest, so thou wilt read them but to make thyself merry, I wish they might as well please thee in the reading as they displease me in putting them forth. I bid thee heartily farewell.

Barnabe Riche

meant nothing less than to put had no intention of putting.

W.I. Gentleman,[23] in Praise of the Author.

Who seeks by Lady Fame to reap renown,
    Must ask consent of worthy virtue's grace:
To her belongs the stallment of the crown.
    She yields all those their just deservèd place,
As tread her path and run her royal race.
    Such rich rewards to each she yields each where
As might become this worthy Riche to wear.

The painful man that tills his ground reaps fruit,
    Each merit hath his meed, pain hath his hire.
Desert requires that fame should not stand mute
    Where wisdom doth to virtue's ways aspire.
The hope of gain doth set men's hearts on fire,
    Then yield him thanks that erst hath undertook,
For thy delight, to pen this little book.

Let Momus'[24] mates chat on in their despite,
    Let wranglers wreak and wrest the worst they may;
The wisest sort will judge and take delight,
    Though jangling jays that know not what they say,
Will oftentimes their witless wits bewray,
    Yet Riche shall reap what he by right hath won,
Deserved praise for that which here is done.

FINIS. g. W.I. Gent.

Baptiste Starre[25]
in praise of the Author.

If due desert should reap reward,
　　Or worthy merit, guerdon have:
Why should not Riche press forth himself,
　　The lovely laurel crown to crave,
Whose life in field that won him praise,
　　He leads at home in Pallas' ways.

Scorn not then Zoilus[26] his good hap,
　　That can his will subdue and tame;
But try to tread his path whereby,
　　Thou mayest thy life with virtue frame;
Allow his pain and pen to write,
　　Who naught pretends but thy delight.

Lo, he who wonted was in field
　　To meet his furious foe in face,
Hath scaled Parnassus' hill where he
　　Attends Minerv' her noble grace.
And there his pen doth play his part,
　　As did elsewhere his shield and dart.

FINIS. g. B.S.

The Printer to the Reader.

The fragrant rose can make no choice,
    Who shall upon him light;
The sprawling spider turns to gall,
    The bee to honey right.

So fares it with this book, whose leaves
    Are open spread to thee;
Make choice good reader of the best,
    Suck honey with the bee.

Misconster not each merry phrase,
    Deem not the worst of it,
Which is not penned to do thee hurt,
    But recreate thy wit.

And for such faults as scaped have
    The press, whereof there's store,
Reprove the printer for his haste,
    Blame not the book therefore.

But as by mirth tis meant to move,
    Thy mind to some delight,
Reward his pain with praise, which did
    These pleasant stories write.

FINIS.

SAPPHO DUKE OF MANTONA

The Argument of the First History.

Sappho, Duke of Mantona,[1] having long time served Claudius the Emperor, by whose magnanimity and martial prowess sundry victories were achieved against the Turks, was by false imposition banished, himself, Messilina his wife, Aurelianus his son, with Phylene his daughter,[2] in which banishment they sustained sundry conflicts of fortune, but in the end, [were] restored again to their former estate and dignity.

The one of the greatest virtues that worldly men can express in the common behavior of this life is neither to wax proud by prosperity, nor to fall into despair by adversity, for Fortune, having a free will to come and go when and where she listeth, the wise man ought not to be sorry when he loseth her, nor to rejoice when he holdeth her, for that the valiant man loseth no reputation when that Fortune faileth him, but is the less esteemed of if he want discretion to bear her mutabilities, the which for the most part is altogether uncertain: now promising good, now performing ill; now lifting up to the tip of the highest dignity, now throwing down to the pit of perpetual infamy; now advancing aloft those that be unworthy, now throwing down the climbers up into extreme adversity. Such are the gifts and graces of Fortune, to have no better thing more certain in them than to be for the most part in all things uncertain, as the sequel of this history shall more better describe, and followeth in this manner.

There was sometime remaining° in the court of the Emperor
Claudius a noble duke whose name was Sappho, Duke of Mantona, who, as well through his own magnanimity and valiance
as otherwise through his great policy and experience in martial
affairs, had achieved many notable victories in the behalf of the
emperor against the Turks, which made him both famous to the
world and feared of his enemies, but most entirely beloved of
the Emperor Claudius. But the wars being once finished and
brought to an end so that the empire remained in tranquility and
peace, soldiers were forgotten, captains were not cared for. Such
as had proffered themselves to fight for the safety of their country were now shaken off, and such were preferred in their rooms°
as had any faculty in them tending to pleasure and delight, as
dancers, pipers, fiddlers, minstrels, singers, parasites, flatterers,
jesters, rhymers, talebearers, news carriers, love makers, such as
can devise to please women with new fangles,° strange fashions,
by praising of their beauties when sometimes it is scarce worthy,
by commending of their manifold virtues when God knows they
have few or none at all. But see, I pray you, how far my wits begin to square.° I pretended but to pen certain pleasant discourses
for the only pleasure of gentlewomen, and even at the very first
entry I am fallen from a reasonable tale to a railing rage, as it
may seem. But I pray you, gentlewomen, bear with my weakness
and, as the preacher in the pulpit, when he is out of his text, will
say for excuse: "Good people, though this be something digress-
ing from my matter, yet it may very well serve at this present."
Take this I pray you for my excuse in like case.

And now to my purpose where I left off before, this noble Duke
Sappho had no skill in courting trade; his head which had been accustomed to bear the lofty helm had now quite forgotten to wear
the wavering plumes, ready to blow away with every wind.[3] His
body, most inured° to wear a coat of steel, could not be brought
in fashion with this quaint and nice° array. His neck he thought
more fitly to paise° the trusty targe° than to be hanged with

---

remaining dwelling.   **rooms** places.   **new fangles** new fashions, foppish or silly finery.   **square** wander.   **inured** familiar
through custom or habit.   **nice** foolish.   **paise** hold suspended.
targe by then a poetic word for shield or buckler.

gems or chains of gold; his fingers, commonly practiced to grasp
the sword or lance, could not be brought in frame to strike the
virginal or lute; his voice served him better to cheer his soldiers
in the field than either to feign or sing ditties in a lady's chamber;
his tongue had more used to speak simply and plain than to dissemble with his friend or to flatter with his foe; his legs had better
skill to march after dub-a-dub-dub than to mince it with a minion,
tracing a pavan or galliard upon the rushes.[4] What should I say
further? This noble duke had no manner of skill in carpet trade.[◊]
But thus it fell out that parasites and flatterers, having once entered credit with the emperor—as surely it is almost a common
infirmity as well among princes as other superior officers to be seduced by flatterers, pickthanks, and tale-bearers—this noble emperor likewise, by the instigation of such as were about him, who,
perceiving the duke to be none of their flattering fraternity and
envying the great reputation wherein the emperor held him, had
so incensed the emperor against him that now his liking was converted into loathing, and his great love turned to a mort[al] hate,
that in the end the poor duke was brought to answer unto many
forged articles surmised against him, who neither in consideration
of his former service done for his country, neither in respect of the
innocency of his cause, could otherwise be dispensed withal than
to be banished into exile, himself, Messilina his wife, Aurelianus
his son, with Phylene his daughter; and although the common
sort of people held him in great honor and much lamented his
case, yet it could not be helped but the emperor's decree, openly
pronounced, must needs take place.

I beseech you, gentlewomen, yet to comfort yourselves. I know
your gentle hearts cannot endure to hear of such ungentle parts,
but these are but the trumps of ordinary fortune, not private to
Duke Sappho alone, but common to all men that be of the like
profession, for what happened better to the most noble captains
of the world, or what other recompense received either Caesar,
Scipio, Hannibal, or many other like, who, having honored their
countries with sundry triumphs and many notable victories, when

carpet trade (unique usage acc. to O.E.D.), amusements in the chamber or boudoir, the kinds of intimate rooms in which carpets were
found; singing, courting etc.

the wars were ended and that there was no more need of them, finished their days in such pitiful plight as I will keep to myself, because, right courteous gentlewomen, I rather desire to draw you into delights than to drown you in dumps◊ by revealing of such unnatural facts as I know your gentle natures are not able to digest.

Thus you have heard how this noble duke, with his wife and children, by sentence of the emperor, were banished from out their native country, as also from any other realms, cities, towns, or territories being within the emperor's dominions. There resteth now for the duke to make such poor provision for his furnishing as his ability might any ways serve him, the which, God knoweth, fell out so mean and scant as it scarcely serveth him to defray his charges to carry him from out those places from whence he was prohibited. And taking his course towards the parts of Macedonia, after a long and weary journey, he arrived at a town called Tariffa, where, being lodged in a mean and simple house, his money now being at the last cast wherewith to bear his charges, his poor wife and children altogether wearied with their long and troublesome travel,[5] and himself all ashamed to be known what he was. Now it fell out that the host of the house many times viewing and casting his eyes upon the Duchess Messilina,[6] who notwithstanding she dissembled her estate and degree, contented to leave her honorable dignity and to participate such equal fortune with her husband and children as their hard haps◊ had conducted them unto, yet her beauty, which could not be blemished with mean and homely garments, had so entangled her arrant host that he could not be merry when he was out of her sweet sight. And now though he perceived his guest began to wax◊ slack in his payment and not able to disburse for his ordinary expenses, yet for the love he bare to his wife, he was contented to chalk up the charges behind the door,[7] hoping in the end to have cleared the scores to his better content; and as time and convenience might serve him, he spared not to let the duchess understand his great liking towards her, assuring her that the courtesy that he used towards her husband was only for her sake, and that if he were

dumps a fit of melancholy or depression.   haps fortunes.   wax grow.

assured his good will might be acceptable in her sight, she might assure herself of such a friend of him as would be as careful of her as her husband to whom she was married.

This lady now having well pondered the words of her amorous host, who would not think but that she was much perplexed in her mind that she who had been born of honorable parentage, espoused to a noble duke, whose dignity in times past surmounted all the rest, whose training up had ever been amongst those of the highest degree, and now that her honorable estate was not only eclipsed by crooked destiny, but also to have her chastity assailed by such a simple coistrel◇ whom she durst not so sharply shake off, as her heart would very well have served, for that she knew the duke her husband was run in his debt, neither could she tell by what means he was able to discharge it, she was therefore constrained with fair speeches to shift him off from time to time, the which the knave perceiving very well, began to think with himself that it was but her husband's presence that hindered him of his purpose, and therefore determined to find a present remedy.

And now coming to his guest, [he] began to reckon with him and to call him to account for the charges wherein he was behind, telling him that at that very instant he had occasion to occupy◇ money, which made him not only to seek up such small sums as were due unto him, but also to try his friends otherwise to serve his turn, and that helping him now at his present need he might then begin again a new score and would bear with him a much longer time.

The poor duke, then enforced to seek out an old salve for a new sore—which is to pray when he was not able to pay— with very courteous speeches desired his host to bear with his inability, assuring him that when time should serve he would so thoroughly recompense him as he should have cause to hold him well contented. But what prayers may prevail where pity is clean exiled, or what gentleness is to be looked for to come from such an ungentle churl◇ whose mind was only set upon rape and ravin,◇ who had premeditated before the drift,◇ which, as he presupposed, was now sorted out as he looked for?[8]

coistrel base knave, varlet.   occupy invest, trade with.   churl lowest rank of freeman, hence low-bred fellow.   ravin rapine, robbery.   drift scheme, plot.

Wherefore, as it were half in a fury, he uttered forth these words: "My friend content yourself and take this for a resolute answer. The money which now resteth in your hands, although I might very ill forbear it as my case standeth, yet for that it is not mine ease to run into any further charges without a better assurance than either words or promises, I am notwithstanding contented to bear with you for that which is already past, minding from this day forward to give no further credit. And for that you are altogether a stranger, unto me unknown, both what you are, from whence you come, whither you will, and where I should find you, I purpose therefore for my better security, and the rather to come by that you already do owe me, to keep your wife in pawn, whom I know is so dearly beloved unto you that for her sake I shall the sooner hear from you again. Otherwise I know not where to inquire after you, nor how to come by that [which] is my due, which I am not well able to forbear, neither do I mind clearly to lose."

The poor afflicted duke, having never fallen before into [a] cut-throat's hands—persuaded indeed that the tenor of this varlet's words and the keeping of his wife tended to no other end but for his better assurance to come by his money—was constrained to make a virtue of necessity, and was so much the better pleased for that his wife might still remain free from further travel, and thinking in time to settle himself and to recover his wife and children about him, with this resolution he began to relate unto his wife with what salutations his gentle host had greeted him withal, desiring her to comfort herself for a season, assuring to do his best endeavor and to set up his sails to the prosperous gales of fortune.

This good lady, hearing her husband's discourse, uncertain what to do, wept bitterly, as well for grief to lose his presence as for that she should be left in the house of the arrant knave her host; but like a wise lady, hearing the alleged reasons of her lord and husband, did think it not for the best to increase his old sorrow with a new grief, contented herself, uttering these words:

"Dear husband, knowing all that you have said to be very just and true, I am contented for a certain time to force my will in hope that hereafter we may live together, joining ourselves in the company of our children, and this I would desire you, that so

often as you can, by convenient and trusty messengers, to send
me word and intelligence of your health and estate, because the
same should bring greater contentation unto me than the welfare
of mine own self."

This said, she embracing him very lovingly, and he kissing her
with great sorrow and grief, took his leave and bade his lady
and spouse heartily farewell, leaving with her Phylene her dear
daughter.

Thus himself, with Aurelianus his little son, departed from
Tariffa towards the famous city of Caire,[9] and as they passed
through a wilderness, having lost their way, wandering two or
three days without any manner of food saving hips, haws, and
sloes° such as they could gather in the desert, the poor child
being overcome with faintness, not longer able to travel, began
to complain to his afflicted father, desiring him to sit down to
rest himself a time. The woeful father, tormented in his mind to
see his poor distressed child, sat him down under a tree, where,
after a while recounting to himself his sundry misfortunes, being
oppressed and wearied with travel, he fell into a sound sleep. The
child, after he had a while rested himself, leaving his father asleep,
began to seek about for something to slake his hunger. And as
he was straying thus about the woods, it fortuned the Duke of
Vasconia, having lost his company in the pursuit of a stag where
he had been a hunting, and as he was crossing the next way to
go to the city of Messina where he held his court, having in his
company but the Lord of Sura with three or four serving men,
he fortuned to espy the child running in the bushes all alone,
and calling the child unto him he said: "Alas my little boy, what
makest thou in this place? Art thou here alone, or how camest
thou hither, I pray thee tell me?"

"Forsooth, godfather," quoth the child, "I came hither with
my father who lies asleep hereby, and I was seeking something to
eat, for by my troth I am so a-hungered that I could eat worse
meat than a piece of roasted pig, and that with all my heart."

hips, haws, and sloes the fruit of the wild rose; the fruit of the
hawthorne; the fruit of the blackthorn. Riche did not attempt to find
eastern Mediterranean equivalents of these favorite English plants.

The duke, greatly pleasuring to hear the pretty answer of the child, replied in this wise: "How sayest thou, my little knave, wilt thou be my boy and dwell with me, and I will give thee good meat thy belly full, how sayest thou, wilt thou go with me?"

"Yea forsooth, godfather," quoth the child, "on that condition you will give me roast meat enough, I will go with you, for I think I did not eat my belly full of roast meat this month and more."

The duke then commanded one of his men to take up the child whom he carried away with him, and now perceiving it to be both well-favored, quick-witted, and very apt to learning, he brought it up at school, where he proved not only wise and learned, but also in many other exercises convenient and fit for gentlemen he commonly excelled every other man. And thus leaving him at school, I will convert my tale to his woeful father, who, when he was awaked and missed his pretty son, began to pry about in every bush, seeking and calling: "What Aurelianus, Aurelianus, where be you Aurelianus?" But in the end when he could nowhere find him, thinking assuredly that he had been devoured by some wild beast, began with pitiful exclamation to cry out:

"O Fortune, Fortune, more than fickle, who in a moment hoist a man up to the highest degree, and by and by, in less space than in the twinkling of an eye, she throweth him down again so low, as more misery is prepared for him in one day than she advanced him in an hundred years, which I now prove and have experience in myself, and so much the more, the greater is my grief, who have been nourished delicately amongst my friends, maintained still in most prosperous estate, hoping for the full perfection of my felicities by marrying a noble dame with whom I pretended◊ to spend the residue of my life according to the scope and lot appointed by the almighty God. But now behold all my enterprises be quite plucked back, and my purposes turned clean topsy turvy in such wise that from honorable estate I am driven to wander like a vagabond, driven from post to pillar, from country to country, from region to region, to sequestrate◊ myself from amongst my friends without any assured place where to make my abode. Oh froward fate, how canst thou be so hard-hearted and void of pity still to prosecute thy cruel pursuit, first

pretended intended.   **sequestrate** isolate.

to deprive me of my honorable dignities, then to banish me from amongst my loving friends, thirdly to separate me from Messilina, my well-beloved wife, more dear unto me than the balls of my unhappy eyes, and not yet contented, but now to bereave me of my sweet infant, my only hope of comfort in my old age. O death, death, the end of all sorrows and the beginner of felicities, now make sharp thy dart and give no longer delay of life. Dispatch, dispatch at once the most unfortunate man that lives this day on earth. For what avails my life if in the gulf of sorrow and grief I drown the pleasures of the same? But ah, I see right well, thou preservest the same of purpose but to delight in my griefs and to triumph over my adversities."

And herewithal the brinish tears so streamed down his cheeks that he was not further able to speak one word, but running up and down the woods, sighing and sobbing in great anguish of mind, and his body much enfeebled for want of food and sustenance, he fortuned to meet certain laboring men that dwelt in a poor village not far from the place, who, perceiving by his gesture that he was passionated in his thoughts, they began with such courtesy as they had learned in the country to demand the occasion of his grief.

But he, knowing very well how far they were unable to minister relief to the least of his afflictions, could render no other answer than piteous sighs and sobs; but the poor peasants, when they had better beheld the tallness of his stature, the seemliness of his countenance, and the comeliness of his personage, were greatly moved with compassion towards him, and with such bad eloquence as their skill would permit, began to persuade him to walk with them to their cabins, where he might refresh himself with such homely junkets° as was provided for their own suppers. The duke, contented to yield to their requests, walked along with them, where he remained all the night very pensive and heavy in his heart, and began to think with himself that there was no more hope left for him to hear of his son, and therefore began to imagine how he might render some relief to his poor wife and daughter whom he had left as you before have heard.

junkets sweetened curds served with cream; any dainty cake or sweet-meat.

Now there was dwelling hard by the place a nobleman that was lord of the village, who, having intelligence of this distressed stranger, caused him to be sent for, before whom, when the duke was presented, after many questions debated between them, the nobleman demanded of the duke what countryman he was, and how he had been trained up, and then if he could be contented to play the servingman, and would be careful and diligent in his master's affairs, that then he would be contented to receive him into his service and would reward him accordingly as he was able to deserve.

The duke, all ashamed to be known what he was, reverently made answer that he was born in the country of Achaia, and that he had been trained up in service with sundry noblemen, and would be very well contented to do his best endeavor to serve him with the best service he could do.

Thus the poor duke became a servingman, whom we will leave with his master, and return to his wife, who was left in huckster's handling,[10] as you have heard, remained in the house with this varlet, who sought by sundry assays° to satisfy his villainous lust, and like an expert soldier when he cometh to besiege a hold, first sendeth his heralds to summon the fort, proffering many large conditions if they will quietly surrender. But if defiance be made then presently he placeth his battery, thundering forth his cannonshot against the walls, which, if they be so well rampired° that there will no breach be made, yet he ceaseth not with gifts and bribes to corrupt the warders, not caring how he conquereth so he may have the spoil.

This villain in like wise sought first with piteous sighs, which, sauced with sugared words, did serve instead of heralds to persuade her to yield up the keys of the fortress that with peaceable entry he might take possession at his pleasure; but, being by her repulsed, and the flag of defiance displayed upon the bulwark, then with thundering threats he thinketh to make his battery, proffering to cast her into prison for the debt which was owing him for her husband and herself. Otherwhiles again he would tempt her and try her with gifts, thinking that for the necessity

assays military strategems, devices.   **rampired** (orig. rampered), having ramparts, a bulwark.

she was driven into, she would have made sale of that which she preferred before her own life.

This noble dame, perceiving herself so hardly beset on every side, fearing in the end the varlet should work her some greater despite, so enforced herself, with Phylene her little daughter, to fall to work that with weaving and knitting of laces and otherwise with their needles they had gained so much money as she was able to set herself free from out a knave's debt. And thinking with herself that her husband had remained about the city of Caire, to the which he purposed to journey when he departed from her, she determined with all convenient speed to repair thither, as well to comfort herself with the company of her lord and husband as otherwise with her earnings to help to relieve him. But for that she had understanding that the passage by land was not only troublesome but also very inconvenient for her to travel by reason it lay through woods and deserts, she got intelligence of a small bark that was bound thither by sea which only stayed but for a wind to serve her turn. Hereupon she discharged herself from the town of Tariffa, and when weather served, agreeing with the master for her passage, herself with her daughter repaired aboard the bark, which, being put to sea, was forced by the extremity of a contrary wind to put themselves romer° for the safety of their lives to a clean contrary place. And where they meant to have sailed to the city of Caire, they were now arrived at the city of Cherona, where the lady coming ashore, she joyed nothing so much in the narrow escape she had made with life by reason of the tempest, as she sorrowed for being so far driven from her husband, whose fellowship she more desired than either wealth or worldly treasure. But forasmuch as both herself and her daughter were very evil at ease and greatly enfeebled with sickness at the sea and bad living in the ship, she determined to make her abode still at Cherona till she might convey letters to Tariffa that should certify her husband of all that had happened.

In the meantime, her husband, having received some small

romer (term unknown), Cranfill: to let the ship go with the wind and currents rather than to fight the elements; Donald Sampson: to use a sea anchor or running anchor, shaped like a drinking glass or rummer (Ger. roemer). *The Explicator*, xxxiv. 1 (1975) art. 1.

benevolence of his lord and master who had conceived some good liking of him by reason of the skill that he had in the riding of horse, very desirous to render his wife some portion of his good fortunes, who had been so long time partaker of his evil haps, craving leave of his lord for a time, came to Tariffa, where, when he missed his wife whose letters were not yet come from Cherona and therefore could get no intelligence but that she was gone to Caire of purpose to seek him, in a great perplexity he travelled towards Caire where, making great inquiry, could learn nothing of her. From thence he posted from place to place, from city to city, from town to town, but being never the near his purpose, he then began to double his dolors° and with bitter words to curse the celestial signs and planets which reigned at the day of his nativity and hour of his birth, contented to yield himself a captive to mishap, and to surrender himself a subject to fortune's froward frumps.°

Being thus turmoiled with great anguish of mind, wandering to and fro, he was brought so low and bare that he was ready to beg an alms from door to door. And coming to a poor country village, his penury was such that he was glad to become a servant to him that was the sexton of the parish, whom he had not served long but the old sexton his master died, and for that he had now learned to ring bells and had some cunning in the keeping of a clock,[11] the parishioners were contented to place him in his master's room.° The duke, thinking himself more than thrice happy to get so great preferment, thanked Lady Fortune that had so friendly dealt with him, resolving himself to continue the office while he lived; but Fortune, finding him so thankful for a little, dealt more friendly with him as after you shall hear.

But I will first declare how it happened with his son Aurelianus, who was taken up in the woods by the Duke of Vasconia, as before you have heard. (But here I must first remember° you that the duke changed his name from Aurelianus to Silvanus, which name he gave him of purpose for that he was found in the woods.) Silvanus, now having been trained up at school, was come to man's estate, and besides that he had the knowledge of

dolors sorrows.   **frumps** taunts, insults.   **room** position.
remember remind.

good letters, he was comely in his personage and of very good proportion, and in all manner of activities appertaining to a gentleman he exceeded every other that was in the court. Besides, in his demeanor he was so courteous and gentle that he gained the good will and liking both of one and other, but especially of the duke himself, who allowed him such large expenses whereby to maintain himself as brave as the best.

Now this noble duke had no other children but one only daughter whose name was Valeria, in whom it seemed that both virtue and beauty had held some great contention who should bear away the prize, for, although that in beauty and good grace she exceeded every other dame, yet her virtues and good conditions surmounted more her beauty than the finest gold surmounteth lead or dross.

The lady, now having heard great report of the nobleness of Silvanus, who was suspected to be but some poor man's son by reason he was found in the woods, began yet to bear him very good countenance, which at the first proceeded but of the noble nature which ever was accustomed to be favorable to such in whom was found any worthy desert; but, as the fish which by little and little sucketh upon the bait till at the length she swalloweth down the hook whereby she hangeth fast not able to free herself, so this lady Valeria, contemplating herself many times to behold that young gentleman Silvanus, was so far entangled with his sweet and pleasant countenance, that now perforce° her will she was constrained to yield to love, and, feeling herself ensnared and bereaved of her former freedom, being by herself alone, she began to complain as followeth:

"Alas," sayeth she, "is it possible that now, force perforce,° my mind should be so altered that straying from the bounds and limits of vowed chastity I should now become amorous and subject to a certain unacquainted lust? From whence cometh this alteration, or how happeneth this unaccustomed hue? Ah, Love, Love, how hast thou tormented me and taken away the health and soundness of my mind?

"It behooveth me to show myself as issued forth of the noble house of Vasconia, and with the greater care I ought to take heed

perforce in spite of.   force perforce in spite of efforts to resist.

how I degenerate from the noble blood whereof I am descended, rather than to set my mind on a foundling unknown, unto whom, peradventure, if I discover my fondness, will not let to mock me for my labor, and for all the beauty or nobleness of my birth will make me his jesting stock and solace himself with the fondness of my conceits. But stay, stay unhappy tongue that thundereth forth such hateful words against my beloved Silvanus. Oh thrice accursed wench that can so ungently conceive against him that in all his demeanors doth show himself as noble as the best. But of what mettle are either monarch, king or kaiser framed of otherwise than of natural and common earth, whereof other men do come? Or what maketh these differences which by sottish opinion we conceive either of gentle or ungentle otherwise than the show of virtue and good conditions? Then the party whom I love is both virtuous, valiant, sage, of good grace, learned and wise. Vaunt thee then Valeria that thou likest no inferior foundling unworthy of thy love, but a worthy gentleman endued with noble qualities in whom both heaven and nature have forgotten nothing to make him equal to them that march in foremost rank. It is Silvanus whom I love, and of him I pretend to make a lawful husband, for otherwise I detest to lead the filthy life of lawless lust. But thus the bond of marriage being made, I may love and live without offence of conscience, neither shall I do any blot or blemish to the greatness of my house. But if any be so scrupulous as to think by marrying of him I should diminish mine honor, it is the thing that I do least esteem, for what is honor worth where the mind is void of contentation, and where the heart is bereaved of his chiefest desire, the body remaineth restless and the mind is never in quiet. Silvanus, therefore, shall be my loyal husband, meaning thereby neither to offend God nor man."

And now from henceforwards she devised with herself how to make her love known to Silvanus, not sparing when she was out of his presence, before all men, to praise his great perfections wherewith he was enriched, and in his own presence she used such loving countenance towards him that although Silvanus were but young and had never been trained up in the school of love, yet he perceived very well that those friendly glances were lent him of good liking, and those loving countenances were grounded of good will. And albeit he saw the inequality and difference between them both, she being sorted out of royal race, and himself altogether ignorant of his own estate and from whence he was sprung, yet being now led by Love, whose laws have no respect either to estate or dignity, he determined to follow his fortune and to serve her which so lovingly showed herself to requite him with the like. And the more he called to mind the divine beauty of his lady, her graces, wisdom, behavior and courtesy, so much the more increased his desire, fortifying himself against all mishaps and perils that might succeed, and began to debate with himself in this manner:

"How is it possible that I should be so foolish to despise a duty so rare and precious, and to set light by that which the noblest would pursue with all reverence and endeavor? I am not the first that hath obtained the love of a lady. No, no, I see she loveth me, and shall not I requite it by yielding love again? If I were so void of humanity and good nature, besides, I might work mine own overthrow in seeming to despise so noble a lady, so the gods would not let to minister revenge as they did upon Narcissus.[12] But, ah, silly° wretch that I am, what folly is this that I have now premeditated with the peril of mine honor and the hazard of my life? See, see how far my affections begin to stray through the hot assaults of foolish fantasy, enraged with an appetite rising on vain hope. What madness in me to think that Valeria will so much forget the greatness of her house, or yet embase° herself in respect of me, poor silly soul. But what if she would be contented, either in respect of marriage or otherwise in respect of good will, to surrender herself to satisfy my request, how much were I the near my purpose? Alas, nothing at all. The first, I know, should be denied me by the duke her father, and as for any other courtesy, although I know it be far from her thought, yet surely mine own conscience would not suffer me to proffer so great villainy to so noble a lady, neither the reverence and duty which I owe to her father would permit me to requite his gentleness towards me with so great an injury. Cease, therefore, Silvanus. Subdue thy sensuality, that by vanquishing thyself thou mayest set open the gate to fame, who with her

---

silly helpless, deserving of pity.　　**embase** degrade.

trump of everlasting glory, she may advance thee renowned to all posterity.

"But, alas, shall I then give over° to love my Lady Valeria? Reason wills me so to do, but love hath so blinded all my senses that reason giveth no manner of light. What help have I then hereafter to hope for? Alas I know no one, and therefore be content." Herewithal he stayed his travail, resolving with himself to conquer his affections, and being in his chamber taking pen and ink, he sat him down and wrote these verses following:[13]

No shame I trust, to cease from former ill,
   Nor to revert the lewdness of the mind,
Which hath been trained and so misled by will,
   To break the bounds which reason had assigned.
I now forsake the former time I spent,
   And sorry am, for that I was miswent.°

But blind forecast was he that made me swerve,
   Affection fond was lurer of my lust;
My fancy fixed, desire did make me serve,
   Vain hope was he that trainèd all my trust.
Good liking then so dazzled had my sight,
   And dimmed mine eyes, that reason gave no light.

O sugared sweet that trained me to this trap,
   I saw the bait where hook lay hidden fast;
I well perceived the drift of my mishap.
   I knew the bite would breed my bane at last.
But what for this? For sweet I swallowed all,
   Whose taste I find more bitter now than gall.

But lo the fruits that grew by fond desire,
   I seek to shun that pleasèd best my mind;
I sterve° for cold, yet fain would quench the fire,
   And glad to lose that fainest° I would find.
In one self thing I find both bale and bliss,
   But this is strange, I like no life but this.

When he had thus penned these verses, he committed them to memory, and the next day, being in the company of certain

give over cease.   **was miswent** have gone astray.   **sterve** die.   **fainest** most eagerly.

gentlemen and gentlewomen in the court, taking a lute, whereon he could play very well, and having likewise good knowledge in his song and therewithal a very pleasant voice, he began to sing this ditty before mentioned in the midst whereof came in the young Lady Valeria, wherewith Silvanus stayed his song. But she, joining herself to the company, seeing the saint that secretly shrined in her thought, she had vowed her greatest devotion unto, desired Silvanus at her request to begin his song again. Silvanus, making the matter nothing nice° was pleased very well to satisfy her request, and taking the lute began his song, to the which the lady gave attentive ear from the beginning to the ending. And, perceiving the song to be made in some extreme passion forced by love, she demanded of Silvanus who had penned those verses, who answered they were of his own penning, and so lately done that he could not forget them. The lady, then thinking Silvanus to be in love with some other gentlewoman, departed very speedily, as though some sudden motion had happened to her mind; and coming to her chamber, shutting fast the door, she began to say as followeth:

"How much am I unfortunate above all other women, that being a lady of such blood as I am, and yet am happened into so strange a misery, that in manner with mine own mouth I have made request to him, which rather with all humility ought to proffer me his service, and yet am scornfully rejected, and another like to catch the birds whilst I do but beat the bush. Oh Silvanus, Silvanus, deemst thou me no better worth than so lightly to reject my proffered love? And shall another that is much less worthy bear away the sweet fruit of my desired hope, and shall possess without desert the glory due to a firm and faithful friend? No, no, I cannot think thee so ingrate, and my heart foretelleth me that it is impossible my Silvanus should wander so far from equity, but that he is able to discern of colors and will not requite me with wrong for right. I am sure not to be deceived in my love. I know he loveth me, but that he dareth not to disclose the same, fearing I should refuse him and cast him off with shame. I will not let,° therefore, with mine own mouth to bewray° the same

nothing nice without feigning objections.   **let** hesitate, hinder
myself.   **bewray** reveal.

unto him, and to manifest my good will whereby my chaste and honest amity once known unto him, virtue herself may knit the knot between us, which cannot choose but bring forth the fruits of true and perfect friendship.

"And shall I then, being a lady of such degree, be constrained to sue where every other woman of the meanest reputation be ordinarily required, and that with the importunate instance of their suitors? I shall then be noted of boldness and be thought to stray too far from the limits and bounds of modesty, and to make a greater show of lightness than is properly looked for in us who be of the feminine gender; but what strictness is this prescribed to our sex that we should be bereaved of our liberty and so absolutely condemned of lightness in seeking to satisfy our lawful and honest desires; with what trampe° be we tempered withal more than men whereby we should be able to withstand the forces of the flesh, or of power to resist the concupiscences which nature itself hath assigned? We be termed to be the weaker vessels, and yet they would have us more puissant than either Samson or Hercules; if man and woman be made of one mettle,° it must needs follow by consequence we be subject to like infirmities. From whence cometh then this freedom that men may ask what they desire of us, be it never so lewd, and we may not crave anything of them that tendeth to good and honest pretence. It is termed to be but a man's part that seeketh our dishonor by lewd and lawless lust, but to a woman it is imputed for lightness to firm° her lawful liking with pure and loyal love. If men will have pre-eminence to do evil, why should we be reproved for doing well?

"Whereupon stand I then amazed with these fond° opinions? My love is not unlawful, neither before God nor man. I love Silvanus whom I will take for my husband, for otherwise to love him° my heart doth not intend; therefore without any further respite or delay, I will make my love known unto him, and the bond of marriage once confirmed between us shall cover the fault

trampe (Fr. trempe) process for hardening metal; mental humor, mood (cotgrave).   mettle or possibly metal, to accord with tempering.   firm secure.   fond foolish.   otherwise to love him love him without marrying him.

which men would deem; neither shall my mind be altered, either
by the sugared persuasion of friends, neither terrified with any
threats that may be thundered forth by parents' blustering wrath.
I am not so far overwhelmed with pride that in respect for the
greatness of my parentage I should despise a gentleman endued
more with virtue than with riches, though there be some that
be of this condition that they will sooner prefer the greatness
of birth than the greatness of virtue, the abundance of wealth
than the abundance of wit, the perfection of beauty than the
perfection of the mind. But I am out of the number of those
women which care more to have their husbands' purses well lined
with money whereby they may be maintained in their bravery, or
sometimes fix their fancy upon some young man that is of goodly
personage, although void of virtue, quality, and good conditions
that ought to garnish a gentleman and doth more beautify and
enrich him than either the bare show of beauty or any other gifts
of fortune; but I cannot employ my love upon transitory treasure
when the riches of the mind is clean taken away. No, no, it shall
better content me to see a mean gentleman beloved and praised
of everyone for his virtues, than to marry a miser possessed with
all the goods of the world, hated and ill-spoken of for his vices.
Fear not, then, Valeria, to follow thy determination, and to put
in proof what thou hast pretended."◊

Herewithal staying herself, she began to practice the mean◊
in what manner she might bewray her love to Silvanus, seeking for occasion and time meet◊ for her purpose. And although
there remained in her a certain natural shamefastness◊ wherewith maidens are commonly accompanied, which for a time did
close her mouth and made her to defer the time of her resolved[14]
mind, yet in the end thoroughly persuaded in her intent, she
sent one of her maidens, willing Silvanus to come and speak with
her about certain affairs that she had to employ him. The maid
having finished her message, there could never more joyful news
happen to Silvanus, who, entering the chamber of Valeria with
trembling heart, after he had done his reverence, with great fear
and bashfulness said, "For that I understand your ladyship hath

pretended asserted, claimed.   practice the mean calculate.
meet convenient.   shamefastness modesty.

to employ me about certain affairs, I shall think myself the most happiest man in the world if my travail and diligence might any ways do you service, be it that therein I should offer or sacrifice mine honor or life, craving no greater benefit for the satisfaction of all my contentations received in this world than to serve, obey, and honor you, so long as my life doth last."

The lady now, all ravished with joy and contentation, perceiving by his change of color the fault proceeded of vehement love, taking him aside into a window, Love had so closed up her mouth that she knew not how to begin her tale. Her mind was so troubled, her wits so far out of course, that her tongue failed to do his office in such wise that she was not able to speak one only word.

He, likewise perplexed with the like fever, was now astonished to see the alteration of his lady.

Thus these two lovers, like two senseless images, stood still beholding each other without any manner of moving; in the end, the lady taking courage herself, with a trembling voice joined with a maidenlike shamefastness, began to say as followeth:

"Being assured, my Silvanus, of your discretion and wisdom, which nature hath not only endued you withal but art hath also accomplished what nature began to work, I will therefore make no doubt at all to let you know the hidden secrets of my heart, neither will I go about with circumstance to color my words, but, being well persuaded that when you shall both hear and savor my speeches and therewithal sound the depth of my devices, you will easily conjecture that my enterprises be none other than just, and that my alleged reasons are grounded of good pretence.◇ I think sithence your arrival here in the court of the duke my father you have not seen me in any behavior otherwise than virtue doth permit, nor in any my demeanors exceeding the bounds of modesty otherwise than becometh a maiden of my calling, being descended of so worthy a stock; but if this be a fault that being provoked by the pureness of my heart and fidelity of my good will, who to keep the same inviolable do voluntarily offer myself to the honest disposition of your judgment as it shall please you to conceive of me, I have then committed a fault in liking you too well, but I trust nothing at all offended God who knoweth

pretence cause, just claim.

the innocency of my crime. Think not, Silvanus, that I am the friend of Fortune and practice pleasure alone without virtue, for it is modesty that commandeth me and honesty is the guide of my conceits, swearing and protesting by the Almighty God that never man shall touch Valeria except it be in marriage, and he that otherwise would assail me I have a heart that shall encourage my hands to sacrifice my life. And now, Silvanus, if you will not think me more prodigal of my present than your fancy will serve you to take in good part, behold, it is you that I have chosen for my spouse and loyal husband. And although I had determined to dissemble that which now I have laid open unto you, yet reposing myself in your virtue and honesty, I trust I shall not have cause to repent me for anything that I have either said or done."

Silvanus, which all this while hearing this heavenly harmony with full assurance of that he most wished for, albeit he saw no possibility how to bring to pass this desired marriage, yet determined not to refuse so great a preferment being so frank and liberally offered, answered in this manner:

"I know not, madam, with what humility and reverence I might receive and accept this your great bounty and nobleness, so graciously offered unto me. I do acknowledge my condition and state too base, and that my love may be thought to presume too far beyond the bounds of order, considering that my ignobility and birth are no meet° matches for such a peerless princess. Yet this I dare boldly affirm, that if love and entire affection borne to your ladyship might serve to countervail that defect which by place of birth the Destinies have denied me, I dare undertake I should as well deserve to be received as he that is lineally descended from the greatest monarchy of the world. The which love, if till this time I have delayed to open, I beseech you, madam, to impute it to the greatness of your estate, and to the duty of my calling. But now forasmuch as by your own motion, grace, courtesy and great liberality the same is proffered, and that of your own bounty it pleaseth you to accept me for yours, I humbly beseech you not to dispose of me as of a husband, but as of one which both is and shall be your servant for ever."

Thus said, he, taking her by the hand, kissed it with great

meet worthy, appropriate.

devotion, his tongue and wits were so rapt and tied. As the lady perfectly perceived this alteration, and seeing it to proceed of love, replied in this manner:

"Then, my Silvanus, there needeth at this present no further circumstance, but for that I am well assured there are some that will be offended with my choice, but especially the duke my father who will conceive some great displeasure against me, there resteth then that this our contract be kept very secret until it please God to appoint the time that the rest of our determinations may without danger be consummate and accomplished. In the meantime, trusting that your desire is godly and that the friendship you pretend to bear me is founded upon virtue and to be concluded by marriage, receive me for your spouse and lawful wife; you shall have such part in me as without any regard to the obedience and duty that I owe to my parents, I am yours, being ready and disposed to obey you so far as my honor may permit me."

These two lovers, now grounding themselves the one in the other's fidelity, could not so cunningly dissemble and cloak their affections, but that it was easily perceived by their secret glances and countenances conveyed from the one to the other, and, as we have a proverb, "It is ill halting before a cripple," so there were many about the court that were so well studied in the school of love that they were able to have commenced masters of art and could easily conjecture from whence those rolling looks did proceed, that being now assured of that which before was but suspected, the brute° was spread about the court of the love that was between Silvanus and Valeria, that in the end it came to the duke her father's ear, who taking the matter very grievously that his daughter, to whom the inheritance of the dukedom remained after his decease, should so meanly bestow her love upon a foundling found in the woods, and minding to find a remedy for the matter, willed Silvanus that in pain of his life, within twenty days he should depart the court and never after to be seen within the jurisdictions of the dukedom of Vasconia.

Valeria, now having intelligence what had happened, had no leisure to vex or molest° herself when time rather required a

brute (from Fr. bruit), news.   **molest** trouble, annoy.

speedy remedy for the encountering of those mishaps, devised
with Silvanus to convey herself away, contented rather to live in
the fellowship of an honest loving husband with whom she should
hold faithful and loyal company, with what estate and fortune
soever it might please God to appoint, than to live without him,
beautified with the graces and foolish names of honor and pre-
eminence.

Silvanus, contented to satisfy her desire with the hazard of his
life, yielded to her request, and before the twenty days were expired, so cleanly conveyed himself and Valeria away that when
they were missing the duke wist° not which ways to send after
them. Wherefore in a great fury he spared not to send out great
companies, which posting every way, made inquiry and search after them, but all in vain, for Silvanus had so disguised himself and
Valeria that, without any manner of trouble, they quietly passed
the country, and, having freed themselves from out the danger of
the duke, desiring that the day of their marriage might now be
prefixed the which by mutual consent was presently determined,
and by great fortune—or rather conduction by the providence of
God—they happened to arrive in the country village where Duke
Sappho that was father to Silvanus had remained all this while
sexton of the parish. In this village, because it was a place free
from resort—whereby they might remain unknown and in the
better safety—they purposed as well to celebrate their marriage
as for a time to make their abode till matters were better quieted,
and that they might at leisure resolve what course were best for
them to take. Silvanus now having conferred with the priest, the
marriage was appointed, where the poor bellringer, taking the
view of this new married couple, fell in a great liking of Silvanus,
not for that he knew him to be his son, for thereof he could have
no manner of suspicion, as well for that he deemed he had been
devoured in the woods by some wild beast, as also because his
name was changed. But whether it were by the instigation or
secrecy of nature, or otherwise by the will and pleasure of God,
to bring to pass that which afterwards happened in effect, this
poor sexton, I say, led by the secret motion of his own affections,
proffered Silvanus that if his service might any ways stand him

wist knew.

in stead—for that he was a stranger in the place—he should use him in any respect and should find him ready to stand him in such stead as his poor ability might any ways permit.

Silvanus, in like case having forgotten his father, being separated from him in his infancy, yet nothing despising his friendly offer, craved his help for the hiring of a chamber for some reasonable rent till time that he might better provide for himself. The sexton, very glad that he had so good opportunity to pleasure him, brought him with his wife to his own house where he lodged him in the best room that he had, proffering not only his house, but all that was in it to be at their disposition and pleasure. This new married couple, now gladding and sporting themselves with all such sweet embracements as they can better describe which have been possessed with the like delights, but, as some will say, it is the man's part to be first wearied in those venereal sports, so Silvanus, having now well feasted himself with that sweet repast, had leisure to bethink him of his own estate, began inwardly to grow into great sorrow and heaviness, not so much for himself as for his wife, who for his sake had dispossessed herself from so great honor, abandoning her friends, contented to yield herself a thrall° to fortune.

These cogitations did so nip him that he could not so well dissemble his grief but that his wife perceived some disquietness in his mind, and therefore very grievously she demanded of him to show her the cause of his discontentment which by outward appearance seemed inwardly so much to molest him.

Silvanus, hearing his lady's request, answered in this wise: "My dear wife, the sweetest companion that ever man did possess, for so much as you earnestly desire to understand what it is that so much withdraweth my delights, I will not let to bewray the truth, which is this: when I consider with myself of your present estate and condition, who from the tip and height of dignity have not spared for my sake to surrender yourself to become a subject to all mishaps, besieged on every side with the future assaults of ordinary fortune, it maketh me therefore to have the greater care by what means I might endeavor myself to maintain and continue your estate, though not according to your worthiness and calling,

thrall prisoner.

yet according to your well contentment and liking. And hereupon conceiving in my head diverse imaginations, no means but one in my fancy seemeth best, which is that I go to the court of the Emperor Claudius, who at this present is leading a great band to encounter the Turk, at whose hands I doubt not but to receive some good entertainment, and besides the honor and reputation I may gain by good desert, I may likewise reap such living and good liking of the emperor that, in despite of fortune's teeth, we may live hereafter a quiet and honorable life to our great joy and comfort. But when I did consider the beloved company of you, dear wife, I feared to bewray that which now I have disclosed, not knowing in what part you would take it that I should so suddenly depart. Lo, here the cause of my disquietness, which you desire so instantly to know."

The lady which was wise, perceiving the great love that her husband did bear her, when he had stayed himself from talk, with glad and merry countenance answered in this wise:

"Ah, Silvanus, the exemplar of all virtue and gentleness, let death and fortune do what they list, for I count myself more than satisfied of all that is past by the only enjoying of your presence, contenting myself to be a partaker of your misfortunes, and have no doubt but that I can so moderate my affections that during my life I will rest better contented with that which your ability will permit, be it never so mean, than otherwise to be honored with names and titles of nobility in princely state or port° having not your presence. Disquiet not yourself, therefore, but persevere in your determination, and that sorrow which shall assail me by reason of your absence, I will sweeten and lenify° with contentation to see your commendable desire appeased, and the pleasant memory of your valiant facts° shall beguile my pensive thoughts, hoping that our next meeting shall be more joyful and glad than this our parting shall be either heavy or sad."

The lady's answer did wonderfully quiet the mind of Silvanus, and calling his host the sexton unto him whom he had made partaker of his determinations, he departed, leaving his wife such money and jewels as they had remaining. And coming to the court of the Emperor Claudius, he was very well entertained, and

port bearing.   **lenify** soften, mitigate.   **facts** deeds.

the rather for that the emperor had great need of men to supply his army, which had sustained sundry conflicts and diverse overthrows, for the Turk did wonderfully encroach upon the emperor, and had taken sundry cities, towns and castles from him, and was like still every day more to prevail than other, that now the emperor began to repent him of the slender account he had made of soldiers in the time of peace, for that he had too few that were sufficient to serve him in his wars; for instead of experience, valiance, and policy, which three ought to be governors, commanders, and chief officers in a camp, he was glad to prefer vainglory, foolhardiness, and rashness—simple sots that were more fitter to wait in gentlewomen's chambers than to be made captains or leaders in the wars.

The emperor [was] now standing in great distress for want of men, for those that he had made greatest account of in the time of peace were now able to stand him in no stead in the time of wars, and those that had braved it up and down the court in the new cuts, strange fashions, their hair frizzled, looking with such grisly and terrible countenances enough to make a wise man believe they were clean out of their wits, now in the time of wars were glad to run under a gentlewoman's farthingale to hide them. The emperor, I say, being thus perplexed, called to his remembrance the injury that he had done Sappho, whom he had banished only to satisfy the wills of those that were about him, which he knew did hate him more of spite than for any occasion the duke had given. Without any further delay, therefore, the emperor sent sundry messengers into every part of Christendom to make inquiry that whosoever could find the duke should be worthily recompensed, and those proclamations were spread through every region, in city, town and village, insomuch that in this parish where the duke remained sexton, as you have heard, the priest made inquiry on Sunday in the church, as the custom is, that whereas about fourteen or fifteen years sithence the Duke of Mantona was banished by the emperor, which was procured rather by envy than for any desert, as now it was proved, whosoever therefore could give any intelligence of the same duke should be very liberally recompensed by the emperor.

The sexton, now hearing these news, did think it more better to live still in his sexton's room where he remained without envy, than to become again the Duke of Mantona, subject to the spite of hateful persons. But calling to his mind his wife and daughter, which he thought remained yet alive—although he knew not where—and for the great love that he bore to Silvanus, whose wife remained in his house, as you heard, seeing that fortune offered him so good opportunity to pleasure them, only for their sakes resolved himself to go to the emperor. But first, comforting his guest Valeria, whom for a time he should leave in his house only with such servants as herself had about her, he told her that he was well-assured where to find this duke that was so much inquired after, and that he doubted not, if it were but in respect of his good news, he should work Silvanus, her husband, into some credit with the duke who might likewise procure his better preferment with the emperor.

And thus the sexton departed, and with all convenience came to the court of the emperor, to whom, when he had made himself known, he was most honorably received and great joy and gladness was made throughout the whole court; the emperor now in consideration of the injury he had done him did not only restore him to his former room° and dignity, but also advanced him in honor and estimation to be preferred before all other next unto himself.

Thus, after many benefits received of the emperor, the duke prepared himself, accompanied with many [of] his friends, to go to the emperor's camp, of the which he was made general, where he knew well how to behave himself. And giving out new ordinances, he appointed certain such as he himself knew worthy, and gave them charge, amongst the rest seeing Silvanus, who all this while remained in the camp, whom the duke did very well know, although Silvanus did little suspect that a poor sexton of a parish should become a general to an emperor's army. The duke, perceiving himself to be unknown to Silvanus, was contented so to remain for a time, but yet desirous to see what was in him, he gave him the leading of a certain horsemen° with the which Silvanus served so valiantly and therewithal had so happy success that every man extolled up to the heavens the worthiness of Silvanus. This pleased the duke passing well, and the duke, having

room position. **horsemen** a cavalry troop.

now sundry times encountered with the power of the Turks and had given them many overthrows, he was now preparing a great force for the recovery of the city of Cayoe,[15] the which the Turks had taken before from the emperor. And calling Silvanus unto him, he said: "God grant, young gentleman, that your end agree with your good beginning." Then making Silvanus to kneel, he dubbed him knight and made him colonel of twenty ensigns.◊

Silvanus, after he had done his reverence, thanked the duke of the honor and favor which it had pleased him to do him, promising to do so well in time to come as he should not be deceived in his conceived opinion, whereof he gave assured testimony at the assault that was given to the city before mentioned, where he behaved himself so valiantly as he was the first that mounted upon the walls and by his dexterity and invincible force made way to the soldiers in the breach, whereby they entered and took the city, killing and driving out their enemies before them. In many such like attempts Silvanus still showed himself so noble and valiant that his praise and renown was sounded in every place.

The duke now having recovered again all such cities, towns and other forts which the Turk had before taken from the emperor, and therewithal had banished the Turks from out the bounds and borders of the empire, and a league agreed upon between the Emperor and the Turk, the army being broken up and soldiers discharged, every man [was] well recompensed for his service, according as he had deserved. Silvanus likewise, who by his worthiness, having not only made himself famous to the world, but also had well lined his purse with good store of gold, bethinking him now of his fair lady, came to the duke to have taken his leave. But the duke, minding now to perform the good that he meant to Silvanus, was resolved in his mind that Silvanus with his wife should be his guests as well at Mantona where he was duke as they had been before where he was but a sexton, said to Silvanus as followeth:

"Sir knight, what haste is this, that you would so suddenly withdraw yourself from out my company? Belike you have some

---

ensigns companies or troops serving under one banner.

fair wife to whom you make such speed to be gone. But sir, content yourself to bear me company to the emperor's court, where I doubt not but you shall receive some better recompense for your service so happily begun, for it is not requisite° but that the virtue of valiance ought to be rewarded and cherished by princes that be aided in their necessity with the diligence of such virtuous and noble gentlemen as yourself."

Silvanus, greatly comforted with these words of the duke, was well pleased to wait upon him. Thus they took their journey towards the great city of Cherona, which was in the uttermost borders of the emperor's dominions; there the duke purposed to stay a while to recreate himself with the rest of his company.

Now it fortuned that the valiant acts and haughty° enterprises of Silvanus were so renowned and spread that the fame therefore came to the ears of the Duke of Vasconia that was father to Valeria the wife of Silvanus, who with all possible speed made such haste that he came to Cherona where he found Silvanus in the company of the Duke of Mantona, to whom turning himself he said as followeth:

"Sir duke, the only hope that I have—that you will not let to extend justice upon the mischievous and ungracious acts of wicked men—doth let me at this instant to forbear with mine own hands to avenge the wrong that I assure myself to have received of this traitor Silvanus."

The company were wonderfully abashed at these words, but especially the Duke of Mantona, who loved Silvanus more dearly than any other.

But the other, going still forwards in his tale said: "If the heartbreak that afflicteth the soul of a woeful father whose house is made desolate by losing his child by the mischievous enticements of a thief, if this precedent° I say, move you not to minister such speedy revenge as the law doth prescribe, I suppose that all impunity of vice and sin hath place on your behalf." And therewithal staying his talk, but yet by his gesture and countenance so enraged, that he seemed like a man that were besides himself.

---

requisite not right, as required by the nature of things.   **haughty** eminent, courageous.   **precedent** (A. president; C. present), these preceding events.

The Duke of Mantona now perceiving the matter—that Valeria was the daughter of the Duke of Vasconia, whom he supposed to have been of some mean birth and parentage—was wonderfully sorry for Silvanus whose fact° by the law deserved death. And seeing the duke in such a fury he wist° not by what means to work Silvanus' safety, for to entreat the duke he thought it but vain, and to bring Silvanus to answer the fact, he knew the law would condemn him. And therefore knowing where Valeria did remain, whom he knew did love Silvanus as her own life, and thinking that her tears might lenify and soften the hardened heart of the duke her father, he therefore privily sent for her to be brought immediately to the city of Cherona. In the meantime, he committed Silvanus into safe custody and desired the duke at his request to stay himself a while and he should have such justice on Silvanus as himself would require.

Matters being thus pacified for a while, I will in like case let them rest for a time, and will now discourse how it befell to the Duchess Messilina with her daughter Phylene.

You have heard before how by constraint of weather at the sea they were driven to this city of Cherona where the duke now remained, and at her first coming, falling to her work as before she had done at Tariffa, a rich merchant that dwelt in the town, taking the view of this new-come workwoman, fell into so great a liking with her that only to have access to come into her company, he bestowed more money in cloth to make him shirts and handkerchiefs in one week than he was able to wear out in three years after, which he put her to make, whereby he became something well acquainted with her. But to the end that she might think herself something the better beholding unto him, he proffered her a more convenient house than that she was in, which he would furnish with all manner of household stuff for a reasonable rent. She, being very glad of so good an offer, became his tenant. The merchant, now perceiving his time did so well serve him, without any great circumstance declared unto her the great goodwill he bare her, but Messilina so delayed him with such wise and reasonable answers that from time to time the merchant himself could

fact deed, action.   wist knew.

not importunately° crave that which with such modesty she so honestly denied him.

Now there lay in the city of Cherona the old Duchess of Petrona, who, having intelligence of Messilina to be so good a workwoman, she sent for her, to whom she put sundry parcels of work, which she so well finished to the liking of the duchess that from time to time she still plied her with the like, whereby Messilina with her daughter Phylene had continual recourse to the palace of the duchess, where Arabianus, the only son of the Duchess of Petrona—and inheritor of the dukedom, but that he was under-age—did mark and behold the beauty and good grace of this young seamstress Phylene, was so clogged and fettered in the bands of love that all other thoughts seemed loathsome unto him, and every other joy displeasant in respect of the pleasure that he suffered by thinking of his fair Phylene, wherefore baiting himself with hope and tickled only by love, he determined whatsoever happened to love her.

Which being perceived by his mother, she began very sharply to rate° him, blaming him that would so indiscreetly place his love, not weighing his estate and birth as come of princely race, and now would make himself a fable to the world to like of such a one so far unworthy his degree.°

Arabianus, falling down upon his knees, most humbly desired his mother to bear with all that was past, and although it were truth that she had said, that he deemed her for her birth to be unworthy his degree, yet she deserved for her beauty to be compared to the greatest dame and bravest minion° elsewhere. And whereas other girls by artificial means and trumperies do enforce that which the heavens have denied them, yet Phylene had no other ornament than that which nature had enlarged in her; and otherwise for her virtue, wisdom, and modesty, he knew it to be such by report of many as she might be a lantern to the greatest dame that lived.

"Notwithstanding, madam, for so much as you do take my fact° in so ill part, considering the reverence that I owe to the

importunately urgently, persistently.   rate scold.   degree rank in society.   bravest minion most handsome, best dressed favorite or mistress of a king or royal person.   fact behavior.

place which you hold on my behalf, and the duty and obedience that God will and hath commanded that children should bear to those that have begotten and borne them, if it please you to pardon me of this that is past, I protest that from henceforth I will be more wise and better advised how I enter into anything that might turn to any such consequence or any manner of ways to offend you."

The duchess, knowing all to be true that her son had said, very well pleased with his speeches, remained satisfied, thinking in her mind indeed that if Phylene had been the daughter but of some mean gentleman, her son should never have sought further for a wife.

From this time forwards, although Arabianus by the persuasion of his mother had vowed to revolt◊ and let slip the love that he bare to Phylene, yet he could not so clearly lose his liking, but that he did manifest some part of his goodwill by gifts and good countenances which still he bestowed upon Phylene, causing his mother likewise to bestow many liberal rewards upon Messilina. Thus the mother and the daughter perceived themselves a thousand times beholding to the old duchess and her son.

In this mean space, the merchant before mentioned had buried his wife, and knowing no other but that Messilina his tenant had been a widow, he began now a fresh suit, and with great importunity requested her in the way of marriage, and so hardly he laid into her that Messilina, not knowing otherwise how to rid him, confessed unto him that she had a husband alive and therefore might not marry.

The merchant, thinking these to be but delays to shift him off, came to this point that if hereafter he could prove her by her own confession to be a widow, that then before witness she would take him for her lawful husband, and till that time he would no further trouble her till he had made his proof; she, being glad to be at rest, thinking that he should work very wisely to make her confess herself to be a widow, agreed to his request, and witness was had in the matter. The merchant now letting his matter rest a time for his better purpose, in the end coming unto her he told her that although she were so discourteous to forsake his

revolt to cast off.

friendship in every respect, first in the way of good fellowship, and after in the way of marriage, whereby he was driven to go seek farther, but now having found a wife in the country to whom he was assured and meant presently to be married, yet for the old friendship that he bare her, considering that he would presently remain in the country altogether and forsake the city, therefore for her better security and assurance of her dwelling, he would make her a lease of the house that she dwelt in for one and twenty years if it might do her any pleasure, without paying any penny income.

Messilina, giving him great thanks, took his offer very courteously, and the lease was put to making, which the merchant signed and delivered, and here withal desired her single obligation for the performance of some small rent, were it never so little, that she might acknowledge him to be her landlord, the which she never denied to give.

The obligation was made in this manner: "Know all men by this presents that I Messilina, widow," and so forth with words in manner and form of every obligation. This obligation thus made was signed and delivered by Messilina to the merchant, who had now gotten that so long he had sought for, and by virtue of this obligation, craved Messilina to be his wife—she denying his demand. But what could that prevail when he had her own hand and seal to show whereby she confessed herself a widow, and then by her own agreement—as you have heard before—she must yield herself to be his wife?

This matter was long in fending° and proving, insomuch that the duke being now in the town ministering of justice to such as would crave it, the merchant brought the matter before the duke, who, hearing the manner of the bargain and so many witnesses to affirm the same, gave sentence that the merchant ought indeed to have her. But Messilina, falling at the feet of the duke, desiring him with tears to defer his judgment, the duke, now taking better view of the woman, knowing her both by her voice and also by looking well on her face, perceived assuredly that it was his own wife, he called again to the merchant to see his obligation, which, when he had received, he said in this manner:

fending arguing.

"Master merchant, this obligation which you have delivered me, now I have perused with better advice, I find it to be neither sufficient nor lawful, for this woman that you would make a widow without doubt is married and hath a husband. Now she being under covert barne,° your obligation is unpleadable and I know not whom you should blame, whether yourself or the scrivener." And herewithal being replete with great joy and gladness, taking his wife up in his arms very lovingly embraced her, he said:

"Ah, my dear and loving wife, how much am I bound to render innumerable thanks to the almighty God, that when all hope was passed, have yet again recovered my greatest hope and comfort."

Messilina, likewise perceiving her lord and husband, clasping her hands about his neck, was not able to speak a word for joy and contentation; the company that stood by amazed to see this sudden hap° were likewise very joyful to see this friendly meeting. The merchant, seeing how he had been deceived, tore his obligation and departed all ashamed. The duke, now desirous to see his daughter Phylene, caused her mother to send for her, who not knowing her father otherwise than by report, fell down on her knees to crave his blessing. The duke, taking her up, kissing her with fatherly affection, could not stay his tears in remembering her brother Aurelianus, whom he deemed to be dead.

These news were suddenly spread throughout the city of Cherona, insomuch that Arabianus, having now intelligence that Phylene was the daughter of the noble Duke Sappho, certifying his mother the truth which he had learned, without any great deliberation both the mother and the son coming to visit the duke and his company, where they were very well welcomed, but especially to Messilina, to whom the old duchess and her son both had been very bountiful. And when a while they had passed the time with pleasant discourses of all that had passed, the Duchess of Petrona craved Phylene in marriage for her son. The duke, being made privy to the matter, knowing Arabianus to be come of great descent and to be endued with large and fair possessions, seeing him likewise to be a toward° young gentleman, would not stand

covert barne (more usually covert baron) legal cover or protection of a married woman through her husband.   hap chance occurrence. toward promising.

against it, but referred the matter to his daughter's liking. Phylene, who had been greatly bound to the courtesy of the young duke, and had received many gifts and good turns at his hands, would not do as a number of these nice dames that will many times make dainty of that they would fainest° come by, gave her free consent. There was then no more to do but to prepare for the marriage, which was presently solemnized with great pomp and glory.

By this [time] Valeria—whom as you have heard before the duke had sent for—was come to Cherona, who was privily lodged by the duke's commandment in a privy place. The day now being come Silvanus was brought to his answer, he could not deny the fact wherewith he was charged, but that he had stolen Valeria from her father, by which confession the law condemned him to die. There were many that knew the nobleness of Silvanus that began to entreat the Duke of Vasconia to remit the fact,° but all in vain, for the more they entreated, the more he hastened to see execution.

The Duke of Mantona, seeing his great obstinacy, did think it high time to find a remedy for Silvanus, if it might be. Therefore he said: "Sir duke, were it possible that this condemned man, who is like, so far as I can see, to bear the whole brunt, and yet might be enticed to this fact by your daughter's means, or at the least, your daughter must be half partner of this fault and yielded with her good will to come away, for otherwise it had been impossible for him to have brought her from out your court, which, if it be true, if you will needs see justice so duly executed in the one, I cannot see how your daughter can go quit,° but must be as well partaker of the punishment, as she was in the fact by yielding her consent."

The Duke of Vasconia answered: "As it is the office and duty of every good justicer to know the valor° and difference between virtue and vice to the end that all virtuous acts may be honored and the contrary chastised and punished; otherwise he is not worthy the name of a righteous judge but of a cruel and traitorous tyrant. Wherefore, sir duke, you sitting here in the place of justice

fainest most eagerly.   remit the fact pardon the deed.   quit
free.   valor value.

to minister equity and right to everyone that calleth, then I desire that I may have the law extended° upon this wretch Silvanus. As for my daughter that you speak of, as I know not where she is, so I do not desire to learn what is become of her. But this I protest, that if ever I may find her, rather than she should go unpunished, I will not let° with mine own hands to do execution upon her according to her demerits and the filthiness of her fact, from henceforth denouncing her to be any child of mine, and make no better account of her otherwise than to be a filthy strumpet, unworthy of me for her father, or to challenge her descent from such a stock."

The Duke of Mantona was now troubled worse than before, for whereas he had some hope that the humble suit of Valeria should something have moved her father to compassion, he now thought that her sight would rather increase his rage and fury. Again he thought that to bring her into his presence, if he continued in one mood, he might work Valeria so great prejudice as he would be heartily sorry to see. Yet, thinking with himself that it was impossible that a father should be so void of good nature to see the utter ruin of his child without any remorse, he called Valeria to be sent for, who, being conducted to the place, seeing her father and the rest of the company, she began to conjecture that all was not well. But when Silvanus saw his Valeria, wondering by what means she was brought to so evil a banquet, remembering what words her father before had protested, he began with a piteous voice to cry out:

"O my dear beloved wife, the only cause of my joy and quiet, what evil fortune hath conducted thee to this place, what froward fates have forced thee, that thou shouldst be made a companion of my mishaps? O frail and inconstant fortune, how hast thou fronted° my honest desires with such crooked° spite that where I covet the countenance of greatest credit, there am I forced to hazard the loss of life and all? What crooked aspect hath governed my proceedings that the hoped time I spent in this warlike service should thus conclude with his contrary, and I forced, as it were, by fate to follow the unhappy event of the same, wherein I do

extended inflicted.   **let** forbear.   **fronted** defied, set one's face against.   **crooked** (orig. cooked), dishonest, perverse.

confess my predestinate follies. But such are the sundry dealings of this life, as those that tend their steps to monstrous mountains do sometime scarce conclude with mean mole hills. The sundry conflicts of fortune, masking my hope with a show of happy reward, hath not only wracked me, but it threateneth the sequel of worse success, that instead of happy and quiet life, my days shall be abridged with most shameful and vile death. O Valeria, Valeria, the joy and comfort of my life, I shall no more see that incomparable beauty of thine which darkeneth and obscureth the rays and beams of the sun."

Then turning himself to the Duke of Vasconia, he said: "I most humbly beseech your grace to have compassion upon me, not for that I would consume my life in your displeasure, I make offer of the same to your merciful will and disposition, choosing rather to die and to leave your grace satisfied and contented than to live a happy life, your princely mind displeased. And albeit the right good intent and unstained conscience is free from fault, yet the judgment of men hath further relation to the exterior appearance than to virtue's force. Is it a sin to marry? Is it a fault to flee and avoid the sin of whoredom? What laws be these, then, where the marriage bed and joined matrimony is pursued with like severity as murder, theft, adultery? But seeing the fault of this mishap to arise by my predestinate evil luck, I most humbly beseech you to mitigate your rage and to conceive no sinister° opinion of this your worthy daughter, whose smallest grief is my double pain. As for myself, I am well pleased with my misfortune, contented to sacrifice my life, only to receive your clear acquittance for my offence, and will make satisfaction with the price of my blood."

The Duke of Vasconia, bending his brows, answered: "No, traitor, no, it is not thy life that shall appease my fury, but I will so cool the whorish heart of your minion, for whom you seem so much to plead, that I will make her an example to all others for doing of an act so detestable. But what abuse have they committed under the title of marriage, thinking without remorse of conscience by that means to continue their mischief, and their promise and faith that was made under a bush must serve for a cloak and visard for their most filthy whoredom. But what if

sinister ill.

their marriage were concluded and confirmed by God himself? Is Silvanus a man worthy to be allied or mingled with the royal blood of the house of Vasconia? No, no. I vow I will never take sound nor restful sleep until I have dispatched that infamous fact from our blood, and that villain whoremonger with his trull° be used according to their deserts."

Valeria, now knowing how matters were sorted out, and hearing this cruel sentence pronounced by her father, fell down upon her knees and bitterly crying out, she said: "My dear father, most humbly I beseech you, since no other thing may appease your ire than the life of the offender, let not this gentleman abide the penance of that which he never committed; be revenged on me by whom the fault—if a woman's faith to her husband may be termed a fault—is done. And let this unfortunate gentleman depart, who God knows is innocent of any other crime than what he was brought into only by my provocation." And as she was about to have proceeded farther in her talk, her father interrupted her, saying:

"Have you found your tongue now, pretty peat,° then we must have an almond for parrot.[16] How durst thou, strumpet, challenge me to be thy father, that without regard either of my renown or of the honor or my house, thou art content to be abandoned from this noble estate and to become a fugitive and a stranger to follow a rogue up and down the country? No, minion, no, think not that any feminine flattery shall stay me from doing thee to death, nor your darling that stands by you shall escape with his life, verily believing that in time it shall be known what profit the world shall gain by purging the same of such an infected plague. And I do hope besides this, that in time to come men shall praise this deed of mine, who for preserving the honor of my house have chosen rather to do to death two offenders than to leave the one of them alive as less faulty or guiltless[17] than the other."

Valeria, once again falling frustrate° before her father, said: "I most humbly beseech you, for that all other comfort is denied me, that I may crave this only grace at your hands for the last good that ever I hope to receive, which is that you being thus grievously

---

trull prostitute, strumpet.   **pretty peat** girl (term of endearment,
used ironically here).   **frustrate** (C. prostrate), defeated.

offended with me do vengeance at your pleasure upon her who willingly yieldeth herself to the death with the effusion of her blood to satisfy your ire, grant only that Silvanus, who is innocent and free from fault, may go quit."° But her father, no longer able for anger to hear her speak, crieth out to the duke to haste the execution. The Duke of Mantona, whose heart did bleed in his belly for sorrow, perceiving it folly to delay longer time, gave sentence of death and present execution to be made, although he took so great sorrow for them as if his daughter Phylene should have borne them company. But he was not able to help it; the laws and ordinances of the country would not otherwise permit. And, thinking to take his last farewell of Silvanus, he said:

"O Silvanus, the glory and honor of all young gentlemen that ever were, that be now, or shall be hereafter this, whose virtue, valiance and worthy exploits do glister° amongst the multitude as the sunbeams do upon the circuit of the earth, oh that thy hard fortune should conduct thee to such distress that only by thine own valiance and prowess hast escaped so many dangers amongst thy thronged enemies, and now thy ruin and overthrow should be thus wrought amidst thy assured friends that knows not how to help it. What heaps of cares hath besieged me on every side to think that I should crave thy company whereby thou are brought into the midst of so great mischief, which otherwise mightest have escaped this mishap. And thou Valeria, would God thy unfortunate host, which departed from thee thinking to do thy husband pleasure, had remained with thee a poor sexton still, till this present day."

The rest of the company that stood by, hearing the duke to make so great lamentation, was likewise stricken into a marvelous grief and sorrow insomuch that every one that durst speak cried to the Duke of Vasconia for pardon and that he would remit the offence, and what pity it were if he should seek the death of so noble a gentleman as Silvanus had showed himself to be. But the duke, persevering still in one mind, asked them with what face they could make request for a varlet of no reputation whom he had found in the woods and brought him up to that estate he was come to, not knowing who was his father, but by seeming

quit free.   glister shine.

some poor country clown and forgetting himself from whence he sprung, neglecting so many benefits which he had bestowed upon him, would enter into those things so far unseemly and exceeding his degree.

The Duke of Mantona, giving good ear to this tale, remembering his son Aurelianus whom he had lost in the woods about those parts, questioned with the duke of the time and what apparel the child had on at that present, who in all things showed a troth as it was; he demanded further how he knew his name to be Silvanus, or whether he had any other name.

"Yes," quoth the Duke of Vasconia, "his name he said was Aurelianus which myself changed to Silvanus because I found him in the woods."

Herewithal, without any farther stay, the Duke of Mantona running hastily upon Silvanus, embracing him in his arms, crying: "O my son, my son," and with this sudden joy, the tears trickled down his cheeks so fast that he was not further able to speak one word.

The Duke of Vasconia, much amazed to see this sight, but a great deal more glad that Silvanus had found out such a father, and now nothing at all offended with his daughter's choice, came likewise with cheerful countenance and embraced Silvanus, desiring both the duke his father and himself to forgive what was past, and taking Valeria by the hand, he delivered her to Silvanus, promising him for her dowry forty thousand franks in gold presently to be paid, and after his decease to remain for his inheritor. Silvanus, better pleased with Valeria herself than with all the rest that was promised, gave him great thanks, and so did the duke his father.

All the company were replenished with the greatest joy that might be to see this sudden sight, and thus they departed to the palace where the duke kept his abode, where Silvanus was welcomed to his mother, to his sister, to Arabianus and to all the rest, where there was great feasting and triumph, and a bond of everlasting amity between the houses of the Duke of Mantona, the Duke of Vasconia and the Duke of Petrona. And after a while they had feasted and sported themselves, they rode altogether in company to the emperor's court, who received them with so great honor as he could devise, and making himself a partaker of their mirth, wondering to hear the whole discourse how things had happened, when after a while he had feasted them, and showed them as great pleasures as might be devised, he bestowed of them all large and bountiful gifts, but especially of the two young ladies Valeria and Phylene, and this agreeing amongst themselves to meet once a year at the least to sport and make themselves merry, for this season they departed, every one where it liked them best.

OF APOLONIUS AND SILLA

The Argument of the Second History.

Apolonius, duke,[1] having spent a year's service in the wars against the Turk, returning homeward with his company by sea, was driven by force of weather to the isle of Cyprus, where he was well-received by Pontus[2] governor of the same isle, with whom Silla, daughter to Pontus, fell so strangely in love that after Apolonius was departed to Constantinople, Silla with one man followed, and coming to Constantinople she served Apolonius in the habit of a man, and after many pretty accidents falling out, she was known to Apolonius, who, in requital of her love, married her.

There is no child that is born into this wretched world but before it doth suck the mother's milk it taketh first a sup° of the cup of error, which maketh us when we come to riper years not only to enter into actions of injury, but many times to stray from that is right and reason. But in all other things wherein we shew ourselves to be most drunken with this poisoned cup, it is in our actions of love, for the lover is so estranged from that is right and wandereth so wide from the bounds of reason that he is not able to deem white from black, good from bad, virtue from vice, but only led by the appetite of his own affections, and grounding

---

sup (orig. soope), sip.

them on the foolishness of his own fancies, will so settle his liking on such a one as either by desert or unworthiness will merit rather to be loathed than loved.

If a question might be asked, "what is the ground indeed of reasonable love whereby the knot is knit of true and perfect friendship?" I think those that be wise would answer, "desert," that is, where the party beloved doth requite us with the like. For otherwise, if the bare show of beauty or the comeliness of personage might be sufficient to confirm us in our love, those that be accustomed to go to fairs and markets might sometimes fall in love with twenty in a day; desert must then be, of force, the ground of reasonable love, for to love them that hate us, to follow them that fly from us, to fawn on them that frown on us, to curry favor with them that disdain us, to be glad to please them that care not how they offend us—who will not confess this to be an erroneous love, neither grounded upon wit nor reason? Wherefore, right courteous gentlewomen, if it please you with patience to peruse this history following, you shall see Dame Error so play her part with a leash° of lovers, a male and two females, as shall work a wonder to your wise judgment in noting the effect of their amorous devices and conclusions of their actions: the first, neglecting the love of a noble dame, young, beautiful and fair, who only for his good will° played the part of a serving man, contented to abide any manner of pain only to behold him; he again setting his love of a dame that, despising him—being a noble duke—gave herself to a serving man, as she had thought, but it otherwise fell out, as the substance of this tale shall better describe. And because I have been something tedious in my first discourse, offending your patient ears with the hearing of a circumstance overlong, from henceforth that which I mind to write shall be done with such celerity as the matter that I pretend to pen may in any wise permit me, and thus followeth the history.[3]

During the time that the famous city of Constantinople remained in the hands of the Christians,[4] amongst many other noblemen that kept their abiding in that flourishing city there was one whose name was Apolonius, a worthy duke, who, being but

leash a brace and a half of hunting dogs i.e. three.   good will i.e. to gain his favor.

a very young man and even then new come to his possessions, which were very great, levied a mighty band of men at his own proper charges with whom he served against the Turk during the space of one whole year, in which time, although it were very short, this young duke so behaved himself—as well by prowess and valiance showed with his own hands as otherwise by his wisdom and liberality used towards his soldiers—that all the world was filled with the fame of this noble duke. When he had thus spent one year's service, he caused his trumpet to sound a retreat, and gathering his company together and embarking themselves he set sail, holding his course towards Constantinople. But being upon the sea, by the extremity of a tempest which suddenly fell, his fleet was dissevered, some one way and some another; but he himself recovered the isle of Cyprus where he was worthily received by Pontus, duke and governor of the same isle, with whom he lodged while his ships were new repairing.

This Pontus that was lord and governor of this famous isle was an ancient duke and had two children, a son and a daughter. His son was named Silvio, of whom hereafter we shall have further occasion to speak, but at this instant he was in the parts of Africa serving in the wars.

The daughter her name was Silla, whose beauty was so peerless that she had the sovereignty amongst all other dames, as well for her beauty as for the nobleness of her birth. This Silla, having heard of the worthiness of Apolonius, this young duke, who besides his beauty and good graces had a certain natural allurement, that being now in his company in her father's court, she was so strangely attached° with the love of Apolonius that there was nothing might content her but his presence and sweet sight. And although she saw no manner of hope to attain to that she most desired, knowing Apolonius to be but a guest and ready to take the benefit of the next wind and to depart into a strange country, whereby she was bereaved of all possibility ever to see him again, and therefore strived with herself to leave her fondness, but all in vain—it would not be, but like the fowl which is once limed, the more she striveth, the faster she tieth herself.[5]

So Silla was now constrained, perforce° her will, to yield to

attached seized, taken.   perforce in spite of.

love; wherefore from time to time she used so great familiarity
with him as her honor might well permit, and fed him with such
amorous baits as the modesty of a maid could reasonably afford,
which when she perceived did take but small effect, feeling herself
so much outraged with the extremity of her passion, by the only
countenance that she bestowed upon Apolonius it might have
been well perceived that the very eyes pleaded unto him for pity
and remorse. But Apolonius, coming but lately from out the field
from the chasing of his enemies, and his fury not yet thoroughly
dissolved nor purged from his stomach, gave no regard to those
amorous enticements which, by reason of his youth, he had not
been acquainted withal. But his mind ran more to hear his pilots
bring news of a merry wind to serve his turn to Constantinople,
which in the end came very prosperously; and giving Duke Pontus
hearty thanks for his great entertainment, taking his leave of himself and the lady Silla his daughter, departed with his company
and with a happy gale arrived at his desired port.

Gentlewomen, according to my promise, I will here for brevity's
sake omit to make repetition of the long and dolorous discourse
recorded by Silla for this sudden departure of her Apolonius,
knowing you to be as tenderly hearted as Silla herself, whereby
you may the better conjecture the fury of her fever.[6]

But Silla, the further that she saw herself bereaved of all hope
ever any more to see her beloved Apolonius, so much the more
contagious were her passions, and made the greater speed to execute that she had premeditated in her mind, which was this:
amongst many servants that did attend upon her there was one
whose name was Pedro, who had a long time waited upon her
in her chamber, whereby she was well-assured of his fidelity and
trust; to that Pedro, therefore, she bewrayed° first the fervency
of her love borne to Apolonius, conjuring him in the name of the
goddess of love herself and binding him by the duty that a servant
ought to have that tendereth his mistress' safety and good liking, and desiring him with tears trickling down her cheeks that he
would give his consent to aid and assist her in that she had determined, which was—for that she was fully resolved to go to Constantinople where she might again take the view of her beloved

bewrayed revealed.

Apolonius—that he, according to the trust she had reposed in him, would not refuse to give his consent secretly to convey her from out her father's court according as she would give him direction, and also to make himself partaker of her journey and to wait upon her till she had seen the end of her determination.

Pedro, perceiving with what vehemency his lady and mistress had made request unto him, albeit he saw many perils and doubts depending in her pretence,◊ notwithstanding, gave his consent to be at her disposition, promising her to further her with his best advice and to be ready to obey whatsoever she would please to command him. The match◊ being thus agreed upon and all things prepared in a readiness for their departure, it happened there was a galley of Constantinople ready to depart, which Pedro understanding, came to the captain desiring him to have passage for himself and for a poor maid that was his sister which were bound to Constantinople upon certain urgent affairs—to which request the captain granted, willing him to prepare◊ aboard with all speed because the wind served him presently to depart.

Pedro now coming to his mistress and telling her how he had handled the matter with the captain, she liking very well of the device, disguising herself into very simple attire, stole away from out her father's court and came with Pedro, whom now she calleth brother, aboard the galley, where all things being in readiness and the wind serving very well, they launched forth with their oars and set sail.

When they were at the sea, the captain of the galley, taking the view of Silla, perceiving her singular beauty, he was better pleased in beholding of her face than in taking the height either of the sun or star. And thinking her by the homeliness of her apparel to be but some simple maiden, calling her into his cabin he began to break◊ with her after the sea fashion, desiring her to use his own cabin for her better ease, and during the time that she remained at the sea she should not want a bed, and then whispering softly in her ear he said that, for want of a bedfellow, he himself would supply that room. Silla, not being acquainted with any such talk, blushed for shame, but made him no answer

depending in her pretence relating to her plan.   **match** appointment; bargain.   **prepare** repair, go.   **break** negotiate.

at all. My captain, feeling such a bickering within himself, the like whereof he had never endured upon the sea, was like to be taken prisoner aboard his own ship and forced to yield himself a captive without any cannon shot; wherefore to salve all sores, and thinking it the readiest way to speed, he began to break with Silla in the way of marriage, telling her how happy a voyage she had made to fall into the liking of such a one as himself was, who was able to keep and maintain her like a gentlewoman, and for her sake would likewise take her brother into his fellowship whom he would by some means prefer in such sort that both of them should have good cause to think themselves thrice happy, she to light of such a husband, and he to light of such a brother. But Silla, nothing pleased with these preferments, desired him to cease his talk for that she did think herself indeed to be too unworthy such a one as he was, neither was she minded yet to marry, and therefore desired him to fix his fancy upon some that were better worthy than herself was, and that could better like of his courtesy than she could do. The captain, seeing himself thus refused, being in a great chafe, he said as followeth:

"Then seeing you make so little account of my courtesy, proffered to one that is so far unworthy of it, from henceforth I will use the office of my authority; you shall know that I am the captain of this ship and have power to command and dispose of things at my pleasure, and seeing you have so scornfully rejected me to be your loyal husband, I will now take you by force and use you at my will, and so long as it shall please me will keep you for mine own store; there shall be no man able to defend you, nor yet to persuade me from that I have determined."

Silla, with these words being struck into a great fear, did think it now too late to rue her rash attempt, determined rather to die with her own hands than to suffer herself to be abused in such sort. Therefore she most humbly desired the captain so much as he could to save her credit, and seeing that she must needs be at his will and disposition, that for that present he would depart and suffer° her till night, when in the dark he might take his pleasure without any manner of suspicion to the residue of his company. The captain, thinking now the goal to be more than

suffer bear with.

half won, was contented so far to satisfy her request and departed out, leaving her alone in his cabin.

Silla, being alone by herself, drew out her knife ready to strike herself to the heart, and falling upon her knees desired God to receive her soul as an acceptable sacrifice for her follies which she had so willfully committed, craving pardon for her sins and so forth, continuing a long and pitiful reconciliation to God, in the midst whereof there suddenly fell a wonderful storm, the terror whereof was such that there was no man but did think the seas would presently have swallowed them. The billows so suddenly arose with the rage of the wind that they were all glad to fall to heaving out of water, for otherwise their feeble galley had never been able to have brooked° the seas.

This storm continued all that day and the next night, and they, being driven to put romer° before the wind to keep the galley ahead the billow, were driven upon the main shore where the galley brake all to pieces; there was every man providing to save his own life: some got upon hatches, boards, and casks, and were driven with the waves to and fro; but the greatest number were drowned, amongst the which Pedro was one. But Silla herself being in the cabin, as you have heard, took hold of a chest that was the captain's, the which by the only providence of God brought her safe to the shore; the which when she had recovered, not knowing what was become of Pedro her man, she deemed that both he and all the rest had been drowned for that she saw nobody upon the shore but herself.

Wherefore, when she had awhile made great lamentations, complaining her mishaps, she began in the end to comfort herself with the hope that she had to see her Apolonius, and found such means that she brake open the chest that brought her to land, wherein she found good store of coin, and sundry suits of apparel that were the captain's. And now, to prevent a number of injuries that might be proffered to a woman that was left in her case, she determined to leave her own apparel and to sort herself into some of those suits, that, being taken for a man, she might pass through

brooked withstood.   **romer** either to trim the sails, or allow to be driven by the wind, or to use a sea anchor to keep the ship properly oriented to the wind.

the country in the better safety. And as she changed her apparel, she thought it likewise convenient to change her name, wherefore, not readily happening of any other, she called herself Silvio, by the name of her own brother whom you have heard spoken of before.

In this manner she travelled to Constantinople where she inquired out the palace of the Duke Apolonius, and thinking herself now to be both fit and able to play the servingman, she presented herself to the duke, craving his service. The duke, very willing to give succor unto strangers, perceiving him to be a proper smug° young man, gave him entertainment. Silla thought herself now more than satisfied for all the casualties that had happened unto her in her journey, that she might at her pleasure take but the view of the Duke Apolonius, and above the rest of his servants was very diligent and attendant upon him, the which the duke perceiving, began likewise to grow into good liking with the diligence of his man, and therefore made him one of his chamber. Who but Silvio then was most neat° about him, in helping of him to make him ready in a morning, in the setting of his ruffs, in the keeping of his chamber? Silvio pleased his master so well that above all the rest of his servants about him, he had the greatest credit, and the duke put him most in trust.

At this very instant there was remaining in the city a noble dame, a widow, whose husband was but lately deceased, one of the noblest men that were in the parts of Greece, who left his lady and wife large possessions and great livings. This lady's name was called Julina, who, besides the abundance of her wealth and the greatness of her revenues, had likewise the sovereignty of all the dames of Constantinople for her beauty. To this lady Julina Apolonius became an earnest suitor, and according to the manner of wooers, besides fair words, sorrowful sighs, and piteous countenances, there must be sending of loving letters, chains, bracelets, brooches, rings, tablets, gems, jewels, and presents—I know not what. So my duke, who in the time that he remained in the isle of Cyprus had no skill at all in the art of love, although it were more than half proffered unto him, was now become a

smug (orig. smouge), neat and trim.   neat (possibly a misprint for near), skillful and precise.

scholar in love's school and had already learned his first lesson, that is, to speak pitifully, to look ruthfully, to promise largely, to serve diligently, and to please carefully. Now he was learning his second lesson, that is, to reward liberally, to give bountifully, to present willingly, and to write lovingly. Thus Apolonius was so busied in his new study that I warrant you there was no man that could challenge him for playing the truant, he followed his profession with so good a will. And who must be the messenger to carry the tokens and love letters to the lady Julina but Silvio his man; in him the duke reposed his only confidence to go between him and his lady.

Now gentlewomen, do you think there could have been a greater torment devised wherewith to afflict the heart of Silla than herself to be made the instrument to work her own mishap and to play the attorney in a cause that made so much against herself? But Silla, altogether desirous to please her master, cared nothing at all to offend herself, followed his business with so good a will as if it had been in her own preferment.

Julina, now having many times taken the gaze of this young youth Silvio, perceiving him to be of such excellent perfect grace, was so entangled with the often sight of this sweet temptation that she fell into as great a liking with the man as the master was with herself. And on a time Silvio, being sent from his master with a message to the lady Julina, as he began very earnestly to solicit in his master's behalf, Julina interrupting him in his tale, said:

"Silvio, it is enough that you have said for your master; from henceforth either speak for yourself or say nothing at all."

Silla, abashed to hear these words, began in her mind to accuse the blindness of love, that Julina, neglecting the good will of so noble a duke, would prefer her love unto such a one as nature itself had denied to recompense her liking.

And now for a time leaving matters depending,° as you have heard, it fell out that the right Silvio indeed—whom you have heard spoken of before, the brother of Silla—was come to his father's court into the isle of Cyprus, where, understanding that his sister was departed in manner as you have heard, conjectured

depending suspended.

that the very occasion did proceed of some liking had between
Pedro her man—that was missing with her—and herself. But
Silvio, who loved his sister as dearly as his own life, and the
rather for that as she was his natural sister both by father and
mother—so the one of them was so like the other in countenance
and favor that there was no man able to discern one from the
other by their faces, saving by their apparel, the one being a man,
the other a woman—Silvio therefore vowed to his father not only
to seek out his sister Silla, but also to revenge the villainy which
he conceived in Pedro for the carrying away of his sister. And
thus departing, having travelled though many cities and towns
without hearing any manner of news of those he went to seek
for, at the last he arrived at Constantinople, where, as he was
walking in an evening for his own recreation on a pleasant green
yard without the walls of the city, he fortuned to meet with the
lady Julina, who likewise had been abroad to take the air. And
as she suddenly cast her eyes upon Silvio, thinking him to be her
old acquaintance by reason they were so like one another as you
have heard before, said unto him:

"Sir Silvio, if your haste be not the greater, I pray you let me
have a little talk with you, seeing I have so luckily met you in
this place."

Silvio, wondering to hear himself so rightly named, being but
a stranger not of above two days' continuance in the city, very
courteously came towards her, desirous to hear what she would
say.

Julina, commanding her train something to stand back, said as
followeth: "Seeing my good will and friendly love hath been the
only cause to make me so prodigal to offer that I see is so lightly
rejected, it maketh me to think that men be of this condition,
rather to desire those things which they cannot come by than to
esteem or value of that which both largely and liberally is offered
unto them; but if the liberality of my proffer° hath made to seem
less the value of the thing that I meant to present, it is but in
your own conceit,° considering how many noble men there hath
been here before, and be yet at this present, which hath both

liberality of my proffer generosity of my offer.   **conceit** opinion,
fancy.

served, sued, and most humbly entreated to attain that which to you of myself I have freely offered, and I perceive is despised or at the least very lightly regarded."

Silvio, wondering at these words, but more amazed that she could so rightly call him by his name, could not tell what to make of her speeches, assuring himself that she was deceived and did mistake him, did think, notwithstanding, it had been a point of great simplicity◊ if he should forsake that which fortune had so favorably proffered unto him, perceiving by her train that she was some lady of great honor, and viewing the perfection of her beauty and the excellency of her grace and countenance did think it impossible that she should be despised, and therefore answered thus:

"Madam, if before this time I have seemed to forget myself in neglecting your courtesy which so liberally you have meant unto me, please it you to pardon what is past, and from this day forwards Silvio remaineth ready prest◊ to make such reasonable amends as his ability may any ways permit, or as it shall please you to command."

Julina, the gladdest woman that might be to hear these joyful news, said: "Then, my Silvio, see you fail not tomorrow at night to sup with me at my own house where I will discourse further with you what amends you shall make me."

To which request Silvio gave his glad consent, and thus they departed very well pleased. And as Julina did think the time very long till she had reaped the fruit of her desire, so Silvio, he wished for harvest before corn could grow, thinking the time as long till he saw how matters would fall out. But not knowing what lady she might be, he presently—before Julina was out of sight—demanded of one that was walking by what she was and how she was called, who satisfied Silvio in every point, and also in what part of the town her house did stand whereby he might inquire it out.

Silvio, thus departing to this lodging, passed the night with very unquiet sleep, and the next morning his mind ran so much of his supper that he never cared neither for his breakfast nor

great simplicity lack of intelligence or judgement.   **ready prest** (from Fr. prêt, ready), prepared, at hand.

dinner; and the day, to his seeming, passed away so slowly that he had thought the stately steeds had been tired that draw the chariot of the sun, or else some other Joshua had commanded them again to stand, and wished that Phaethon had been there with a whip.[7]

Julina, on the other side, she had thought the clock-setter had played the knave, the day came no faster forwards; but six o'clock being once struck, recovered comfort to both parties, and Silvio hastening himself to the palace of Julina, where by her he was friendly welcomed, and a sumptuous supper being made ready, furnished with sundry sorts of delicate dishes, they sat them down, passing the supper time with amorous looks, loving countenances, and secret glances conveyed from the one to the other, which did better satisfy them than the feeding of their dainty dishes.

Supper time being thus spent, Julina did think it very unfitly[°] if she should turn Silvio to go seek his lodging in an evening, desired him therefore that he would take a bed in her house for that night; and bringing him up into a fair chamber that was very richly furnished, she found such means that when all the rest of her household servants were abed and quiet, she came herself to bear Silvio company, where concluding upon conditions that were in question between them, they passed the night with such joy and contentation as might in that convenient time be wished for, but only that Julina, feeding too much of some one dish above the rest, received a surfeit whereof she could not be cured in forty weeks after, a natural inclination in all women which are subject to longing and want the reason to use a moderation in their diet. But the morning approaching, Julina took her leave and conveyed herself into her own chamber; and when it was fair daylight, Silvio making himself ready departed likewise about his affairs in the town, debating with himself how things had happened, being well assured that Julina had mistaken him, and therefore, for fear of further evils, determined to come no more there, but took his journey towards other places in the parts of Greece to see if he could learn any tidings of his sister Silla.

The Duke Apolonius, having made a long suit and never a

unfitly inappropriate.

whit the nearer of his purpose, came to Julina to crave her direct answer, either to accept of him and of such conditions as he proffered unto her, or else to give him his last farewell.

Julina, as you have heard, had taken an earnest penny° of another, whom she had thought had been Silvio the duke's man, was at a controversy in herself what she might do. One while she thought, seeing her occasion served so fit, to crave the duke's good will for the marrying of his man. Then again she could not tell what displeasure the duke would conceive in that she should seem to prefer his man before himself, did think it therefore best to conceal the matter till she might speak with Silvio to use his opinion how these matters should be handled, and hereupon resolving herself, desiring the duke to pardon her speeches, said as followeth:

"Sir duke, for that from this time forwards I am no longer of myself, having given my full power and authority over to another whose wife I now remain by faithful vow and promise, and albeit I know the world will wonder when they shall understand the fondness of my choice, yet I trust you yourself will nothing dislike with me sith I have meant no other thing than the satisfying of mine own contentation and liking."

The duke hearing these words, answered: "Madam, I must then content myself, although against my will, having the law in your own hands to like of whom you list and to make choice where it pleaseth you."

Julina, giving the duke great thanks that would content himself with such patience, desired him likewise to give his free consent and good will to the party whom she had chosen to be her husband.

"Nay surely madam," quoth the duke, "I will never give my consent that any other man shall enjoy you than myself. I have made too great account of you than so lightly to pass you away with my good will. But seeing it lieth not in me to let° you, having, as you say, made your own choice, so from henceforwards I leave you to your own liking, always willing you well, and thus will take my leave."

earnest penny money paid to seal a bargain, a down payment.
let hinder, prevent.

The duke departed towards his own house, very sorrowful that Julina had thus served him. But in the mean space that the duke had remained in the house of Julina, some of his servants fell into talk and conference with the servants of Julina, where, debating between them of the likelihood of the marriage between the duke and the lady, one of the servants of Julina said that he never saw his lady and mistress use so good countenance to the duke himself as she had done to Silvio his man, and began to report with what familiarity and courtesy she had received him, feasted him and lodged him, and that in his opinion, Silvio was like to speed before the duke, or any other that were suitors.

This tale was quickly brought to the duke himself, who making better inquiry in the matter, found it to be true that was reported; and better considering of the words which Julina had used towards himself, was very well assured that it could be no other than his own man that had thrust his nose so far out of joint, wherefore, without any further respect, caused him to be thrust into a dungeon where he was kept prisoner in a very pitiful plight.

Poor Silvio, having got intelligence by some of his fellows what was the cause that the duke his master did bear such displeasure unto him, devised all the means he could, as well by mediation° by his fellows as otherwise by petitions and supplication to the duke that he would suspend his judgment till perfect proof were had in the matter, and then if any manner of thing did fall out against him whereby the duke had cause to take any grief, he would confess himself worthy not only of imprisonment, but also of most vile and shameful death; with these petitions he daily plied the duke, but all in vain, for the duke thought he had made so good proof that he was thoroughly confirmed in his opinion against his man.

But the lady Julina, wondering what made Silvio that he was so slack in his visitation and why he absented himself so long from her presence, began to think that all was not well. But in the end, perceiving no decoction° of her former surfeit received as you have heard, and finding in herself an unwonted swelling in her belly, assuring herself to be with child, fearing to become

mediation (A.B.C.D. meditation).   **decoction** reduction.

quite bankrupt of her honor, did think it more than time to seek out a father, and made such secret search and diligent inquiry that she learned the truth how Silvio was kept in prison by the duke his master. And minding to find a present remedy, as well as for the love she bare to Silvio as for the maintenance of her credit and estimation, she speedily hasted to the palace of the duke, to whom she said as followeth:

"Sir duke, it may be that you will think my coming to your house in this sort doth something pass the limits of modesty, the which I protest before God proceedeth of this desire that the world should know how justly I seek means to maintain my honor. But to the end I seem not tedious with prolixity of words, nor to use other than direct circumstances, know, sir, that the love I bear to my only beloved Silvio, whom I do esteem more than all the jewels in the world, whose personage I regard more than my own life, is the only cause of my attempted journey, beseeching you that all the whole displeasure which I understand you have conceived against him may be imputed unto my charge, and that it would please you lovingly to deal with him whom of myself I have chosen rather for the satisfaction of mine honest liking than for the vain pre-eminences or honorable dignities looked after by ambitious minds."

The duke, having heard this discourse, caused Silvio presently to be sent for, and to be brought before him, to whom he said: "Had it not been sufficient for thee, when I had reposed myself in thy fidelity and the trustiness of thy service, that thou shouldest so traitorously deal with me? But since that time hast not spared still to abuse me with so many forgeries and perjured protestations, not only hateful unto me whose simplicity thou thinkest to be such that by the plot of thy pleasant tongue thou wouldst make me believe manifest untruth, but most abominable be thy doings in the presence and sight of God, that hast not spared to blaspheme His holy name by calling Him to be a witness to maintain thy leasings,◊ and so detestably wouldst forswear thyself in a matter that is so openly known."

Poor Silvio, whose innocency was such that he might lawfully swear, seeing Julina to be there in place, answered thus:

leasings lies.

"Most noble duke, well understanding your conceived grief, most humbly I beseech you patiently to hear my excuse, not minding° thereby to aggravate or heap up your wrath and displeasure, protesting before God that there is nothing in the world which I regard so much or do esteem so dear as your good grace and favor. But desirous that your grace should know my innocency, and to clear myself of such impositions wherewith I know I am wrongfully accused, which as I understand should be in the practicing of the lady Julina who standeth here in place, whose acquittance for my better discharge now I most humbly crave, protesting before the almighty God that neither in thought, word, nor deed, I have not otherwise used myself than according to the bond and duty of a servant that is both willing and desirous to further his master's suits, which, if I have otherwise said than that is true, you, madam Julina, who can very well decide the depths of all this doubt, I most humbly beseech you to certify a truth if I have in anything missaid or have otherwise spoken than is right and just."

Julina, having heard this discourse which Silvio had made, perceiving that he stood in great awe of the duke's displeasure, answered thus: "Think not, my Silvio, that my coming hither is to accuse you of any misdemeanor towards your master; so I do not deny but in all such embassages° wherein towards me you have been employed, you have used the office of a faithful and trusty messenger. Neither am I ashamed to confess that the first day that mine eyes did behold the singular behavior, the notable courtesy, and other innumerable gifts wherewith my Silvio is endued, but that beyond all measure my heart was so inflamed that impossible it was for me to quench the fervent love or extinguish the least part of my conceived torment before I had bewrayed the same unto him, and of my own motion craved his promised faith and loyalty of marriage. And now is the time to manifest the same unto the world which hath been done before God and between ourselves, knowing that it is not needful to keep secret that which is neither evil done nor hurtful to any person. Therefore, as I said before, Silvio is my husband by plighted faith, whom I hope to obtain without offence or displeasure of anyone,

minding intending.　　　**embassages** the carrying of messages.

trusting that there is no man that will so far forget himself as to restrain that which God hath left at liberty for every wight,° or that will seek by cruelty to force ladies to marry otherwise than according to their own liking. Fear not then my Silvio to keep your faith and promise which you have made unto me, and as for the rest, I doubt not things will so fall out as you shall have no manner of cause to complain."

Silvio, amazed to hear these words, for that Julina by her speech seemed to confirm that which he most of all desired to be quit of, said: "Who would have thought that a lady of so great honor and reputation would herself be the ambassador of a thing so prejudicial and uncomely for her estate. What plighted promises be these which be spoken of? Altogether ignorant unto me, which if it be otherwise than I have said, you sacred gods consume me straight with flashing flames of fire. But what words might I use to give credit to the truth and innocence of my cause? Ah, madam Julina, I desire no other testimony than your own honesty and virtue, thinking that you will not so much blemish the brightness of your honor, knowing that a woman is or should be the image of courtesy, continency and shamefastness, from the which so soon as she stoopeth and leaveth the office of her duty and modesty, besides the degradation of her honor, she thrusteth herself into the pit of perpetual infamy. And as I cannot think you would so far forget yourself, by the refusal of a noble duke, to dim the light of your renown and glory, which hitherto you have maintained amongst the best and noblest ladies, by such a one as I know myself to be too far unworthy your degree and calling, so most humbly I beseech you to confess a truth: whereto tendeth those vows and promises you speak of, which speeches be so obscure unto me as I know not for my life how I might understand them?"

Julina, something nipped with these speeches, said: "And what is the matter that now you make so little a ˈunt of your Julina, that being my husband in deed have the   ˈo deny me to whom thou art contracted by so many solemn oaths? What, art thou ashamed to have me to thy wife? How much oughtest thou rather to be ashamed to break thy promised faith and

wight man, person.

to have despised the holy and dreadful name of God. But that time constraineth me to lay open that which shame rather willeth I should dissemble and keep secret, behold me then here, Silvio, whom thou hast gotten with child, who if thou be of such honesty as I trust for all this I shall find, then the thing is done without prejudice or any hurt to my conscience, considering that by the professed faith thou didst account me for thy wife and I received thee for my spouse and loyal husband, swearing by the almighty God that no other than you have made the conquest and triumph of my chastity, whereof I crave no other witness than yourself and mine own conscience."

I pray you gentlewomen, was not this a foul oversight of Julina, that would so precisely swear so great an oath that she was gotten with child by one that was altogether unfurnished with implements for such a turn? For God's love take heed, and let this be an example to you, when you be with child, how you swear who is the father before you have had good proof and knowledge of the party, for men be so subtle and full of sleight that, God knoweth, a women may quickly be deceived.[8]

But now to return to our Silvio, who, hearing an oath sworn so divinely that he had gotten a woman with child, was like to believe that it had been true in very deed; but remembering his own impediment thought it impossible that he should commit such an act, and therefore half in a chafe, he said:

"What law is able to restrain the foolish indiscretion of a woman that yieldeth herself to her own desires? What shame is able to bridle or withdraw her from her mind and madness, or with what snaffle° is it possible to hold her back from the execution of her filthiness? But what abomination is this, that a lady of such a house should so forget the greatness of her estate, the alliance whereof she is descended, the nobility of her deceased husband, and maketh no conscience to shame and slander herself with such a one as I am, being so far unfit and unseemly for her degree. But how horrible is it to hear the name of God so defaced, that we make no more account but for the maintenance of our mischiefs, we fear no whit at all to forswear His holy name, as though He were not in all His dealings most righteous, true, and

snaffle a simple bridle.

just, and will not only lay open our leasings° to the world, but will likewise punish the same with most sharp and bitter scourges."

Julina, not able to endure him to proceed any farther in his sermon, was already surprised with a vehement grief, began bitterly to cry out uttering these speeches following:

"Alas, is it possible that the sovereign justice of God can abide a mischief so great and cursed? Why may I not now suffer death rather than the infamy which I see to wander before mine eyes? Oh happy and more than right happy had I been if inconstant fortune had not devised this treason wherein I am surprised and caught. Am I thus become to be entangled with snares, and in the hands of him who, enjoying the spoils of my honor, will openly deprive me of my fame by making me a common fable to all posterity in time to come? Ah, traitor and discourteous wretch, is this the recompense of the honest and firm amity which I have borne thee? Wherein have I deserved this discourtesy? By loving thee more than thou art able to deserve? Is it I, arrant thief, is it I upon whom thou thinkest to work thy mischiefs? Doest thou think me no better worth but that thou mayest prodigally waste my honor at thy pleasure? Didst thou dare to adventure upon me, having thy conscience wounded with so deadly a treason? Ah, unhappy and above all other most unhappy, that have so charily° preserved mine honor, and now am made a prey to satisfy a young man's lust that hath coveted nothing but the spoil of my chastity and good name."

Herewithal the tears so gushed down her cheeks that she was not able to open her mouth to use any further speech.

The duke, who stood all this while and heard this whole discourse, was wonderfully moved with compassion towards Julina, knowing that from her infancy she had ever so honorably used herself that there was no man able to detect° her of any misdemeanor otherwise than beseemed a lady of her estate. Wherefore being fully resolved that Silvio his man had committed this villainy against her, in a great fury drawing his rapier, he said unto Silvio:

"How canst thou, arrant thief, show thyself so cruel and careless to such as do thee honor? Hast thou so little regard of such

leasings lies, falsehoods.   **charily** carefully, cautiously.   **detect** accuse.

a noble lady as humbleth herself to such a villain as thou art, who, without any respect either of her renown or noble estate, canst be content to seek the wrack and utter ruin of her honor? But frame thyself to make such satisfaction as she requireth—although I know, unworthy wretch, that thou art not able to make her the least part of amends—or I swear by God that thou shall not escape the death which I will minister to thee with my own hands, and therefore advise thee well what thou doest."

Silvio, having heard this sharp sentence, fell down on his knees before the duke, craving for mercy, desiring that he might be suffered to speak with the lady Julina apart, promising to satisfy her according to her own contentation.

"Well," quoth the duke, "I take thy word, and therewithal I advise thee that thou perform thy promise, or otherwise I protest before God I will make thee such an example to the world that all traitors shall tremble for fear how they do seek the dishonoring of ladies."

But now Julina had conceived so great grief against Silvio that there was much ado to persuade her to talk with him. But remembering her own case, desirous to hear what excuse he could make, in the end she agreed, and being brought into a place severally° by themselves, Silvio began with a piteous voice to say as followeth:

"I know not, madam, of whom I might make complaint, whether of you or of myself, or rather of fortune, which hath conducted and brought us both into so great adversity. I see that you receive great wrong, and I am condemned against all right: you in peril to abide the bruit° of spiteful tongues, and I in danger to lose the thing that I most desire. And although I could allege many reasons to prove my sayings true, yet I refer myself to the experience and bounty of your mind."

And herewithal, loosing his garments down to his stomach, and showed Julina his breasts and pretty teats surmounting far the whiteness of snow itself, saying: "Lo, madam, behold here the party whom you have challenged° to be the father of your child; see, I am a woman, the daughter of a noble duke, who

severally apart from the others.   bruit noise, gossip.   challenged declared.

only for the love of him whom you so lightly have shaken off, have forsaken my father, abandoned my country, and in manner as you see, am become a servingman, satisfying myself but with the only sight of my Apolonius. And now madam, if my passion were not vehement and my torments without comparison, I would wish that my feigned griefs might be laughed to scorn and my dissembled pains to be rewarded with flouts. But my love being pure, my travail continual, and my griefs endless, I trust madam, you will not only excuse me of crime but also pity my distress, the which I protest I would still have kept secret if my fortune would so have permitted."

Julina did now think herself to be in a worse case than ever she was before, for now she knew not whom to challenge to be the father of her child. Wherefore, when she had told the duke the very certainty of the discourse which Silvio had made unto her, she departed to her own house with such grief and sorrow that she purposed never to come out of her own doors again alive to be a wonder and mocking stock to the world.

But the duke, more amazed to hear this strange discourse of Silvio, came unto him whom, when he had viewed with better consideration, perceived indeed that it was Silla the daughter of Duke Pontus, and embracing her in his arms, he said:

"O the branch of all virtue and the flower of courtesy itself, pardon me I beseech you of all such discourtesies as I have ignorantly committed towards you, desiring you that without further memory of ancient griefs, you will accept of me who is more joyful and better contented with your presence than if the whole world were at my commandment. Where hath there ever been found such liberality in a lover, which having been trained up and nourished amidst the delicacies and banquets of the court, accompanied with trains of many fair and noble ladies, living in pleasure and in the midst of delights, would so prodigally° adventure yourself, neither fearing mishaps nor misliking to take such pains as I know you have not been accustomed unto? O liberality never heard of before! O fact that can never be sufficiently rewarded! O true love most pure and unfeigned!"

Herewithal, sending for the most artificial° workmen, he pro-

prodigally recklessly.   **artificial** clever at artifice.

vided for her sundry suits of sumptuous apparel, and the marriage day appointed, which was celebrated with great triumph through the whole city of Constantinople, everyone praising the nobleness of the duke; but so many as did behold the excellent beauty of Silla gave her the praise above all the rest of the ladies in the troupe.

The matter seemed so wonderful and strange that the bruit° was spread throughout all the parts of Greece insomuch that it came to the hearing of Silvio, who as you have heard, remained in those parts to inquire of his sister. He, being the gladdest man in the world, hastened to Constantinople, where coming to his sister he was joyfully received and most lovingly welcomed and entertained of the duke his brother-in-law. After he had remained there two or three days, the duke revealed unto Silvio the whole discourse how it happened between his sister and the lady Julina, and how his sister was challenged for getting a woman with child. Silvio, blushing with these words, was stricken with great remorse to make Julina amends, understanding her to be a noble lady, and was left defamed to the world through his default. He therefore bewrayed the whole circumstance to the duke, whereof the duke being very joyful, immediately repaired with Silvio to the house of Julina, whom they found in her chamber in great lamentation and mourning, to whom the duke said:

"Take courage madam, for behold here a gentleman that will not stick both to father your child and to take you for his wife— no inferior person but the son and heir of a noble duke, worthy of your estate and dignity."

Julina, seeing Silvio in place, did know very well that he was the father of her child, and was so ravished with joy that she knew not whether she were awake or in some dream. Silvio, embracing her in his arms, craving forgiveness of all that passed, concluded with her the marriage day, which was presently accomplished with great joy and contentation to all parties. And thus Silvio, having attained a noble wife, and Silla his sister her desired husband, they passed the residue of their days with such delight as those that have accomplished the perfection of their felicities.

bruit gossip, news.

OF NICANDER AND LUCILLA

The Argument of the Third History.

Lucilla, a young maiden endowed with singular beauty, for want of a convenient dowry was restrained from marrying her beloved Nicander; in the end, through the great magnificence of the courteous young prince Don Hercules, the only son and heir of Alfonso, Duke of Ferrara, she was relieved with the sum of 2,000 crowns, the which money being received by the father of Nicander, the marriage was performed to the great contentation of the noble young prince, but especially to the two young lovers Nicander and Lucilla.

In the time that Alfonso—first of that name and third duke of Ferrara—governed that state,[1] there was in the city of Ferrara a gentle young gentlewoman named Lucilla, born of a noble family, but by the frowardness of blind Fortune reduced to greater poverty than her virtues did deserve, whose beauty appeared to be such in the prime and flower of her years as it filled with marvel all those that cast their eyes upon her. Of this gentlewoman was fervently enamored a gallant young gentleman whose name was Nicander, and in like sort born of noble blood, and desired nothing more than to be joined with her in matrimony. But she, being as it is said poor, though of noble parentage and endued with singular virtues, the father of the young gentleman disdained her, who—as for the most part we see old men naturally inclined to covetise°—regarding rather the wealth that their daughters-in-law are to bring into their families than either birth, virtue, or gifts of the mind, could in no wise be persuaded or entreated to content his son in that behalf and to suffer him to enjoy his love by taking her to wife, alleging that the first thing that was to be considered in marriage was the dowry, and [then] the woman, for that the virtues of the women do not enrich the houses wherein they came (said he) but the quality of goods and wealth that they brought with them.

The covetous disposition of the father of Nicander was cause that these two young folk languished in miserable love; for although their flames were of equal force and heat, yet the young gentlewoman, being of a very honest mind, nor the young gentleman never thinking upon any other means than honestly to enjoy his desire without touch or breach of her honor, and the obstinate wilfulness of the old man being cast as a bar or block between the unity and concord of their two minds, they lived in great torment, each consuming and, as it were, melting always with desire for love of each other. Whilst their mutual love continued in this sort each day with less hope than other through the obstinacy of the old carl,° it happened that Don Hercules, the duke's only son and heir, being then in the freshest time of his youth,[2] passing by the street where this gentlewoman dwelt, saw her standing in her door appareled in white, which kind of attire increased greatly her natural beauty. And considering somewhat curiously the comeliness and excellency of her personage, together with her perfection of beauty, he received with such force into his imagination the first impression of them both that from thence forward her lively image seemed continually to be before his eyes, by the consideration whereof he grew by degrees to conceive so vehement a desire to enjoy the singularity which he saw in her that he thought it impossible for him to live if he did not attain it.[3]

And ofttimes discoursing to himself thereof, he would say, "what injury hath fortune done unto this fair gentlewoman, that as nature hath been liberal in bestowing of beauty upon her meet° for any great princess, she hath not likewise caused her to be born

covetise inordinate desire, lust.   carl churl, villian.   meet
worthy, suitable.

of some king or mighty prince, which if she were, I would never cease till I had found the means to get her to be my wife, and so enjoy her as mine own with the safety of her honor and with the satisfaction and contentment of my father."

But in the end, although he saw her degree to be far unequal to his to wish or to procure any such match, yet ceased he not by all the means he could to win her good will, and now by one device and now by another to induce her to love him and to yield to his fervent desire. But all in vain, for where many others would have taken it for a great good fortune that such a prince should have fallen in love with them, Lucilla, considering the baseness of her degree in respect of the high estate of her new lover, reputed it to be a great mishap unto her, as she that considered that[4] she could not nourish or entertain any such love but with the harm and prejudice of her honor. Besides that, she feared lest that Nicander should once perceive that this young prince hunted after that haunt, he would forsake her for fear of further displeasure, wherefore to avoid both inconveniences, whereas till then she was wont to show herself sometime at the door, sometime at the windows, she now retired herself in such sort that she could never be seen but on Sundays and holidays as she went to a little church near adjoining to the house. Wherefore Nicander, not a little marveling and greatly troubled in spirit, fearing that Lucilla—wavering as women use to do—had forsaken him and turned her affection elsewhere. As one full of jealousy and grief, for fault of better comfort, he would watch his times and follow her to that church, there to feed his fancy with a look or two which yet amid his misery he seemed to esteem as a relief, without the which he could not live. Finally, not being able to endure those torments that this absence and strangeness of his lady caused him to feel, he sent unto her a convenient messenger with a letter containing this effect:[5]

The bird which long hath lived in pleasant field,
    Esteems no whit his cage of wreathèd gold,
The dulcet note wherewith he pierced the sky,
    For grief of mind, he cannot then unfold.
Yet lives he still, but better were to die,
    More worse than death, even such a life have I.

The turtle° true, of his deceasèd mate
    Bewails the want, he recks° no more of bliss.
The swelling swan doth hardly brook the place,
    When he his best belovèd bird doth miss.
Such is my joy, Nicander must needs die,
    Lucilla doth his wonted presence fly.

How can I live, that double death possess?
    How should I joy, that drenchèd am in thrall?
What food may feed or bear a pleasant taste,
    Whereas the heart lies bathèd still in
    Whereas the heart lies bathèd still in gall?°
If this be life, then life be far from me.
    And welcome death, to set Nicander free.

What cause my dear, hath thy Nicander wrought,
    That makes thee shun in whom thou shouldst delight;
What moves thy mind to mew thee up so close,
    And keep thee from thy best beloved sight?
If I offended have, then charge me when and how,
    Nicander shall him clear, or to thy mercy bow.

If no offence, but fond conceit hath taken hold,
    Condemn him not, that shows his guiltless hand,
Who hitherto hath never meant the thing
    That justly might against your honor stand.
If guilty I, I ask no other grace,
    Give doom of death, and do my suit deface.

I say no more, but as I do deserve,
    So show the fruit of my deservèd hire;
Seem not so strange unto thy faithful friend,
    Whose absence sets my scorching heart on fire.
But as my love to thee no tongue can tell,
    Esteem the like of me, and so farewell.
              Thine own Nicander.

The young gentlewoman who had fixed all her thoughts and
settled all the contentments of her heart only upon Nicander,

turtle turtledove.   **recks** cares, heeds.   **gall** secretion of the
gall-bladder, hence bitterness of spirit, rancor.

neither desiring anything in the world so much as to please and
content him, felt an intolerable perplexity of mind in that she saw
him grieve thus at her late strangeness, and yet thought it better
that he should complain than come by any knowledge of the love
that Don Hercules did bear her; wherefore, hiding from him the
matter, replied in this sort:

The bird which is restrained
    Of former heart's delight,
I must confess, twixt life and death,
    Doth alway° combat fight.

So doth the heart compelled,
    By hest° of parent's will,
Obey for fear, yet forced by love,
    Continues constant still.

No absence by consent,
    My dear Nicander, I
Have wrought to work thy woe, from thee
    Like Cressid false to fly.[6]

Nor shall I live to loathe
    What may content thy mind;
Hap life or death, as true as steel
    Thou shalt Lucilla find.

Thy ears shall never hear
    Nor eyes shall never see,
That any wight shall reap the fruit
    Which planted was for thee.

Then frame thyself, my dear,
    To take against thy will
Our absence in good part, till time
    May better hap fulfil.

And there withal receive
    This pledge to cure thy pain:
My heart is thine, preserve it well,
    Till we two meet again.
                Ever thine Lucilla.

alway throughout all time.   **hest** injunction, command.

This sweet answer mitigated not a little the mood of the young gentleman, and so he framed himself the best he could to tolerate the absence of his Lucilla. On the other side Don Hercules, who in like manner found himself deprived of the sight of that young lady whom he loved extremely, was very much discontented, and perceiving that neither messages nor fair offers with large gifts sent unto her, whereof never any were accepted, could once move her to show herself courteous unto him of so much as a look, and, considering the poverty wherein her mother lived, now in her later years, began to imagine that it would be much easier for him, by offering her liberally wherewithal to marry her daughter to persuade her to yield her into his hands, than to win the young gentlewoman to his desires.

Wherefore, having sent a fit person to Lucilla's mother to let her understand that if she would be content that the young prince might enjoy her daughter, he would give her such a dowry in recompense of his pleasure that no gentleman of what degree soever should for her poverty refuse to take her to wife; whereas, if she refused that good offer, she should thereby be constrained through necessity either to bestow her upon some artificer or craftsman, or, if she would needs marry her to a gentleman, she must give her to some such as was so poor as that she should live all the days of her life in want and misery. The which, in effect, would be nothing else but to be cruel towards her own daughter in barring that good hap which he did offer, besides the favor that he should be able to show in furthering her marriage to both their endless comforts. The mother being often solicited and summoned to this effect, and on the one side punished with poverty, and on the other charged with years, both which pressed her very much, after diverse discourses made to and fro with herself, lastly she said,

"And whereto ought I to have regard but to the wealth and profit of my daughter, which both she shall reap abundantly if by the giving of herself unto this young prince he doth bestow upon her that dowry which he hath promised. And although in doing thereof, there be some touch° and spot to my daughter's honor and mine, yet shall it be so recompensed with the benefit

touch blemish, stain.

of her dowry that the profit will be greater than the harm. And if therein be any offence, the blame thereof is not to be imputed unto me but unto my evil fortune that hath brought me into this miserable necessity. Besides that my daughter, being already eighteen years of age and of most singular beauty, and myself already so old that from day to day I may look to go to my grave, I might happen to die and leave her without any government or oversight, and she, stirred with those appetites whereto young folks are inclined through the frailty of her sex and the poverty wherein I shall leave her, be brought to yield herself into the hands of some such one as would not have due regard unto her calling, but bring her unto the spoil."◇

And after these and such like discourses sundry times had with herself, finally she sent him word that if it would please him, she would gladly speak with him herself, which he, having understood, caused her to be brought one evening into a place where they two alone might talk, and there having given her opportunity to say what she would, thus she began:

"Sir, the weapons wherewith necessity and my poverty hath assaulted me have been so sharp and so piercing that although I have endeavored all the ways I could devise to resist and defend myself from them, yet in the end I have been forced to yield as vanquished and overcome, and constrained to do that with my daughter as to think of it only I am so abashed that I dare not for shame lift up mine eyes to behold you. But forasmuch as no other thing hath persuaded me thereunto but the desire which I have to get her a dowry wherewith I may afterward bestow her honestly, I beseech you to be content to extend your liberality in such sort as she may have that large dowry which it hath pleased you to promise me."

"Thereof I assure you," said the prince, "and larger too than hath been spoken of to you besides; and also I will minister such relief unto you for your own state that you shall have cause to give me thanks for the same."

Then replied the old gentlewoman and said: "Since that you perceive, sir, that no desire to make merchandise of my daugh-

bring her unto the spoil to rob a person of goods, hence to injure in respect of character; here to ruin her honor.

ter, but extreme poverty whereunto my froward° fortune hath brought me, doth drive me to this exigent, I do likewise beseech you that you will come unto my daughter at such time as I shall devise most convenient, with as much regard unto her credit as may be possible."

"I will therein be ruled wholly by you," answered the young prince, "and look in what sort you will appoint me to come, so shall it be."

"The first thing then, sir," said she, "that I think requisite, is that you come alone without any company, when I shall assign you the time, so that the thing rest secret between you and me and my daughter, and no occasion be given to publish it whereby my daughter might lose her good name."

This courteous young prince was therewithal well content, and that being concluded and agreed upon, she said further, "I know, sir, the honesty of my daughter to be such that if I should open my lips unto her of any such matter, she would not only reject any persuasion that I might use unto her, but also rid herself out of my house. And therefore lest that should happen, and to the end that you may have your desire and she have a dowry wherewith she may be married, if not with all the honor that the state and calling wherein she was born doth require, yet with the least harm that may be possible, since my hard hap is such, and that my poverty doth so constrain me, I have determined to do herein as you shall hear. My daughter useth to lie in a low chamber° near unto the street door of my house, in the which chamber I myself in like sort am wont° to lie whensoever we two remain alone in the house, as oftentimes we do. And commonly I, rising early in the morning about such business as I have, do leave my daughter in bed, where she sleepeth sometimes two hours or three after that I am gone. Tomorrow morning therefore will I rise and leave her alone in that chamber, and will set open the street door so as you shall not need but to push at it and the chamber door likewise. You shall come very early as we have concluded, all alone, and entering into the chamber, there shall you have my daughter and abide with her as long as it shall please yourself.

froward adverse.   **low chamber** a room on the ground floor.
wont accustomed.

But I do once again, sir, beseech you as I have done before, that
the matter may pass secret and not to be imparted to any other
than to us three, to the end that where I suffer myself to be led
through necessity to do that which I do, and with an intent to
place my daughter in marriage by the means of that dowry which
you do give her, the case being known, we escape not eternal
shame and infamy."

At this device the young prince paused a while, thinking it
strange that he should go to a young maid that not only was
unwilling, but also not so much as made privy of his coming, did
what he could to refuse that mean and to persuade the mother
to devise some better. But at the last, seeing none other could
be found more fit for the purpose, being pricked forward with
the vehemency of that appetite which love had stirred up in him,
considering himself to be a prince and a gallant young gentleman,
and that he should be alone with his love, thought that it should
not be hard for him to win her to his will, and so [was] content
to do as the old gentlewoman had devised. And being parted
each from the other, he began to attend the coming of the next
morning, and all that night, which seemed longer unto him than a
whole year, he lay with his thoughts and imaginations in the arms
of his Lucilla. As soon as the day began to peep, Don Hercules,
all alone, as he had promised to the mother, went to the house of
his lady, and finding the doors open according to promise, entered
into the chamber wherein Lucilla lay, and having barred the door
approached near the bed wherein she lay.

It was in the month of July, which season in that country is
extremely hot, by reason whereof Lucilla, tumbling from one side
of the bed unto the other, had rolled off all the clothes wherewith
she had been covered so as she had left herself all naked, and
in that sort he found her with corals° about her neck and arms
which, with the difference of their ruddy color, did set out and
beautify greatly the excellent fairness of her white body. She lay
asleep upon her back, with her hands cast over her head, as for
the most part young women are wont to do, so that forthwith
the young prince discovered her from top to toe; and, considering
with a greedy eye all her whole body, not only he commended her

corals (orig. coralies), red coral made into jewelry.

to himself so naked as he had done whilst she was appareled, but also did so singularly well like her in that state that he thought he saw rather some divine thing or some goddess come down from heaven to heap him with happiness than a mortal creature, and began to allow and commend his own judgment in that he had placed his love upon so excellent and rare a piece. And therewith bowing down himself to give her a kiss and so to awaken her, behold she opened her eyes, which right well resembled two fair shining stars. And where she was used to see none other body in that chamber but her mother when she waked, now seeing this young prince standing thus[7] over her, and finding herself in that sort all naked, she gave a great screech and said:

"Out alas sir," for she knew him straightway, "what evil hap hath brought you hither at this time?" And in so saying as one wonderfully ashamed to be seen in that plight, she wrapped about her one of the sheets and began with a loud voice to call her mother.

But perceiving that her mother would not hear and that she called in vain, she began to imagine that she was consenting unto his coming thither, and lamenting with tears that trickled down her cheeks like drops of dew hanging upon roses in a May morning, she said: "Alas now, I see my mother also hath betrayed me."

Which thing the young prince understanding, said unto her: "Trouble not yourself, nor grieve not, fair damsel, at my coming hither, but rather rejoice that your singular beauty hath so enflamed me, as one in a manner forgetting my estate, have been contented to come hither all alone as a private man to enjoy your company, if it will please you to accept my good will, which though a thousand other dames of this city do wish and would be glad of, yet have I deemed none of them worthy thereof but yourself. And seeing your mother, who hath that power over you that in reason she ought to have over her child, and knoweth best what is for your good and commodity, doth consent hereunto; you, in my judgment, are not but to show yourself in like sort content. For in giving yourself to me, you do not abase or cast yourself away upon any vile person, but show yourself courteous unto a prince whom your beauty hath made thrall,° and in whom

thrall prisoner.

you shall find nothing but grateful courtesy, to your benefit and satisfaction."

And with these and other like words stretched forth his hand toward her breasts, that were like two little balls of ivory, and drawing near her to kiss her, she with her hand thrusting him modestly back, said thus:

"Sir I beseech you, by the princely nobility that is in you and by that love which you say you bear me, that it will please you not to force me or to seek at my hands anything against my will; and that since my mother, who ought to have been the chief defender of mine honesty, hath abandoned and forsaken me, you will yet of your courtesy vouchsafe to give me the hearing of a few words, which the special care I have of mine honor doth force me to express."

The courteous young prince, at this request, stayed himself proceeding any further, and not being desirous to have her but with her own good will, stood still to hear what it was that Lucilla would say unto him, yet ever hoping with fair means to win her at the last. And she, weeping very tenderly, began to say unto him in this sort:

"I am very sorry, most noble prince," quoth she, "that Fortune hath been so much mine enemy, that she hath made me a woman far unworthy and unmeet for you, for that you, being so great a prince as you are, and I so mean a gentlewoman, I see so great a space and difference between your high estate and my low degree that between us there can be no proportion° or convenient equality. For the which cause, sir, I, considering mine own estate, and not minding to exceed my calling, have a good while since chosen Nicander to be my lover, who, in respect of his blood, though he be richer than I, is no whit nor more nobly born than myself am.[8] By reason of which conformity of blood and birth, our love is likewise grown to be equal, and equal the desire in us both, he to have me to his wife, and I to have him for my husband. But the covetousness—let it be lawful for me to say so—of his father is such that although he knoweth me to be a gentlewoman born, yet because I am not of that wealth as to bring him so great a

proportion (orig. portion, restored from the Ital. source convenienza), balance, harmony.

dowry as his riches perchance require, he despiseth me and will not yield by any persuasion his good will and consent that we may match together according to our desire. Nevertheless sir I, considering how fervently this young gentleman loveth me, and that already we are in mind united and knitted together with consent, faith, and love, do yet believe assuredly that God of his special goodness and favor will grant us his assured grace that we may one day be joined together in the holy state of matrimony. Which thing, if it should happen and come to pass, I not having anything else to bring with me for my dowry but my virginity, am determined and fully resolved, by God's help, to give it unto him as pure and unspotted as I brought it from my mother's womb. And if my unhappy chance and fortune be such as that I cannot have Nicander to my husband, I have concluded with myself, by the grace of God, never to couple myself to any man living, but to give and vow me wholly unto almighty God, and in his service to spend my days a virgin in continual fasting and prayer. Therefore, most excellent prince, if honesty, if justice, if religion have that power and force in your noble mind which in reason they ought to have, I do beseech you, and for that love's sake that you say you bear me, that you will preserve and keep unstained my honesty, and that it would please you with the sound discourse of reason to temper that fervent appetite which hath brought you hither to the prejudice and breach of my honesty and credit, in doing whereof you shall show yourself to be indeed that noble prince that the highness of your birth and blood doth promise you should be, whereas if you should force and violate me, a virgin, and a weak maiden without defence, there could thereof ensue naught else to me but dishonor and reproach, and withal small praise would it be unto your excellency, when it shall be said that you had overcome a simple damsel."

And here being interrupted with sobs and tears exceeding for the grief of her mind, casting down her eyes for shame and sorrow, she held her peace, attending what her hap and the goodness of the prince should dispose of her, in whose courtesy she had reposed all her hope and confidence.

This young prince, understanding the honest desire of Lucilla, first praised her greatly to himself for the chasteness of her mind,[9] and, being moved with the magnanimity of his noble mind, though he were pricked with the sharpest dart of the blind boy's° quiver, and that his ardent appetite did still stir him to the accomplishment of his desire, yet conquering himself with reason, he turned all the love which erst he bare unto this young lady into compassion of her estate, and thus he said unto her:

"The virtue and honesty of thy mind, fair damsel, do require that I should make no less account of thine honor than if I were come hither to no other intent than to defend it against any other that should go about to stain or spot it. Therefore not only thou needest not to fear any violence at my hands, but also mayest hope that I will not fail to further this thy chaste purpose so that thou mayest enjoy that young gentleman which thou hast chosen for thy husband with all the honor and satisfaction that appertaineth to the honesty of thy mind. And therefore, since nothing else doth let thee from the getting of him but the poverty of thy state whereunto thy froward fortune hath unworthily brought thee, I will myself supply in that behalf that wherein she hath failed, and correct with my liberality the injury that she hath done thee."

And having so said, he himself openeth the door and called her mother, who had gotten herself into a chamber and there sat bewailing the misery of her state whereby she had been driven in such sort to prepare a dowry for her daughter.

She being come, he said unto her, "Gentlewoman, if erst I came hither as a lover unto your daughter, now I will depart and leave her as if I were her brother, leaving her honor no less safe and untouched than I found it, for so deserveth her virtue that I should deal with her. And forasmuch as I perceive she is in love with a young gentleman whom I well know, and is in my opinion very worthy of it, and that he in like force is in love with her, and that only the want of a reasonable dowry is the cause that she cannot become his wife as she desireth, I am content to bestow upon her for her contentment that sum for her dowry which I had purposed to have given her in recompense of my contentation, to the end that this her honest desire may have that effect which is most convenient to so great and well grounded an affection, and that her great honesty and virtue do deserve. Therefore send you

blind boy's cupid's.

this day unto my treasurer, and he shall forthwith disburse unto you two thousand pound, which shall be the dowry of this your gentle and honest daughter."

And turning himself toward the young gentlewoman, he said unto her, "and as for you, fair damsel," quoth he, "I crave nothing else now at your hands but that you keep this faith of yours wherewith you are linked unto your lover inviolate and unspotted, even as I do leave you inviolate and unspotted in your mother's hands."

How great the joy of the mother was when she saw the honesty of her daughter, as it were, resaved out of this young prince's hands by the force of her own virtue, may better be imagined than expressed with words. But above all joys, the joy of Lucilla exceeded all other when she understood that through the magnificence and liberality of the noble young prince, she was to have her Nicander for her husband.

And turning her eyes full of modesty towards him she said, "I could not, sir, have had any more certain and infallible token of your love toward me than that which now of your great courtesy and bounty you have showed me, which I acknowledge to be so great that I am bound to yield your excellency my most humble and infinite thanks. But forasmuch as words do fail me wherewith I might do it, I must beseech you that it may rest in your discreet judgment to consider how much I confess myself to be your debtor when words do[10] fail me to yield you at the least thanks for so great a benefit. This only will I say unto your grace, that the remembrance of so noble an act shall never wear out of my mind, and that I will, so long as I live, pray unto almighty God so to preserve and maintain your noble person, as you of your goodness have saved mine honesty, and so to grant you the accomplishment of all your noble desires, as you have offered me to make me content of mine by having my Nicander to be my husband. Unto whom, as well, because I have ever been so disposed, as for that it hath pleased your excellency to command me, I will always keep sound and unstained that faith which through your courtesy shall join me to him in marriage."

The damsel seemed unto the prince at that instant to be in manner greater than she was in deed, when she once stood assured of the safeguard of her honesty, and, delighting no less in the excellency of her mind than he had before done in the beauty of her body, he departed from her.

And having caused the two thousand pound to be paid unto her mother as he had promised, he went unto the duke his father and told him all that had passed between Lucilla and him, the manner whereof liked so well the duke that he concluded with himself that all the virtues that ever had been before that time in his progenitors would be most excellently joined in him.

This young prince required his father to send for Nicander's father, and to persuade him to agree that his son might match with Lucilla since that she was provided and furnished with so reasonable a dowry; which thing the duke did with a very good will, for that he knew that if his son should have taken in hand to persuade the old man to any such matter, it might have stirred some suspicion in his head why the prince should so do. And having sent for him accordingly, when he was come, the duke, after some familiar speeches of course and courtesy, told him he was desirous that his son Nicander should take Lucilla to be his wife, who as well for her birth as for the rare gifts of her mind, as he had learned, was worthy to be wife to any great lord. The old gentleman answered that although she had those virtues and gifts which he spake of and were very well born, yet had she not any dowry convenient or agreeable to his wealth whereby she might deserve to be matched with his son.

"Yes, marry,"◊ said the duke, "for I myself, because I would not have so great virtue as is in her to be oppressed by fortune's spite, have bestowed upon her two thousand pound to serve for her dowry."

The old man, hearing of such a sum, was very well content to do as the duke would have him, and the next day, through the liberality of the prince, the marriage was concluded and knit up which had so long been delayed and hindered by the covetousness of the old man and the poverty of Lucilla, with the infinite joy and contentment of the two young lovers who had long wished and desired that happy day.

What virtue, or what continence of Alexander or of Scipio may be compared to this? Scipio abstained from the young gentle-

marry exclamation of surprise, a variant of "by mary".

woman which was presented unto him in Spain, Alexander from
Darius his daughter,[11] but it was very easy for either of them so
to do, as well because they were in the fury of war and the sounds
of drums and trumpets, as for that those women were of a strange
nation and enemies unto them, and never before that time seen of
any of them, much less desired. Whereas this young prince, who
even bathing, as it were, in bliss, living at his ease and pleasure
in the flower of his youth and in the heat of his amorous flames,
had a young gentlewoman of a rare beauty, not of strange nation or any otherwise to be hated, but extremely beloved, in his
hands, and voluntarily yielded and committed unto him by her
own mother, and yet not only tempered himself and refrained to
defile her chaste and honest body, but also bestowed liberally her
dowry upon her to the end that another might enjoy her and be
her husband whom she had chosen to love and like of, did without all question far exceed all human courtesy in so noble and
so virtuous an act. Whereby he made apparent that although
he were pricked forward with the sharp spurs of Love and his
sensual appetite, yet was he of that highness of courage and of
that constancy of mind that he was able not only to conquer
himself, but also to subdue the forces of love, whereunto both
mortal men's valor doth commonly yield, and the very power of
the gods themselves—if we shall believe the fables of the ancient
writers—hath showed itself oftentimes inferior.

And thus this honest damsel Lucilla, by the means of her
chastity the virtue and excellency whereof did win and master
the heart of that young prince much more than the perfection of
her bodily beauty had done before, obtained the thing she most
desired and joyed in, which was to have Nicander to her husband, with whom she lived ever after in great contentment and
happiness, still nourishing with kind and loving demeanor each to
other that fervent affection which, from their first acquaintance,
had taken full possession of both their liberties.

OF FINEO AND FIAMMA

The Argument of the Fourth History.

The hard adventure of Fineo with his beloved Fiamma who, after sundry conflicts of fortune, were in the end sold as slaves to the King of Tunis, who, seeing their perfect love, caused them to be married, and after honoring them with sundry presents sent them home to Savona where by their parents and friends they were joyfully received.

In Genoa, one of the fairest and most famous cities in Italy, there was sometime a young gentlewoman of excellent beauty called Fiamma, that was in love with a young gentleman of Savona—a city subject to the state of Genoa, and distant from thence about thirty miles[1]—whose name was Fineo, and their love being mutual and tending to no other end than to be linked and joined together by marriage, they would not long have stayed to bring their honest desires to a good end and conclusion had not the father of the gentlewoman refused his consent and showed himself contrary to this their love and goodwill. For he, misliking with the match either for that he purposed to place her better or because he would not have her married to any other man that should carry her out of Genoa, did ofttimes chide and reprehend his daughter for casting her affection upon that young gentleman that was a stranger unto them and in effect but a subject, though he were both of blood and richesse° equal unto them.

But for all that the father could do, or any other of her friends, the fire which love had kindled in this young couple's breasts slaked° no whit at all, but still increased—both hoping in the end to win her friends' goodwill and attain the fruits of their desired love. This young damsel had to her brother a stout and valiant young gentleman, who, being offended greatly that Fineo should continue his love toward his sister and follow the pursuit of that which he knew well enough her friends were unwilling to yield unto, had caused him to be spoken unto, and to be warned that he should desist and leave to solicit her; but he, for all that, ceased not, but continued his suit. Wherefore this brother of hers determined to make him leave off by force and dint of sword. For although there was at that time a very strait° law in the city that no man should wear his sword, and pain of death appointed for him that should hurt any man with any weapon, yet both these gentlemen wore their swords, for that they both had charge of soldiers that lay then in garrison for the defence of the city.

And having one day met Fineo in the street alone, and himself being very well accompanied with other gentlemen, he began to give him evil language. And being a gentleman of great courage, and though he were a stranger there, not being able to endure to be injured in words, said to him boldly and roundly again that if they two were alone he durst not use those speeches unto him, for he would well give him to understand that he was no man to take wrong at his hands, and that time and occasion would serve one day, he doubted not, to make him know that he had offended one that would bear no coals.° Whereupon his adversary, having drawn forth his sword whilst he was yet speaking, ran fiercely upon him, thinking to have stricken him. But Fineo, also a very lusty gentleman and quick of eye and nimble of hand, drew out his sword and not only warded the blow of his enemy but also hurt him, though but lightly in the hand. Forthwith they that were with the young gentlewoman's brother environed him and took him prisoner and delivered him into the hands of the magistrate

richesse wealth, opulence.   slaked became less intense, abated.
strait strict.   bear no coals put up with no insults.

or chief officer of the city. And the penalty being such as is before mentioned for hurting of any man within the city, and especially a gentleman, Fineo was condemned to lose his head.

Nevertheless, he being very well friended and supported by many principal gentleman of the city, they labored so much for him that they obtained that he should not be beheaded but that his penalty should be converted unto another punishment very little better if it were no worse. For having bound him fast hand and foot, they laid him in a small boat, and in very stormy weather set him in the main sea and there left him to the rule and government of Fortune, and to the disposition of God and mercy of the waves and winds. The boat was a long while beaten and tossed by the rage and fury of the seas, and poor Fineo, under diverse and sundry storms and shapes, had before his eyes a thousand times the presence of death. Yet in that fearful and mortal peril he ceased not to call upon the name of his dear Fiamma, and in that extremity and imminent danger did he yet in manner glorify himself and think himself happy that he should end his life for the love of his lady.

While he was thus tossed and tormented, still looking for none other but present death, the tempest began to cease and the storm and rage of seas to be assuaged. When lo, he discovered a frigate of Moors that went a-roving° and were then new gone abroad to spy whether the storm which was then past had not happily prepared for them some occasion of gain and booty.[2] These Moors had no sooner discovered this little boat thus fleeting at all adventures, but hoping to find therein some prey for their profit, they made toward it; and having at the boarding thereof found Fineo bound hand and foot, and perceiving by his countenance and apparel that he was no very base person, they untied him and set him in their frigate as a slave to row until such time as they should determine further what to do with him who, although that servitude and captivity were grievous unto him, yet considering with himself that it was better for him to be in the power of men, though they were infidels, than in the power of seas and winds. He comforted himself that yet if he lived he might still hope through the goodness of God one day to be so happy as to

a-roving sailing as pirates.

enjoy his lady and love—he framed himself to bear with patient mind that heavy yoke of his captivity.

Fiamma, having understood the unfortunate accident happened to her lover, believing certainly that he was dead and that she should never see him again. Wherefore she herself resolving that she would no longer live, gave herself to devise what kind of death she were best to choose, and in doubt thereof she passed some few days dissembling still in the house her sorrow and grief with a merry and cheerful countenance, as though she had clean forgotten and not once remembered her lover Fineo. But in the end, after long debating with herself, she resolved to die the same kind of death and to make that end which she imagined Fineo had done.

There was another gentleman of the city who was no less enamored of this gentlewoman than Fineo was, who, supposing that now, since she saw there was no remedy for her to recover her lover whom both she and all the city accounted certainly to be dead, he might perchance by suit obtain her good will and so procure her to be his wife with the consent of her friends. And therefore, not long after the mischance of Fineo, he caused her father to be dealt withal for the bestowing of his daughter upon him. And the father, being willing enough to agree thereunto, and having questioned with his daughter thereupon and finding her to give sober and obedient answer with few words, presupposing that she was willing to do as he would have her, made promise of her unto this young gentleman and agreed upon the dowry and all other circumstances necessary for the coupling of two such persons together.

The night that went before the day appointed for their marriage, Fiamma, calling unto her a Moor that was slave in her father's house and had the keeping of a small boat of the gentleman's —wherein when he list to disport himself, he was wont to take the air upon the sea in time of fair weather, and to go to their houses of pleasure whereof that coast is very plentiful,[3] and them of exceeding beauty—which Moor had lived so many years in that thraldom that he was now become so old, as she thought, she needed not to fear any force or violence at his hands, she began to persuade him to put on a desire to deliver himself out of captivity so as he might live the rest of his years in liberty and at his ease; whereunto, finding him ready and willing if the means or occasion were offered him, she gave him in hand a good round sum of money which she had laid together and made him promise to carry her into the sea in the boat whereof he had the custody, and afterwards to do that whatsoever it were that she should command him.

This wicked and faithless Moor, seeing himself not only to purchase his liberty but also make so great a gain of ready money that he was not like at any time after to live in want or poverty, was [not] only thankful in his mind toward the young gentlewoman, but straightway began to purpose and to devise to make a greater gain of her own person by carrying her unto the King of Tunis and selling of her unto him at a very high price. And with this intention, the mischievous knave assured her that he would do in all points as she would have him. Wherefore, when all the rest of the house were in their first sleep, the damsel, with this wretched Moor, went out of her father's house and got her into the boat, and the weather being very fair, the knave began to row and make sail along the coast toward Ligorno,° from which, by break of the day, they were not very far. When this young gentlewoman saw that she was now so far from home that she needed not to fear to be driven back again to Genoa, she willed the Moor to row to the shore and to land himself, and then to shove off the boat again, for that her determination was so to die, swallowed up with the waves of the sea as she supposed her Fineo to have been. But the wicked knave, who had a farther fetch° in his head and thoughts far differed from the gentlewoman's, made her believe that they were yet near unto Genoa and advised her to be content that they might go somewhat farther to the end that her father, if he sent after them, might not overtake them.

Nevertheless, she, having oftentimes urged him to do as she erst bade him, and he still protracting the time and shifting her off with one tale or another, she began to suspect his drift. The morning therefore being well spent, she made as though she would have looked over the boat side into the water, or have washed her hands in the sea, and on the sudden would have cast herself overboard. But the crafty Moor, suspecting her intent, caught hold

Ligorno It. Livorno; Engl. the city of Leghorn in N.W. Italy.   **fetch** trick.

of her about the middle, and not only held her from throwing herself into the sea, but also bound her fast hand and foot, and whereas she of her courtesy had both set him at liberty and liberally bestowed good store of wealth upon him, he, as a treacherous infidel, bereaved her of her liberty, making her an unfortunate slave under his disposition, and being moved with a greedy covetous mind, thought that too little which she had given him, and therefore determined, as is afore said, to sell her person and to increase his goods by that means.

The desolate damsel, when she saw herself so used by that villain, full of woe and grief, ceased not to rebuke the vile caitiff that little regarded her speeches, the breach of his faith and promise, and blaming herself for trusting of him, and then repenting when it was too late that she had not obeyed her father and followed the advice of her friends, she began to curse her destiny and her cruel fortune and to cry out upon the heavens that had made her become the unfortunatest young woman that ever loved man.

And whilst she was thus lamenting her hard hap, and the Moor as fast as he could with his oars laboring to speed his voyage, a little foist or galley of Moors that went prowling° up and down the coast, having espied the small boat, drew near unto it and boarded it. And having found this young gentlewoman being bound therein, they would have taken her away, but the old knave offering to resist them and to keep her out of their hands, they took her away from him perforce, and wounded him very sore, and asked of her in their language from whence she came, and what she was. But she, not understanding them, could make them no answer, but only with tears and weeping make them to understand that she was a woeful and unfortunate damsel. But the old Moor, feeling himself wounded to death, before he died told them both of what place and parentage she was, and laid before them by plain reason how great a booty they might account they had made that morning if they did carry her unto the King of Tunis, as he had thought to have done, and sell her unto him. He being dead, they despoiled him and took from him all that which Fiamma had given, and so he, having thought by treachery and breaking of his faith to make a great gain, lost

prowling (orig. prolling).

both his life and all that which he had gotten of the unadvised and evil-counselled young gentlewoman. And having placed her in their foist° and comforted her as well as they could, they took their way straight toward Tunis.

It fortuned that the other frigate of Moors that had found and taken Fineo (as is already said before) met with this other foist or galley, wherein Fiamma was, and assaulted it, and having fought together a good while—for that the other resisted and defended themselves stoutly—in fine, the frigate wherein Fineo was—who in the encounter and during the fight had showed great valor among the rest—overcame the other and took from them all that they had, so that Fiamma and Fineo were both now together in the compass of one small vessel. And although in that extremity of both their evil fortunes, it was a great comfort for these two lovers to see one the other, and that both longed and desired extremely to embrace each other, and to tell the one to the other their accidents and unfortunate adventures, nevertheless Fineo made signs to Fiamma that in nowise she should take knowledge or acquaintance of him, and accordingly she dissembled and made no show but as one [who] had never seen him.

Fineo, for the valor and courage which he had showed in the battle, was delivered of his chains and much made of among the Moors until such time as they had conducted both him and her—as they did very shortly after—unto the King of Tunis. Who, having seen and considered Fineo and understood by the pirates that his comely personage was accompanied with great valor, brought him and took him to his service in good place near his own person. And being moved with the beauty of the young gentlewoman, bargained for her likewise for a great sum of money, and caused her to be put in the Cube° which is a place where he keepeth his concubines (as the Turk doth his in his seraglio) among a great many of other women, and esteemed her very much for that the rovers—who had learned of those others that they overcame all that which the old Moor had declared unto them of her calling and condition—did assure him that she was a gentlewoman born of a noble family in Genoa.

foist a light galley propelled by oars and sails.   **Cube** (derived from the It. original "cuba"), Cinthio's name for the seraglio.

Fineo, by his service and discreet behavior, became in short
time very dear unto the king, so that in less than the space of one
whole year, the king, of special trust, gave him the charge of the
gate of the Cube, which office the kings of Tunis are never wont
to give but unto such as are in singular favor about them, in the
which Fineo, to his great contentment, had the commodity° daily
to see his Fiamma, and she had no less comfort and satisfaction to
behold and look upon him, which opportunity they enjoyed and
handled so discreetly that they never gave any cause of suspicion
to any person of their fervent good will and affection.

The manner or custom of the king was to cause his concubines
to come unto him, and to lie with them by order as they had
been bought or come to his hands. By reason of which custom,
for that there were very many bought before the coming thither
of Fiamma, there was already a whole year and a half well-nigh
passed after her sale, and yet her turn was not come to be called
for.⁴ But remaining now but three others to be brought unto the
king before her, Fineo considering to his intolerable grief that
she was, ere it were long, to be likewise called for, began to be
tormented with incredible passion and anguish of mind. And his
woe increased ten thousand fold by fear and imagination which
he conceived that—she being above all the king's concubines far
the fairest—when he had once enjoyed her he would take her to
be one of his wives, which fear did no whit less torment and afflict
Fiamma than it did her lover.

Whilst both these young lovers lived in this sort there chanced
to arrive at Tunis a ship of Savona with certain merchants of that
city, who, seeing Fineo there and knowing him, were wonderfully
amarvelled finding him alive, for that he had been lamented at
Savona of all his friends for dead. Fineo likewise knowing those
merchants, and having authority and means to pleasure them in
the court, welcomed them and made much of them in friendly
sort; and demanding of the state and welfare of his father and
brother and other friends, they certified him that they were all
well, and that when they should understand that he was alive and
in so good a case they would be very joyful and think themselves

commodity convenience, advantage.

happy if they might hope to see him once come again, as they doubted not but one day he would and might.

These merchants, having dispatched their business, departed thence and by them Fineo wrote letters to his father and to his brother certifying them of his being in Tunis and how that Fiamma was with him, and that he desired to deliver himself out of bondage, and her with him, which thing he thought he might easily bring to pass if his brother would come thither, and withal described unto them a plot which he had cast for the execution of his intent and desire.

They being returned safe unto Savona, delivered the letters unto the father and brother of Fineo, who, with the rest of his friends and in effect all the whole city, were very glad that his fortune had not been altogether so froward toward him as they had supposed.

And his brother, according to his instructions, prepared a very pretty frigate, very well appointed and furnished with merchandise, among which there were many trifles and things of price meet◇ for ladies and gentlewomen. And being arrived therewith at Tunis, Fineo brought them unto the king, whom they presented with some things of small price, which were very grateful and acceptable unto him, and among other speeches they said that they had aboard many pretty things for dames and ladies, which thing the king understanding, commanded Fineo that the chiefest of them might be brought into the Cube to show such things as they had unto his concubines, by which occasion he got that opportunity which he looked for to confer and deal more privately with them without suspicion and to give the better order for the accomplishment of as much as he had devised.

Fineo and his brother therefore being come into the Cube showed forth among those women such wares as they had brought to please their fancies, and gave unto them all some one trifle or another, as a gentle present to the first, and the brother of Fineo presented Fiamma, among the rest, with a very fair purse richly embroidered with gold and pearl, in the which there was enclosed a letter written by Fineo by the contents whereof she might understand at large all that which he did wish and would have her to

meet suitable.

do to make their escape together and to rid themselves out of that
thraldom and captivity. As soon as the two brethren had done
that° they came for and were departed, Fiamma, by their manner gathering that the gift of the purse contained some mystery,
withdrew herself into a secret place, and having opened it, she
found therein the letter which, when she had read, she thanked
almighty God that of his goodness had showed her the way to deliver herself out of captivity and from becoming dishonestly the
concubine of an infidel king.

And when this appointed day for the performing of their purpose was come, Fiamma, in the night when all was silent and
others slept, came to a window barred with iron where Fineo and
his brother were attending for her, who, with certain instruments
which they had brought for that purpose, brake and wrested° the
grate of the window, and taking her away with them they got her
into their bark and hoisted sail and directed their course with
a merry wind toward the coast of Italy, which served them very
fair all that night long and the most part of the next day. In
the morning, Fiamma being missed and Fineo likewise, the king
was advertised of their escape, who, perceiving the merchants to
be gone also, rested assured that it was a set match made for
the stealing of Fiamma away. And being full of rage and despite
towards them all, he caused certain galleys and other light vessels to be armed in all haste, and to be sent after them, giving
straight charge and commission to his captains that either they
should bring Fineo and the damsel with the chief of the merchants alive unto him because he would cause them all three to
be buried alive,[5] or that if they could not get them alive, they
should bring their three heads for that he would have them be
set over the Cube for an example and a terror to all others.

But before those galleys and other vessels could be in a readiness to depart, Fortune, not having yet her fill of persecuting and
afflicting these two poor lovers, caused a contrary wind with an
extreme storm and tempest to arise, by force whereof the vessel wherein they were was not without great danger driven back
again to Tunis with so much grief and sorrow of all them that

that that which.   wrested detached, tore out.

were in it as they may imagine that know the cruelty and barbarousness of that people. But in the beginning of the storm, the brother of Fineo, despairing of his life, as he that was assured either to be drowned by rage of the wind and seas, or else to die in torment if he returned into the hands of those infidels, got himself into his cockboat° and therein hazarded his life, and after much ado and a thousand perils of present death recovered the coast of Italy at the last, and returned home to Savona full of woe with heavy tidings declaring unto his father that either the frigate would be lost or else driven back again to Tunis, where he was well assured that both his brother and the young damsel his lover should be murdered in most cruel manner. At which doleful news, the father, as if he had seen his son lie dead before him, began to weep and lament, complaining of his hard destiny that caused him to live so long, or reserved him to see those cruel and bitter days.

Fineo, seeing himself brought to so hard an exigent,° for that their vessel was now driven back near unto Tunis, and knowing that he should feel the smart of his fault and the king's anger in sharpest manner and sort, being determined to live no longer and to prevent the cruelty of the king, drew out his sword and would therewith have stricken himself to death. But Fiamma catching him by the arm:

"Alas, Fineo," quoth she, "what shall become of me if you be dead? Shall I remain behind to endure cruel torments that I know this infidel hath prepared for me? Yet rather since that death must needs deliver us of our misfortunes, before you execute upon yourself this your determination, rid me out of the world and deliver me from the pains which already I feel in my imagination, wherewith I assure myself they will bring me to a shameful death." And with these words, offering her breast unto him, she requested him to strike her with his sword.

But Fineo bade her be of good comfort, "for your beauty, my Fiamma," said he, "being so singular as it is, I know will save you, and therefore you need not fear, and I alone should be the man that they would plague and torment to death for us both, and

cockboat   a small boat usually carried aboard ships.   exigent
situation requiring immediate action.

therefore, my dear, suffer me to die before, and content thyself to live and vouchsafe sometime to remember thy unfortunate Fineo when he is dead."

Whilst they were thus talking and debating which should first die, the people which the king had sent out to apprehend them came and boarded their frigate and took them both, whom they bound in chains and brought on land to the presence of the king, who, as soon as he beheld the beauty of Fiamma, felt his former wrath and cruelty intended° to relent, and in much milder manner than the two captives hoped or looked for, he said unto her:

"Tell me what moved you, I pray you, fair damsel, to run away and fly from me at whose hands you had no cause to look for any other entreaty than loving and friendly?"

Fiamma, who in that year and a half that she had been in the Cube, had learned the language indifferently well, made answer unto him that no cause or meaning to fly from him, but her earnest desire to enjoy Fineo, whom she had loved and chosen for her husband many years before, had forced her to do that which she had done.

And herewith she told him the beginning of their acquaintance and love, and how many perils and dangers they had run through, still hoping one day to come unto that happy hour wherein their troubles should have an end and that they might be honestly united and enjoy one another. And finally, casting herself at his feet, with abundance of tears she besought him with all humility to pardon her if she had offended him, and withal to forgive Fineo since that long and faithful love had made them to procure the accomplishment of their desires.

The tears of Fiamma and the only name of Love were of such force and virtue in the heart of the king, though he were barbarous and cruel of nature, that the ire and hatred which he had conceived against them before was then converted and changed into pity and compassion of their misfortunes. And where before he had appointed a cruel death to be their punishment, he now determined to overcome with his courtesy the frowardness of their perverse fortune and to make them, after so many perils and dangers, contented and happy, and to see an end at last of their

intended inclined.

miseries by making them to enjoy their long-hoped-for desires. Wherefore, having caused them to be both forthwith unbound, he took from his own finger a marvelous fair and precious ruby, and giving it unto Fineo, he said unto him:

"Since your fortune hath been such that after so many strange adventures and through such dangers you are fallen unto my hands, I for my part will not be he that will extinguish or quench the flames of so fervent and constant love, or unloose or dissolve the bands wherewith your hearts be bound and knit together. And therefore, Fineo, I do not only pardon you both, but also I will have thee, before thou depart hence, to wed this damsel with this ring, and to take her for thy wife, and that she henceforth enjoy thee forever as her husband."

It is not to be demanded whether the two lovers—who looked for none other of the king's courtesies than death—were glad to hear him use those speeches, yea or no? But both being fallen on their knees, and in humblest manner having yielded their thanks unto his majesty, Fineo in his presence wedded Fiamma and took her for his wife to the unspeakable joy and contentation of both their hearts and minds. And the king, to honor their marriage, caused a sumptuous feast to be prepared with no less charge and abundance of all things than if he had married a daughter of his own to some great lord or chief man of that country.

And after certain days, the two young married lovers being desirous to return into their own country, he gave them very rich and costly presents, and sent them honorably accompanied home to Savona, whose arrival was no less marvelous than joyful to the father and brother of Fineo and to all the city, they having been assuredly esteemed and accounted as dead. Afterwards they went to Genoa to Fiamma's father and brother, certifying of all that had happened, who then, persuading themselves that God and Nature had created those two young folk to be matched and joined together in wedlock, were well contented with that which they saw was God's will should be. And being gone both to Savona, the father embraced and accepted Fineo for his son-in-law, and the brother for his brother-in-law. And the two young lovers lived ever after in great happiness and felicity, giving by this success of their hard fortune an assured argument and a notable example whereby we may learn that though froward fortune do for a while cross and molest the desires and travails of men, yet in the end she cannot let,◊ but that of necessity those things must come to pass which God by his divine providence, wherewith he ruleth the whole world, hath appointed shall take effect.

let hinder.

OF TWO BRETHREN AND THEIR WIVES

The Argument of the Fifth History.

Two brothers making choice of their wives, the one chose for beauty, the other for riches; it happened unto them after they were married, the one of their wives proved to be of light disposition, the other a common scold, in what manner they lived with their husbands and how, in the end, the first came to live orderly and well, but the other could be brought by no device to any reason or good manner.

Gentlewomen, before I will proceed any farther in this history I must desire you to arm yourselves with patience in reading hereof, that if you find anything that might breed offence to your modest minds take it in this sort, that I have written it only to make you merry, and not to set you a snarring° or grudging against me, for although I mean to present you with a chapter of knavery, yet it shall be passable and such as you may very well permit. And the matter that I mind to write is upon this question, whether a man were better to be married to a wise harlot or to a foolish overthwart° and brawling woman. This question I know will seem very doubtful unto some, and yet in my opinion very easy to be answered; and to speak my mind without dissimulation of both

snarring snarling.   overthwart froward, testy.

those evils, I think the first is least and therefore is to be chosen. And herein I could allege for my better proof an example of the ancient Romans, who in all their governments were most wise and politic, amongst whom the infirmity of the first was borne withal because it proceeded of the frailty of the flesh, but the outrage of the second was ever condemned for that it did abound from a wicked and mischievous mind. And in common reason, it is less noisome[1] for a man to live accompanied with a wife who, although she will sometime fly out,◊ can so wisely dissemble with her husband that he shall never so much as suspect her, whereby he shall receive no discontentment in his mind, than to be bedfellow with Xantippe,[2] a common scold, who daily and hourly will be checking, taunting, and railing at him in such sort that he shall think himself most blessed and happy when he is farthest from her company. But for your better confirmation, I have set forth this history of two brethren, the one of them married to a wench that could so cunningly behave herself towards him that he had thought she had believed there had been no other god but himself, and yet, by your leave, she would take reason when it was proffered her. But what of that? The heart never grieves what the eyes see not.[3] The other was married to a dame that from her navel downward was more chaste and continent, but otherwise of her tongue such a devil of hell that the poor man her husband could never enjoy merry day nor hour, although he devised many a pretty remedy, as by the reading of the process of this tale you shall better perceive, which followeth in this sort.

There was sometime remaining in a famous city[4] two brethren. The eldest, according to the custom of the place, enjoyed his father's goods and possessions after his death, whereby he was well able to live; the youngest had neither lands nor livings, saving that his father had trained him up in learning whereby he was able to govern himself in all manner of companies wheresoever he became.◊ These two brethren, being weary of their single lives, disposed themselves to marriage. The eldest, being of himself well able to live, sought a wife only for her beauty without any other respect either to her conditions or riches, and as the proverb

---

fly out i.e. escape her cage; run free.   **became** i.e. went.

is, "he that seeks shall find," so in the end he lighted on a gentlewoman called by the name of Mistress Dorothy, whose beauty indeed was very excellent and therewithal had a passing ready wit. Marry, her training up had not been after the best nor worst manner, but, as a man might say, after the common sort.° This gentlewoman he married, who could so well handle him with kissings, cullings° and other amorous exercises that her husband thought himself the most fortunate man that lived to light on such a wife, although she cunningly armed his head with horns° as after you shall hear.

The second brother, left as you have heard without maintenance or living, sought for a wife only to relieve his want, and fortuned to hit of a widow indeed with great wealth, but in conditions so overthwart and so spiteful° of her tongue that the poor man had not been married fully out a month but he more than a thousand times cursed the priest that married him, the sexton that opened the church door when he went to be married, yea, and his own unhappy legs that had carried his body to be yoked to so great a mischief. But because I do mind more orderly to tell you the manners of these two gentlewomen, I will first begin with Mistress Dorothy, whose husband, after they had been a while married, fortuned to fall sick, and then, according to that country manner,° a doctor of physic was presently sent for, who, coming many times to visit his patient, began to behold and contemplate the lively beauty of this gentlewoman and lent her many rolling looks and secret countenances in such sort that Mistress Dorothy, being well practiced in the art of love and seeing Master Doctor to be a man as sufficient to content a gentlewoman in her chamber that was whole as to minister medicines to those that were sick, did not only requite him again with look for look, but she yielded him a large usury and paid him more than forty in the hundred.[5] Master Doctor, who was likewise skillful enough, could well perceive whereto those looks did tend. Upon a time being alone in her company, he said unto her as followeth:

common sort just average.   **cullings** hugs.   **armed his head with horns** made him a cuckold.   **spiteful** (orig. spitful, with connotations lost in the modernizing).   **country manner** custom of the country.

"Mistress Dorothy, if the experience which I have learned in physic's art might crave credit and make my tale to be the better believed, assure yourself then that I mind to say nothing but that shall be to your own behoof,° and the reason that makes me to enter into this discourse is the pity that I take to see so proper a gentlewoman as yourself should be so deceived in a husband, who, although you shall find him both honest, gentle and loving, yea, and peradventure may content you with such rights as appertain to the marriage bed, yet assure yourself he shall never be able to get you with child, considering your natures and complexions° be so far different the one from the other, whereby you are like forever to remain without issue. And one of the greatest comforts that may happen unto us in this world is to see ourselves, as it were, regenerated and born anew in our children. And barrenness, in the ancient time, hath been accounted not only infamous, but also most hateful amongst women, insomuch that Sara gave her own handmaid to her husband because she could not herself conceive a child.[6] But I would wish women more wit than to follow Sara's example. God defend° they should be so foolish [as] to give their maidens to their husbands; I would wish them rather themselves to take their men. It hath been ever holden for the greater wisdom rather to take than to give,[7] and sure they shall find it more for their own profits that if their husband's want be such that he is not able to get a child, to take help of some other that may supply his imperfections. But I trust I shall not need to use many persuasions, considering that every wise woman will think that I have reason on my side. Thus, Mistress Dorothy, you have heard the sum of my tale, protesting that if my service may any ways stand you in stead, I am as ready to obey as he over whom you have power to command."

Mistress Dorothy, who all this while had well pondered his words, knew very well how to whet Master Doctor on, and the more to set his teeth on edge,° answered him thus: "I perceive, Master Doctor, you are something pleasantly disposed, and hereafter when I shall find my husband's infirmity to be such as you

behoof benefit.   complexions temperaments; the ensemble of the humors making up the physical constitution and personality of the individual.   defend forbid.   set his teeth on edge here, to whet his appetite.

have said, I mean to send for you, desiring you that you would not be out of the way to help me when I have need."

The doctor knew not well how to understand these words—whether they were merrily spoken or otherwise in disdain of his former talk—answered thus: "Alas Mistress Dorothy, pardon me if my words seem anything offensive unto you, assuring you that in this mean space that I have made my recourse to your husband—whose health, by the sufferance of God, I have now well restored—am myself fallen into a fever so extreme as neither Galen, Hippocrates, Avicenna, Pliny nor any other that ever gave rules of physic could yet prescribe a medicine for the malady or diet to suppress the humor that feeds it.[8] I shall not need to use long circumstance in the matter, knowing your wisdom to be such that you can well conceive the sum of all my grief. It is your beauty that is like to breed my bane, and hath already driven me into the greatest depth of danger, unless some plaints of pity may prevail to yield remorse to him that vows himself to do you service during life."

Mistress Dorothy, seeing the matter sorted out as she looked for, could tell well enough how to handle Master Doctor, and to make him the more eager, she delayed him off with doubtful speeches, but yet fed him still with such enticing and pleasant countenances that ministered great hope of comfort to his disease, she answered thus:

"And could you then find in your heart, Master Doctor, to deceive your very friend of his dear and loving wife? How can you offer him so manifest an injury, to whom you are so lately linked in so great a league of friendship as is between my husband and yourself. I cannot think, Master Doctor, that it is good will that hath caused you to move this suit unto me, but rather to see how I were disposed, or peradventure you use these words for exercise's sake, knowing the fashion of you men to be such as by praising of our beauty you think to bring us into a fool's paradise, that we will give credit straightway that you love us so soon as you shall but tell us the tale; but for my part, Master Doctor, although I want wit to encounter you with words, so likewise I want wit to believe anything that you have said to be otherwise than words of course."

These speeches did engender such a number of sweet and sour

alterations in Master Doctor that for his life he wist not how to understand them; one while they were like to drive him to despair, another while they something quieted him with hope, but in the end, determining to follow what he had begun, he said:

"Sweet mistress, most humbly I desire you to account of me,° not according to my deserts which as yet are none at all, but according to the dutiful service which hereafter I vow faithfully to do unto you. And for the better testimony of my words which, as you say, seem to be of such ordinary course, I desire no other credit may be given them than shall be agreeable to my deeds, when it shall please you to command. But alas for the injury which you speak of that I should offer to your husband, who indeed I make account to be my very friend, what is he, I pray you, that is able to prescribe laws to love? And as love is without law, so it is without respect, either of friend or foe, father or brother, rich or poor, mighty or weak, virtuous or vicious; the examples are so many and general that I should but waste the time to repeat them. But Mistress Dorothy, I protest the very cause that maketh me to move this matter unto you is for no ill will that I bear to your husband, but for the good will I bear to your sweet self. You may use your husband as your husband and me as your friend, glad to stand at reversion° when your husband may take his fill of the banquet and be glutted with more than enough. Further, if you make so great account of your husband's good liking as you say, what wives be ever better beloved or more made of by their husbands than those that have discretion to help their friends when they need? But what sottish opinion is this which so many doth hold, that they think it so great an injury for a man to seek the wife of his friend when he is attached by love, whose arrest° neither gods nor men have been ever able to resist. But I pray you, Mistress Dorothy, if I might ask you this question, would you not think your good will better bestowed upon your husband's friend than his foe? If you love your husband, I am sure you will say I have reason. What should I longer trouble you then with circumstances; I know you are wise, and now I desire

account of me consider me.   **stand at reversion** accept what is left after those with priority have been served.   **arrest** imprisonment, state of being captive to love.

you for the good will that you bear to your husband, to pity me his friend, whom I trust you will restore with one drop of mercy, and the rather for your husband's sake."

How think you, gentlewomen, be not these gentle persuasions to be used by a doctor? Marry he was no doctor of divinity and therefore you need not follow his doctrine unless you list◊ yourselves. But this pitiful gentlewoman, seeing Master Doctor at such desperate points, for fear of damning her own soul that so dear a friend to her husband as Master Doctor was should perish and be so wilfully cast away through her default, she received him for her friend, and so I pray God give them joy.

But it fortuned afterwards this gentlewoman to light into the company of a lawyer, who, perceiving this dame to be of such excellent beauty, joining himself something near her, he said: "Gentlewoman, although I have no skill in the art of painting, yet assure yourself your form and passing beauty is so surely engraven and fixed in my mind that although yourself were absent I could draw your perfect counterfeit,◊ saving that I think all the apothecaries in this city were not able to furnish me with colors to make the perfect distain◊ of the beauty in your face."

Mistress Dorothy, knowing whereto these speeches pretended, answered: "Indeed, sir, it should seem you would prove a passing painter that can so cunningly paint forth with words that which I know is too far unworthy of so excellent a flourish as you would give it."

"Mistress," quoth the lawyer, "if I have committed any offence in these words which I have spoken, it is in that I have taken upon me to praise your beauty, and not able to give it such due commendations as I see it doth deserve, the sight whereof doth so captivate my affections and hath so crippled all my senses that it hath caused me in manner to forget myself, no marvel then, though my tongue doth fail and is not able to express the perfection of you, unto whom with vow of continual service I subject my life, living and liberty, if it please you to accept of it."

list choose to.   counterfeit portrait.   distain imbue with color other than the natural one; he means a color so rare that it could not be counterfeited with dyes, but he comes close to saying the opposite.

This gentlewoman, that had yet but one friend to trust upon besides her husband, began to think that store was no sore° and therefore determined not to forsake his friendly offer. But first she demanded of him of his faculty and what trade of life he used, to which he answered that he was a gentleman appertaining to the law.

"It may well be so," quoth she, "for I perceive by your experience that this is not the first plea that you have framed."

"And yet believe me," quoth the lawyer, "I was never brought before to plead at beauty's bar. But since my hap is such, I humbly hold up my hands, desiring to be tried by your courtesy and mine own loyalty, contenting myself to abide such doom and judgement as it shall please you to appoint, being the chief and sovereign judge yourself."

She, replying, said: "Seeing you have constituted me to give sentence at my pleasure, it is not the office of a good justicer to be partial in his own cause, and therefore this is the hope that you shall look for at my hands, that if hereafter in your deeds I shall see as plain proof of perfect good will as your words by pretence import likelihood of earnest love, you shall find me ready to render such recompense as shall fall out to your own contentation and liking."

This comfortable answer very well pleased him, and within a very little space after, he so handled the matter that he had entered his action in her common place. Thus what between Master Doctor on the one side, who was still ministering of physic unto her so long as there were any drugs remaining in his storehouse, and the lawyer on the other side, who sufficiently instructed her with his law, they used such haunt unto this gentlewoman's company that the one began to grow suspicious on the other, and each of them desirous to have her several° to himself, began in the end to inveigh the one against the other: the doctor against the lawyer, and the lawyer against the doctor, and to tell her to her face what they suspected the one against the other. But Mistress Dorothy, being very angry with them both that would so narrowly look into her doings, did think it had been sufficient for

store was no sore having something in reserve was not a bad idea.
several separately, privately.

reasonable men that she had received them into her favor, and as often as it has pleased them to come she welcomed them as themselves did desire—and what can a man desire any more than to drink so often as he shall be a-thirst? But with fair speeches she contented them both for a time, but she thought in th'end to find a remedy for that mischief.

And thus it fell out that a soldier who was lately returned from the wars—I guess about the same time that King Henry the Fifth was returned from the winning of Agincourt field⁹—this soldier, I say, braving it about the streets of the city—as commonly the custom of soldiers is to spend more in a month than they get in a year—as he roamed to and fro and fortuned to espy this blazing star looking out at a window, was suddenly stricken into a great maze◇ to see this lamp of light than ever he had been in the field to see the ensigns of his enemies, and was so far overcharged with her love that but for fear to have been marked◇ by the passers-by, he would have stood still gazing and looking upon her; but learning in the end that she was the mistress of the house, he began to devise how he might make her understand the fervency of his love, on which he determined to write unto her. But then he knew not how to begin his letter, because soldiers are very seldom accustomed to endite, especially any of these loving lines. And to speak unto her, he was likewise to learn how to use his terms, neither wist◇ he how to come into her presence. But you shall see Fortune favored him, for in an evening as he passed through the street, she was sitting alone in her door to take the air, and coming unto her, not knowing for his life how to begin his tale, in the end: "Mistress," quoth he, "I pray you is your husband within?"

"No, surely, sir," quoth she, "he is abroad in the town, but I know not where."

"And I would gladly have spoken with him," quoth the soldier, "if he had been within."

"Believe me, sir, he is not within," quoth she, "but if it please you to leave your errand with me, at his coming home I will show him your mind."

great maze i.e. greater amazement.   **marked** noticed.   **wist** knew.

"In faith, mistress," quoth the soldier, "my errand is not great. I would but have craved his help in choosing me a wife because I perceive he hath some experience in the faculty, or else I think he could never have chosen so well for himself."

"If your errand be no other than this," quoth Mistress Dorothy, "you may at your own leisure come and do it yourself, and as for my husband's experience that you speak of, although peradventure it be not fitting to your fancy, yet I am well assured that he hath made his choice of such a one as he himself very well liketh."

"I believe it well," quoth the soldier, "and if without offence I might speak it, I swear so God help me, I like his choice so well that I would think myself more than a thousand times happy if I might be his half,◇ or if my unworthiness deserved not so great a portion, I would crave no more than yourself would willingly bestow on me according as you should see me able to deserve it."

"Why sir," quoth Mistress Dorothy, "I do not understand whereunto your speeches doth tend, neither what part you would have me to give you when I have already bestowed of my husband both my hand, my heart, my mind and good will."

"Alas, gentlewoman," quoth the soldier, "these be none of them that I would crave. There is yet an overplus which you have not yet spoken of, which if you please to bestow of a soldier, I should think myself the happiest man alive, whose love and good liking towards you is such that I trust in time to come yourself will judge me worthy for my well deserving zeal to have deserved hire."

"Soldiers are seldom seen," quoth Mistress Dorothy, "to march under the banner of Venus, but whatsoever you be, do you think to overthrow my virtues with the assault of your wanton persuasions, or would you make me believe that you love me as you say when you have no more respect to the hurt of my soul?"

"Gentlewoman," quoth the soldier, "I am not able to encounter you with words because it hath not been my profession nor training up, but if you doubt of my love and good liking, please it you to make trial. Command anything that yourself shall think requisite, which if I do not perform to the uttermost, then esteem my love indeed to be but feigned, and where you think that I go

might be his half might enjoy half what he enjoys.

about to seek the prejudice or hurt of your soul, believe me I never meant it."

Mistress Dorothy, who had been well acquainted before with many suitors, had never been apposed° with such a rough-hewn fellow that was so blunt and plain, as well in his gesture as in his terms, began to think with herself that he might well be a soldier, for she knew that they had little skill in the courting of gentlewomen. Yet she perceived by his countenance the vehemency of the love he bare unto her, and perceiving his plainness, she began to think him more fit for her diet than either Master Doctor or Master Lawyer, that could not be contented the one with the other when she gave them both so much as they could crave. And, therefore, thinking with herself that to lose any longer time were but a point of folly, taking the soldier by the hand, she led him up into a chamber where other speeches were passed between them in secret which I could never yet understand. And what they did farther when they were by themselves, gentlewomen, I pray guess you, but this I must advertise you of,° that before they came forth of the chamber again, the soldier had pleased Mistress Dorothy so well that both Master Doctor and Master Lawyer were put quite out of conceit, so that from that time forwards when they came of their visitation, the gentlewoman was not well at ease, or she had company with her, or she was not at home that they could no more speak with her, which turned them both into a wonderful agony. The doctor had thought she had forsaken him for the love of the lawyer; the lawyer he thought as much by the doctor, that in the end, not knowing otherwise how to spit out their venom against her, they devised each of them a letter which they sent her. The first of these letters delivered unto her came from the doctor, which letter he left unpointed° of purpose, because that in the reading of it, it might be pointed two ways, and made to seem either to her praise or dispraise; but Mistress Dorothy herself, in the reading of it, pointed it as I have set it down, and followeth in this sort:[10]

"And who would have thought, Mistress Dorothy, that for the loving advertisements° given you by your friend, you could so

apposed confronted.   advertise you of draw your attention to.
unpointed without punctuation.   advertisements attentions.

lightly have shaken him off. If I burdened you with anything that
might seem grievous unto you, think it was love that led me unto
it, for that I protest inwardly in my mind, I never did esteem
you otherwise than for as honest a gentlewoman as lives this day
in Bridewell.[11] I have heard say some have been scourged more
upon evil will than for any deserts whereof they might justly
be accused, so if it be my hap to suffer undeserved penance, I
must impute it to my own misfortune, but yet contrary to my
expectation, considering how I have ever taken you to be given in
your conditions to practice unseemly, filthy and detestable things.
I know you have ever abhorred to live chastely, decently and
orderly; you have ever been trained up to be wanton, proud and
incontinent; you never took delight in that [which] was good,
honest or commendable; you wholly gave yourself to lewdness,
lust and lechery; you were an open enemy to virtue, a friend to
vice. . . . What should I say? I do but waste the time in the
setting of you forth,° and therefore will leave you like as I found
you."

This letter brought Mistress Dorothy unto such a fury when
she had perused it that she swore by no beggars° she would be so
revenged upon the doctor that she would make him a spectacle
to all the physicians in the world, how they should abuse an
honest gentlewoman while they lived. And in the midst of her
melancholy, her dearest friend the soldier happened to come in,
whom she made partaker of all her secrets, showing him the letter
which Master Doctor had sent her; and as they were devising
how to use revengement, a messenger was knocking at the door
to deliver a letter from the lawyer, the tenor whereof followeth in
this manner:

"May this be the reward of my true and faithful love which so
firmly I have borne thee? Or is this the delight of thy dalliance
which so many times thou hast used with me, so carelessly to
shake me off, as though I had committed some notable abuse,
when indeed I have loved thee a great deal more than I perceive
thou art worthy of? O feminine flattery, O feigned fawning, O

setting of you forth giving a close description.   swore by no
beggars was so determined, that no amount of begging could change
her mind? (Cranfill, p. 297).

counterfeit courtesy, O deep dissimulation. But what hope is otherwise to be looked for in these kites° of Cressid's kind?[12] Or what constancy may any man think to find in a woman? No, no, if a man may generally speak of their sex, you shall never find them but counterfeit in their courtesy, feigned in their friendship, dissembling in their deeds, and in all their actions most dangerous for men to deal withal. For if she have a fair face, it is ever matched with a cruel heart; their heavenly looks with hellish thoughts, their modest countenances with merciless minds; they have wit but it is in wiles; if they love it is too vehement; when they hate it is to the death. But good God, with how many fopperies are they accustomed to feed fools, I mean such as be lovemakers and suitors unto them, whom they delay with as many devices as they be in number that seeks to serve them. Some they lure with looks, some they practice with promises, some they feed with flattery, some they delay with dalliance, some they wind in with wiles, some they keep with kisses, some they diet with dissimulation. One must wear her glove, another must wear her garter, another must wear her colors, another shall wear the spoil of as much as she can get from all the rest by cozenage,° and yet to see how dainty these darlings will seem to those that be not acquainted with their customs were able to dash a young man out of countenance.° I warrant you, they can make it more nice° than wise, more coy than comely, more fine than honest. And to whom do they make the matter most dangerous but to them that deserveth best to be rewarded, for where they see a man that is drowned in affection towards them, over him they will triumph, and can tell how to ride the fool without a snaffle.° One while they will cross him with froward° language, then again comfort him with some feigned look. Now she drives him into desperation with frowning face, by and by she baits him again with banquets of uncertain hope. Such is their evil nature, as I say, that they will show themselves most squeamish and dainty to him that loves them most entirely, and him that seeks them least dishonestly, him they reward with their coldest courtesy. For better

kites a bird of prey in the hawk family.   **cozenage** deception, cheating.   **countenance** composure.   **nice** foolish; wanton.
snaffle simple horse-bridle.   **froward** perverse.

proof, let a man seek to win one of these tender pieces that goes for a maid honestly and in the way of marriage, and I warrant you she will make the matter more coy and nice to him that means good earnest than to another that comes but to try and prove them. And what signs of shamefastness will they seem to make when a man doth but touch them, feigning themselves to be too young, when indeed if they once passed the age of fifteen years— if they were not afeared of breeding of bugs in their belly—by their good wills they would never be without the company of a man. Thus to conclude, their nature is openly to scorn all men, be their loves never so honest, and secretly to refuse no man, be his lust never so lewd. Full aptly did Solomon in his Proverbs compare you to wine that can make us so drunken with your devices, that notwithstanding we see the snares with our eyes which you have set to entangle us, we cannot shun the bait which we know will breed our bane.◊ Thus much, Mistress Dorothy, I have thought good to signify unto you whose discourtesy at this time hath caused me so generally to inveigh against your whole sex, not otherwise minding to accuse yourself particularly, knowing that if you should otherwise have used me than you have you should have digressed and swerved from your kind, and so I leave you."

Gentlewomen, I beseech you, forgive me my fault in the publishing this infamous letter; I promise you I do but signify it according to the copy which this unhappy lawyer sent to Mistress Dorothy. And when I had well considered the blasphemy that he had used against your sex, I cut my pen all to pieces wherewith I did copy it out, and if it had not been for the hurting of myself, I promise you I would have cut and mangled my own fingers wherewith I held the pen while I was writing of it; and trust me according to my skill, I could well have found in my heart to encounter him with an answer in your defence. But then I was interrupted by another, as you shall well perceive, for the soldier, which you have heard spoken of that was remaining with Mistress Dorothy, when he had perused this letter, was put into a wonderful chafe, and in the midst of his fury he uttered these words:

breed our bane cause our ruin.

"Ah most vile and blasphemous beast, what art thou that with such exclamations goest about to defame those whom by all honest humanity and manhood we be willed specially to love, honor and reverence, what art thou? A man, a devil, or a subtle lawyer, yea surely, and so thou mayest well be, and herein hast thou showed thyself no whit at all to digress from thy profession. For as at the first the laws were constituted to minister justice and to give every one his right, so now are they made by the practice of a number of pettifoggers◊ the instruments of all iniquity and wrong. Even so, that worthy sex which at the first were given unto man by the almighty God himself to be his chiefest comfort and consolation, see here the practice of a wicked caitiff, who with his eloquence would persuade us that they were our greatest ruin and desolations. Ah, wicked wretch that thou art, how thinkest thou to escape thus to blow forth thy blasphemy against those blessed ones whom God hath perfected above all other creatures? For at their first creation, they were made of the most best and purified mettle of man, where man himself was framed but of slime and dross.[13] What reason then that being at the first framed most pure and perfect creatures but that they should continue their first perfection to the end of the world. And like as at the first they were made more excellent than man, where should we now seek for grace, virtue and goodness, but only in the feminine sex according to their singular creation?

"I trust this is so evident that there is no man able to deny it, and enough to prove that as women at the first were created most perfect, so they have still remained the storehouse of all grace, virtue and goodness, and that if there be anything found in us men that is worthy of commendation, we are only to give thanks to women from whom we receive it, as being descended from out their entrails. But with how great and manifold miseries should we men be daily afflicted were it not for the comfort we find at women's hands. For besides that by their industry we be neatified,◊ made more cleanly and kept sweet, who otherwise of ourselves we should become to be most filthy and loathsome creatures, so at all times and seasons they be so necessary and

pettifoggers legal practitioners who engage in quibbling and caviling practices.   **neatified** to be made clean, orderly.

convenient about us that it were impossible for us to be without their blessed companies. First, in our health they content us with their familiarity, in our sickness they cherish us, in our mirth they make it more abound, in sorrow their company doth beguile our pensive thoughts, in pleasure they be our chief delights, in pain their presence breedeth comfort to our grief, in wealth what greater treasure than to enjoy our beloved, in want what greater wealth than a loving and faithful wife, in peace we labor still to get their liking, in wars they make us show ourselves more valiant. But how is it possible that women should behave themselves but that there are some that will find fault with them? First, if she be familiar we judge her to be light, if she seem anything strange in her conversation ah, we say, she is a dangerous dame, if merry we think her to be naught, if sad we say she is more grave than honest, if she be talkative we say she is a tattling housewife, if silent we say she is a sheep, if cleanly in her apparel we say she is proud, if plain or homely we say she is a dowdy or a slut, if they deny us their courtesy when we sue unto them we say they be cruel tigers, bears and bugs, if they have compassion of us we discredit them amongst our companions.[14]

"But see here the cunning of a caitiff that would wrest the words of Solomon to the dispraise of women because in his Proverbs he compareth them to wine; but to interpret the words of Solomon by Solomon himself, in another place of the same Proverbs, he willeth wine should be given to comfort those that be feeble and weak. Now compare these places together and see what harm he hath done to women, and, in my opinion, he could not more aptly have made a comparison, for as wine is a comfort to those that are feeble and weak, so are women our greatest solace both in sickness and in health. But if any will say that wine maketh us drunken, and from reasonable men to become more brute than beasts, I answer that the fault is not to be imputed to the wine but to the beastliness of him that taketh more than enough, for there is nothing so precious for our behoofs° but by our own abuse we make it seem most vile and loathsome. And thus granting Master Lawyer his comparison to be true, he hath done little hurt saving he hath showed himself a diligent scholar to his master the Devil,

behoofs use, benefit.

who is father of all lies, in maintaining so manifest a lie against such harmless creatures."

There were many other speeches pronounced by this soldier in the behalf of women which I have forgotten to recite. But I pray, gentlewomen, how like you by this soldier? Do you not think him worthy a sergeant's fee for his answer? In my opinion, you ought to love soldiers the better for his sake.

But to return to Mistress Dorothy, those two letters had so vexed her that there was nothing in her mind but how she might be revenged. Her friend the soldier promised for her sake that he would so cudgel both Master Doctor and the lawyer that they should not in one month after be able to lift their arms to their heads, saving he wist not how to get them into a place convenient, for it was dangerous to deal with them in the open streets. Mistress Dorothy, giving him twenty kisses for his courtesy, told him she would devise to bring them into some place where he might work his will.

Presently after, Mistress Dorothy sent for Master Doctor whom she knew very well how to handle, and in a mild manner she began greatly to blame him that being wise as she knew him to be would so rashly judge of her, for that he might well know that there was some great cause that moved her to use him as she had done otherwise than he had conjectured. And thus, with many other like speeches, she so smoothed the matter with Master Doctor that she made him believe her husband had some suspicion in their familiarity and that by his commandment she had abstained [from] his company for a time.

"The which, Master Doctor," quoth she, "I did for no evil will that I bear you, but for a time to blear my husband's eyes, thinking in the end so to have handled the matter that we might have continued our accustomed friendship without any manner of suspicion." And then drawing forth the letter which the Doctor had sent her, she said: "But see, Master Doctor, your good opinion conceived in me? Lo, here the reward that I have for my courtesy bestowed of you, thus to rail and rage against me as though I were the most notable strumpet in a country."

The doctor, knowing in what form he had wright° the letter, and desirous again to renew his late acquaintance, answered that
wright i.e. written.

he never writ letter unto her whereby he had given any occasion
for her to take any grief.

"No[t] have?" quoth Mistress Dorothy. "Read you then here
your own lines," taking him the letter which the doctor, as I told
you before, had left unpointed, and therefore in the reading he
pointed it after this manner:

"And who would have thought, Mistress Dorothy, that for the
loving advertisements° given you by your friend, you could so
lightly have shaken him off. If I burdened you with anything that
might seem grievous unto you, think it was love that led me unto
it, for that I protest inwardly in my mind, I did never esteem
you otherwise than for as honest a gentlewoman as lives this day.
In Bridewell, I have heard say, some have been scourged more
upon evil will than for any deserts whereof they might justly
be accused; so if it be my hap to suffer undeserved penance, I
must impute it to mine own misfortune, but yet contrary to my
expectation, considering how I have ever taken you to be given
in your conditions: to practice unseemly, filthy, and detestable
things, I know you have ever abhorred; to live chastely, decently
and orderly, you have ever been trained up; to be wanton, proud
and incontinent, you never took delight; in that was good, honest
or commendable, you wholly gave yourself; to lewdness, lust and
lechery, you were an open enemy; to virtue a friend; to vice. . . .
What should I say? I do but waste the time in the setting of you
forth, and therefore will leave you like as I found you."

"I pray you, Mistress Dorothy," quoth the doctor, "where is
this railing and raging you speak of? I trust I have written nothing that might discontent you."

Mistress Dorothy, perceiving the knavery of the doctor and
seeing the matter fall out so fit for her purposes, first giving him
a friendly buss° she said: "Alas my dear friend, I confess I have
trespassed in misconstruing of your lines. But forgive me I pray
you, and now have compassion of her whose love toward you is
such that it is impossible for me to live without your good liking.
And seeing that my husband's jealousy is so much that you can
have no longer access to my house but it must needs come to his
ear by such spy and watch as he hath laid, neither myself can

advertisements attentions.   buss kiss.

go abroad to any place but I am dogged and followed by such as he hath appointed. But now if your love be but half so much towards me as I trust I have deserved and hereafter do mean to requite, I have already devised a mean how forever I might enjoy my desired friend without either let or molestation of anyone, seem he never so much to be offended at the matter."

The doctor, the gladdest man in the world to hear these news, answered: "And what is it then that should make you stagger° or doubt of the friendship of your loving doctor, no not if thereby I should hazard the loss both of life and goods?"

"Alas," quoth Mistress Dorothy, "God defend I should work you so great a prejudice, and I beseech you use no more such speeches unto me that I should go about to put you into any such peril the remembrance whereof is more grievous unto me than if I had felt the force of a thousand deaths. And now behold my determination and what I have devised: you have a house not far hence standing in the fields which you keep for your solace and recreation in the time of summer. To this house I have devised how you may so secretly convey me that you may there keep me at your pleasure to your own use and to my great contentation, where I may at pleasure enjoy him more dearly beloved unto me than the balls of mine own eyes." And herewithal she gave him another Judas kiss that the doctor desired her of all friendship not to be long in her determination for that he was ready to follow her direction whensoever it would please her to command, yea, if it were presently he was ready.

Mistress Dorothy, who had driven the matter to that pass she looked for, said: "Nay, Master Doctor, there resteth yet another thing. My husband's jealousy, as I told you, is such that there must be great circumspection used in the conveying of me away, and therefore give ear to that I have devised: I have in my house a certain malle° with stuff° that is left with me to be sent by the carriers into the country, whereof my husband doth know very well. This stuff I will cause to be secretly taken forth and to be sent to the carriers trussed up in some other thing without any knowledge to any saving to my maid that shall work this

stagger hesitate.   **malle** (Fr. malle), trunk.   **stuff** a textile fabric, usually of wool.

feat herself, whose trustiness I know to be such as there is no suspicion to be had in the matter, the which, when she hath done, she shall truss up me in the same malle. Then see that you fail not tomorrow in the evening about eight-of-the-clock, disguised in a porter's weed, to come to my house to inquire for the same malle, which you shall say you will bear to the carriers. My maid, who shall of purpose be ready to wait for your coming at the hour, shall make no bones° to deliver you this malle, and thus without either doubt or jealousy of anyone, you may carry me into the fields where for your better ease you may take me forth, and disguising ourselves, we may walk together to your house aforesaid, where I may remain without any manner of suspicion or knowledge to any, so long as it shall please yourself."

"O most excellent device," quoth the doctor, "I have this matter already at my finger's ends, and I warrant you, you shall see me play the porter so cunningly that how many so ever I meet there shall none of them be able to suspect me." Thus with a feigned kiss that she again bestowed of him, for that time they departed.

Mistress Dorothy in like manner sent for the lawyer, whom she handled in like sort as she had done the doctor, making him believe that her husband's jealousy was such as she durst no more come in his company. But of herself she loved him so entirely that she would hazard anything for his sake, and because he should the better believe it, "tomorrow," quoth she, "in the afternoon, my husband will be forth of the doors, wherefore I pray you fail not about three-of-the-clock to come and visit me when we shall have leisure to disport ourselves to our better contentation."

Many like enticing words she used, which so persuaded the lawyer, then dreading no bad measure at all, he promised her not to fail but he would keep his hour and thus departed very joyful that he had again recovered his mistress. And the next day, even as it had struck three-of-the-clock, he was knocking at the door of this gentlewoman, who, looking for his coming, was ready to receive him, and up they go to a chamber which she had appointed for the purpose, where for a time she dallied him off with devices. And suddenly her maid, according as her

make no bones make no objections, scruples.

mistress had given her instruction, came hastily to the chamber door, calling her mistress, saying that her master was come in and had asked for her. Mistress Dorothy, who was not to learn to play her part,[◊] seemed to be stricken into a wonderful fear.

"Alas," quoth she to the lawyer, "for the love of God keep yourself secret for a time, that I may go down and rid him away, if it be possible," and thus going her way down, she shuts the door after her.

The lawyer, who was ready to beray[◊] himself for fear, crept under the bed where she let him alone the space of an hour, and then coming up into the chamber and could not see him, she began to muse what was become of him. He, hearing one was come in at the chamber door, began to pry[◊] out under the bed's feet, and, perceiving by the skirt of her gown who it was, with a faint voice he said: "Alas, my dear, what news? Is your husband gone?"

"Ah my loving friend," quoth she, "I was never so hardly beset sith I was born. My husband is come home with three or four of his friends, which he met withal in the city, and be come out of the country of purpose to make merry with him, and here they be appointed to sup, and hither be come to their beds so long as they remain in the city, and this chamber is appointed for two of them to lie in that for my life I know not what shift[◊] to make nor how to convey you hence."

"Alas," quoth the lawyer, "then am I utterly undone. For the love of God, devise some means to convey me out of the house, for I would not remain all night in this perplexity,[◊] no not for all the gold in the world."

Mistress Dorothy, making a little pause, suddenly as though she had an invention but even then come in to her head, she said: "I have this only remedy left. Here is in the house a malle full of stuff which should this night be sent to the carriers; my device is therefore to take forth the stuff and lay it aside till sometime the next week when I will make shift to send the stuff away very well, and you shall be presently packed up in this malle, which my

---

part needed no coaching on how to act.   beray (orig. beraie) here, befoul or beshit.   pry peer.   shift contrivance, trick. perplexity trouble, distress.

maid shall do while I am below with my husband and his friends. And so causing a porter to be sent for, he shall carry you to your chamber, or to any other place where it shall please yourself, so that my husband, seeing this malle go forth of doors, will think it is the stuff which he knoweth this night should be sent."

"No better device in the world," quoth the lawyer, "and let the porter convey this malle to my chamber, you know where, and deliver it to my man as sent from his master, and will him to give him forty pence for his labor."

The matter thus determined, Mistress Dorothy sent up her maid with this empty malle wherein she trussed up the lawyer, and there she left him lying from five-of-the-clock until it was past eight. And in the summer season, the weather being very hot, the lawyer had like to have been smothered where he lay. At the length, according to pointment,° comes Master Doctor disguised like a right porter with a long gaberdine down to the calf of his legs,[15] and he inquires for a malle that should go to the carriers.

"Yea marry," quoth the maid, "if you please to come in, it is ready for you."

The doctor, being a good sturdy lubber, took up the malle very easily for fear of hurting the gentlewoman's tender ribs whom he had thought he had upon his back, and thus forth of doors he goes, taking the next way towards his lodging.

Mistress Dorothy, with her beloved soldier whom she had made privy to her device, stood where she might see Master Doctor in his porter's weed° going with his carriage, whereat when they had awhile sported themselves, the soldier followed Master Doctor an easy pace, but only to keep the sight of him, and the doctor took his way through the streets with a main° pace till he had recovered the fields where, looking about him to see what company was stirring, saw nobody near him but the soldier, whom he did not know, and then, crossing the way from the common paths, he came to the side of a bank, and being weary—as he was not to be blamed considering the knavish burden that he had borne upon his back—he, laying down the malle tenderly upon the side of the bank, seeing nobody but the soldier who was but a little

pointment the time appointed.   **weed** clothes.   **main** vigorous.

distance from him, said: "Ah, my sweet wench, I can see no creature stirring in all the fields but one man which is coming this way, who so soon as he is past, I will undo this malle."

The lawyer in the malle, when he felt the porter lay him down, was in a good hope that he had been in his own chamber, but hearing by these speeches that he was in the fields, began to conjecture assuredly that the porter had spoken those words to some woman that was in his company with whom he was confederate for the stealing of such things as they should find in the malle, and that when they should open the malle and find him there, they would not stick to cut his throat for fear lest he should bewray° them, and for the only spoil of such things as he had about him, that the lawyer was in such a perplexity that he wist not for his life what he might do. One while he had thought to have cried out for help. Then he thought it would the sooner bring him to his end. And as he continued thus in the midst of his muse, the soldier was come to the place, and, speaking to the doctor, he said: "Porter it seemeth thou hast been knavishly laden, for I perceive thou art very hot. But what hast thou in thy malle, I pray thee, that thou art carrying this way so late in the evening?"

"Marry," quoth the doctor, "I have ware there such as it is."

"Hast thou ware, knave?" quoth the soldier. "Is that a sufficient answer?" "What ware is it, men's ware or women's ware?"

"Sir, I know not," quoth the porter, "I have but the carrying of it to a gentleman's house that is here hard by." "Well," quoth the soldier, "undo your truss, for I will see what wares you have there, before you and I depart."

"Why sir," quoth the porter, "should I be so bold to undo a gentleman's malle that is delivered me in trust to be carried? No, sir, you shall pardon me,° [even] if you were my father."

And here withal he took the malle upon his back and began to go his ways. But the soldier, knowing better what was in the malle than the porter himself that carried it, and being provided for the purpose with a good cudgel, let drive half a dozen blows at the malle as it lay upon his back, so surely that the lawyer cries out, "alas, alas, alas."

bewray betray.   **pardon me** not make me do this.

"Why, porter," quoth the soldier, "have you quick° wares in your malle? No marvel you were so dainty in the showing of it."

Herewithal the doctor laid down his malle, and kneeling down to the solder, said: "Ah, sir, for the love of God be content and I will not let° to confess the whole truth unto you; I have a gentlewoman in my malle which I have stolen from her husband, and seeing you to be a gentleman but young in years, and impossible but that you should love the company of a fair woman, behold, I will deliver her unto you to use at your pleasure, and when you shall see time to restore her unto me again, desiring you sir, of all courtesy, to seek no other displeasure against us."

"You have said well," quoth the soldier, "but is she such a one as to be liked—fair, fresh, and young?"

"Trust me, sir," quoth the doctor, "if she be not as fair and well liking as any dame within the walls of this city, make me an example to all other how they shall dissemble with a gentleman such as you are."

"Thou sayest well," quoth the soldier, "and now I think [it] long till I have a sight of this paragon which thou hast so praised unto me."

"You shall see her straightway," quoth the doctor.

And here withal he began to unlace the malle with much expedition, which when he had unloosed at the one end that he might come to the sight of this gentlewoman's face, as he had thought, he said to the soldier: "See here the sight which you so much desire."

And pulling the end of the malle open with his hands, the lawyer thrust forth his head and looked with such a piteous countenance as though he had been ready to be turned off the ladder.° But the doctor, seeing a face to appear with a long beard, was in such a maze that he could not tell in the world what he might say. The soldier, who had never more ado than to forbear laughter to see how these two the one beheld the other, said to the doctor: "And is this the fair gentlewoman that thou hast promised me? Hast thou nobody to mock but me, that with such commendations thou givest praise to a woman whereby to set my teeth an

quick live.   let refuse.   turned off the ladder hung.
set my teeth an edge whet my appetite.

edge° and then in the end thus delude me? But I will teach thee
how to play the knave again while thou livest." And herewithal
he laid on with his cudgel, sparing neither head, shoulders, arms,
back nor breast, and so be-bumbasted° the doctor that for the
space of a quarter of a year after he was not able to lift an urinal°
so high as his head.

The lawyer, who had nothing out of the malle but his head,
seeing this fray, struggled so much as he could to have got forth
and to have run away while the porter was a-beating,° but it
would not be. His arms were so surely laced down by his sides
that for his life he could not get them forth.

The soldier, when he had thoroughly requited Master Doctor's
knavery that he had used against his beloved mistress in his letter,
left him, and began to bend himself towards the lawyer. The
lawyer, seeing the soldier coming, had thought verily that he had
been some goodfellow° that was walking there so late, to have
taken some prey, said: "O Sir, for the love of God spare my life,
and take my purse."

To whom the soldier answered, "Nay, villain, my coming is
neither to take thy life nor thy purse, but to minister revengement
for thy large speeches, which like a discourteous wretch thou hast
used against a woman," and therewithal laid upon him so long as
he was able to fetch any breath, and then calling the porter unto
him, he said: "Let these words which I mind to speak suffice for a
warning to you both: if ever I may learn that any of you hereafter
this do use any misdemeanor towards any woman, either by word
or writing, assure yourselves that although I have but dallied with
you at this time, I will devise some one mean or other to minister
revenge, that all such as you be shall take an example by you,
and thus I leave you," going his way to his sweetheart—telling her
the whole discourse how he had sped—by whom he was welcomed
with a whole last° of kisses etc.

And now to return to those two that were left in the fields,
as you have heard. The doctor, taking good view of the lawyer,

---

be-bumbasted soundly beat.   **urinal** a doctor's flask for examining urine, then a basic medical practice.   **a-beating** being beaten.
goodfellow thief.   **last** a unit of measure, in all commodities
different, but always a large quantity or number.

knew him very well, but the doctor was so disguised in his porter's apparel that the lawyer did not know him, but said unto him: "A mischief light of all such porters that when they be put in trust with carriages into the city will bring them into the fields to such banquets as these."

"Marry," quoth the doctor, "a mischief take all such burthens that when a man hath almost broken his back with bearing them and then shall receive such a recompense for his labor as I have done."

"Villain," quoth the lawyer, "why didst thou not carry me to my chamber as thou wert willed when thou didst receive me?"

"I would I had carried thee to the gallows," quoth the doctor, "so I had escaped this scourging. But I perceive the banquet was prepared for us both," and herewithal with much ado he got off the porter's coat, and making himself known unto the lawyer, each of them conferred with the other how cunningly they had been dealt withal, and did think it not best for them any further to deal in the matter for fear of further mischief, but with much ado got them home where the lawyer kept his bed very long after. But the doctor took spermaceti° and such like things that be good for a bruise and recovered himself in a short space.

Now it fell out afterwards that this soldier, who lived in great credit with Mistress Dorothy, as he had well deserved, was employed in the king's wars against foreign foes with a great number of others, where he spent his life in his prince's quarrel. And Mistress Dorothy, sorrowing a long time the loss of so faithful a friend, seeing the diversity of men, that she had made her choice amongst three and had found but one honest, feared to fall into any further infamy, contented herself to live orderly and faithfully with her husband all the rest of her life. And her husband, who never understood any of these actions, loved her dearly to his dying day.

And now to say something of the other brother and his wife, which as you have heard was such a notable scold that her husband could never enjoy a good day nor merry hour. She was such a devil of her tongue and would so crossbite him with such taunts and spiteful quips as, if at any time he had been merry in

spermaceti substance found in sperm whales, used medicinally.

her company, she would tell him his mirth proceeded rather in the remembrance of that she had brought him than for any love that he had to herself. If he were sad, it was for grief she was not dead, that he might enjoy that she had. If he used to go abroad, then he had been spending of that he never got himself. If he tarried at home, she would say it was happy he had gotten such a wife that was able to keep him so jolly. If he made any provision for good cheer or to fare well in his house, she would bid him spend that which he himself had brought. If he showed himself to be sparing, then she would not pinch° of that which was her own. Thus, do what he could, all that ever he did was taken in the worst part. And seeing that by no manner of fair means he was able to reclaim her, in the end he devised this way: himself, with a trusty friend that he made of his counsel, got and pinioned her arms so fast that she was not able to undo them, and then putting her into an old petticoat which he rent and tattered in pieces of purpose, and shaking her hair loose about her eyes, tore her smock sleeves that her arms were all bare, and scratching them all over with a bramble that the blood followed, with a great chain about her leg wherewith he tied her in a dark house° that was on his backside,° and then calling his neighbors about her he would seem with great sorrow to lament his wife's distress, telling them that she was suddenly become lunatic, whereas by his gesture he took so great grief as though he would likewise have run mad for company.° But his wife, as he had attired her, seemed, indeed, not to be well in her wits, but, seeing her husband's manners, showed herself in her condition to be a right bedlam.° She used no other words but cursings and bannings,° crying for the plague and the pestilence, and that the Devil would tear her husband in pieces. The company that were about her, they would exhort her, "Good neighbor, forget these idle speeches which doth so much distemper you, and call upon God and he will surely help you."

she would not pinch she would be generous (B. she would not be pinched).   dark house darkness was part of the treatment for lunatics, and some asylums were kept dark.   backside perhaps a house at the rear of their dwelling.   for company to keep her company.   bedlam an insane person so-called after the name of the asylum near London: Bethlehem Hospital.   bannings chidings, angry language.

"Call upon God for help?" quoth the other. "Wherein should he help me, unless he would consume this wretch with fire and brimstone. Other help I have no need of."

Her husband, he desired his neighbors for God's love that they would help him pray for her, and thus altogether kneeling down in her presence, he began to say *Miserere*° which all they said after him. But this did so spite and vex her that she never gave over her railing and raging against them all. But in the end, her husband who by this shame had thought to have reclaimed her, made her to become from evil to worse, and was glad himself in the end clean to leave and to get himself from her into a strange country where he consumed the rest of his life.

Thus to conclude, besides the matter that I mean to prove, men may gather example here when they go a-wiving not to choose for beauty without virtue, nor for riches without good conditions. There be other examples if they be well marked, worth the learning, both for men and women, which I leave to the discretion of the reader.

Miserere one of the penitential psalms beginning "Have mercy upon me, O God".

OF GONSALES AND
HIS VIRTUOUS WIFE AGATHA

The Argument of the Sixth History.

Gonsales,[1] *pretending*° *to poison his virtuous wife for the love of a courtesan, craved the help of Alonso, a scholar something practiced in physic, who in the stead of poison gave him a powder which did but bring her in a sound sleep during certain hours; but Gonsales, judging indeed that his wife had been dead, caused her immediately to be buried. The scholar, again knowing the operation of his powder, for the great love he bare to Agatha, went to the vault where she was entombed about the hour that he knew she should awake, when after some speeches used between them, he carried her home to his own house where she remained for a space. In the meantime Gonsales, being married to his courtesan, was by her accused to the governor for the poisoning of his first wife, whereof being apprehended he confessed to the fact and was therefore judged to die, which being known to Agatha, she came to the judge, and clearing her husband of the crime, they lived together in perfect peace and amity.*

There was sometime in the city of Seville in Spain a gentleman named Gonsales, who, though he were a man of years sufficient

pretending intending.

to be staid and to give over the wanton pranks of youthful folly, yet was he by nature so inclined to follow his lusts, and withal so variable and so unconstant, that he suffered° himself to be ruled wholly by his passions, and measured all his doing rather by his delights and pleasures than by sound discourse and rule of reason. This gentleman, falling in love with a gentlewoman of the said city whose name was Agatha, sought all the means he could to have her to wife. And her friends, although they were well enough informed of the disposition of Gonsales whereby they might have feared the entreaty of their kinswoman, for that they knew him very rich and her dowry not to be very great, they were well content to bestow her upon him, and thought that they had, in so doing, placed her very well. But before the first year of their marriage was fully expired, Gonsales, following his wonted° humor and waxing° weary of love, grew to desire change, giving thereby a notable example for women to learn how little it is to their commodity° or quiet to match themselves to such that be rather rich than wise, and how much it were better for them to be married to men than to their goods.

For being come to sojourn in that street wherein he dwelt, a notable courtesan, who to the outward show was very fair though inwardly she was most foul, as she that under a goodly personage did cover a wicked and dangerous mind, corrupted with all vices, as for the most part all such women do. It was Gonsales' chance to be one of the first that fell into those snares which she had set for such simple° men's minds as haunt after the exterior appearance of those things which their senses make them to delight in, and not considering the danger whereunto they commit themselves by following of their disordinate appetites, do suffer themselves to be entrapped by such lewd dames, among which this, forsooth, was one that was of singular skill to captive men's minds, which by experience and by the natural disposition of her mind bent wholly to deceit and naughtiness, had learned a thousand guiles and arts which way to allure men with the pleasantness of her baits. Wherefore, after he was once entangled with her snares, he fell so far beyond all reason and past all belief to dote upon this

suffered permitted.   **wonted** usual.   **waxing** growing.
commodity advantage, profit.   **simple** foolish, unintelligent.

strumpet, that he could find no rest nor no contentment but so long as he was with her. But she, being as dissolute a dame as any lived in the world and as greedy likewise of gain as ever any was of her profession, would not content herself with Gonsales alone, but yielded unto as many as list to enjoy her if they came with their hands full and spared for no cost to reward her liberally— which thing was unto him that was so besotted on her so grievous and intolerable that nothing could be more.

There was at that same time a scholar in the city that studied physic with whom Gonsales had familiar acquaintance, and the scholar thereby having access and conversation° in his house began so fervently to be in love with Agatha his wife that he desired nothing so earnestly in the world as to enjoy her and to win her good will. Wherefore having, as I have said, free access to her house and to declare his affection unto her without suspicion, he ceased not by all the means he was able to devise to solicit and to procure her to yield unto his desire. With his endeavor and earnest suit, although it were unto Agatha noisome and displeasant as she that was disposed to keep herself honest, and that she could in that respect have been very glad that he would forbear to frequent her house, yet knowing her husband to be a man of no very great substance and but slenderly stuffed in the headpiece, and that he delighted greatly in the familiarity of the scholar, she forced herself to endure with patience the importunate molestation which he still wearied her withal, taking from him nevertheless all hope to obtain at any time any favor at her hands, and cutting him short from all occasions as much as she could whereby he might have cause either to molest her, or to look for anything to proceed from her that were less than honest.

The scholar, perceiving that his own travail to win her affection was but labor lost, thought best to try if by the allurement or persuasion of any other he might haply° move her to show herself more courteous and favorable unto him. Wherefore having found out an old mother Eleanor, a disciple of the Spanish Celestina[2]—such a one as was most cunning and skilful in mollifying of women's minds to work them afterward to receive the impressions of their lovers—he caused her to take acquaintance of

conversation close social affiliation.   **haply** by chance.

Agatha, and by degrees, as though she had been moved with pity and compassion of her case, to declare unto her the love which her husband bare unto the courtesan, and to show her how unworthy he was that she should be true unto him. And in the end, passing from one speech to another, she said plainly unto her that it was a great folly, since her husband did take his pleasures abroad with other women, to stand to his allowances and to take the leaving of his strumpets, and therewith to be content; and that if she were in her case and had a husband that would strike with the sword, she would undoubtedly requite him and strike with the scabbard, so she counselled her to do likewise.

Agatha, being a very discreet gentlewoman and loving her husband as an honest gentlewoman ought to do, said to her in answer of her talk that she would be right glad to see her husband be such a man as she wished him to be and as he ought to be. But that since she saw it would not be and that he could not frame° himself thereto, she would not take from him or bar him of that liberty which either the custom of the corrupted world or the privilege that men had usurped unto themselves had given unto them, and that she would never, for her part, violate or break that faith which she had given him, nor slack or neglect that care and regard of her honor which all women by kind and nature ought to have as the thing that maketh them to be most commended throughout the world, let her husband do what he list, and like and love as many other women as pleased him. And that she thought herself so much the rather bound so to do, because he did not in the rest misuse her [in] any way, or suffer her to want anything that reasonably she could desire or crave at his hands; and for that she had not brought him in effect any other dowry worthy to be accounted of than her honesty, wherefore she was fully resolved never to vary from that constant resolution. And finally, showing herself somewhat moved and stirred with choler, she told her that she marveled at her not a little that being a woman of those years, that she should rather reprehend and chide young folk if she should see them so bent, than encourage them to evil, and mused much she could find in her heart to give her such counsel, which she assured her was so displeasant and

frame adapt, adjust.

so ungrateful as if from henceforth she durst presume to speak thereof any more, she would make her understand perchance to her smart° how ill she could away with such panderly practices.

This old hag, having had her head washed thus without soap,° departed from Agatha and came unto the scholar and told him in brief how ill she had sped° and in what sort the honest gentlewoman had closed her mouth, whereof the scholar was very sorry. Yet for all this, he thought he would not give over his pursuit, imagining that there is no heart so hard or flinty but by long love, by perseverance, prayer, and tears, may in the end be mollified and wrought to be tender.

In this mean season Gonsales, still continuing his old familiarity with the scholar, and having made him privy of° the love he bare unto the courtesan and what a grief it was unto him to see her enjoyed by any other than by himself, one day among other talk between them of that matter, he said unto the scholar that it never grieved him so much to have a wife as it did then, for that if he had been unmarried he would have taken Aselgia°—for so was the courtesan named—to be his wife, without whom he could find no rest nor quiet in mind. And so long as every man hath a share with him in her, he accounted himself as ill as if he had had no part in her at all, and thereto said further, that assuredly if it were not for fear of the law, he would ease himself of that burden by ridding of Agatha out of the world. Thereunto replied the scholar, saying that indeed it was a grievous thing for a gentleman to be cumbered with a wife whom he could not find in his heart to love, and that in such a case he that did seek the best way he could to deliver himself of that yoke was not altogether unexcusable, though the rigor of justice had appointed severe punishments for such as violently should attempt or execute any such thing, but that men that were wise could well enough find out the means which way to work their intents without incurring any danger of the law for the matter. Which language indeed he used unto him but to feed his humor and to

smart pain, penalty.   head washed thus without soap proverbial, meaning "having been well scolded" (Cranfill, p. 309), submitted to insult.   sped fared, succeeded.   privy of party to, informed of.   Aselgia (Gr.) unchaste, in opposition to Agatha, chaste.

see whereunto that talk in fine° would tend. And according to his desire, before it was long Gonsales, having used the like speeches two or three times and still finding him to soothe° his saying, took one day a good heart unto him and brake his mind unto the scholar at large and in plain terms to this effect:

"Alonso," for that was the scholar's name, "I do assure myself, and make full account that thou art my fast friend as I am thine, and I doubt not but that the friendship which is between us doth make thee no less sorry than myself to see me grieve with this continual trouble of mind wherein I live, because I cannot compass to take this woman whom I love so dearly to be my wife and by that means come to have the full possession of her unto myself, which is the thing I do desire above all other things in the world. And forasmuch as I do persuade myself that by thy means and with the help of thy profession I may hap to find some remedy for my grief, I have thought good to tell thee a conceit° which I have thought on oftentimes, wherein I mean to use thee and thy assistance for the better accomplishment of my purpose in that behalf. Assuring myself that thou wilt not refuse or deny me any furtherance that thy skill may afford me, or shrink and draw back from the performing of any friendly offer whereby I may come to find° some ease of mind and be delivered of that intolerable torment of spirit wherewith I am oppressed for the love of this Aselgia in whom I have fixed and set all my joys and delights. Thou shalt therefore understand that I am determined as soon as I can possible, to rid my hands of Agatha my wife, and by one mean or other to cause her to die, and I have been a good while° about the execution of this my intent. But because I could never yet devise the best way to perform it so that her death might not be laid unto my charge, I have delayed it hitherto, and perforce content to bear the heavy burden of my grieved mind till now, which henceforward I am resolved to bear no longer. If thou wilt, according to my trust in thee and as the friendship which is between us doth require, grant me thy furtherance and helping hand. Wherefore, knowing that through thy long study in physic

in fine in the end.   **soothe** argue as true, confirm.   **conceit** idea, device.   **come to find** (A. come by to find; reading from C.). **been a good while** (A. been a this good while; reading from C.).

thou hast attained so great knowledge that thou canst devise a number of secrets whereof any one might be sufficient to bring my purpose to effect, I do require thee to fulfil my desire in that behalf and to give me thy help to bring this my desire to pass—which if thou do, I will acknowledge myself so long as I shall live to be so much bound unto thee that thou shalt command me and all that I have in any occasion of thine as freely and as boldly as thou mayest now anything that is thine own."

The scholar, when he had heard Gonsales and his demand, stood still awhile as musing upon the request, and in the meanwhile discoursed with himself how by the occasion of this intent and resolution of Gonsales he might perhaps find out a way to come by the possession of Agatha, and to have her in his hands and at his devotion. But, keeping secret his thoughts and meaning, he made him answer,◊ that true it was that he wanted not secret compositions◊ to make folk die with poison so as it could never be discerned by any physician, or other, whether the cause were violent or no, but that for two respects he thought it not good to yield unto his request. The one, for that physic and physicians were appointed in the world not to bereave men of their lives but to preserve them, and to cure them of such diseases as were dangerous and perilous unto them. The other, because he did foresee in what jeopardy he should put his own life whensoever he should dispose himself to work any such practice, considering how severely the laws have prescribed punishments for such offenses. And that it might fall out, how warily soever the thing were wrought, that by some seldom or unlooked-for accident, the matter might be discovered—as for the most part it seemeth that God will have it—in which case he were like to incur no less danger than Gonsales, and both assured without remission to lose their lives. And that therefore he would not, for the first respect, take upon him to do that which was contrary to his profession, nor for the second, hazard his life to so certain a danger—for so hateful a thing as those practices are to all the world.

Gonsales, very sorry to hear his denial, told him that the laws and duties of friendship doth dispense well enough with a man,

made him answer answered him.   **compositions** (A. compassions; reading from B.).

though for his friend he strain sometime his conscience, and therefore he hoped that he would not forsake him in a cause that
concerned° him so weightily as that did. And that neither of
those two respects, if they were well considered, ought to be able
to remove him from pleasuring of his friend. For that nowadays,
as well were they accounted and esteemed physicians that killed
their patients as they that did cure them, and because the thing
being kept secret between them two alone, he needed not to doubt
or fear any danger of his life by the law. For if it should by any
mischance happen that he should be imputed or burdened° with
poisoning of his wife, he assured him that he would never whilst
he had breath confess of whom he had the poison, but would
rather suffer his tongue to be pulled out of his head, or endure
any torment that might be devised.

The scholar, at the last seeming to be won by the earnestness
of his petition, said that upon that condition and promise of not
revealing him at any time, he would be content rather to show
himself friendly unto him than [be] a true professor of his science
or an exact regarder of his conscience, and that he would do as
he would have him.

And having left Gonsales very glad and joyful for that his
promise, he went home and made a certain composition or mix-
ture of powders, the virtue whereof was such that it would make
them that took any quantity thereof to sleep so soundly that they
should, for the space of certain hours, seem unto all men to be
stark dead. And the next day he returned to Gonsales to deliver
it° unto him, saying: "Gonsales, you have caused me to do a
thing I protest I would not do for my life.° But since you may
see thereby that I have regarded more your friendship than my
duty or the consideration of that which is honest and lawful, I
must require you eftsoons° to remember your promise, and that
you will not declare to any creature living that you have had this
poison of me."

Which thing Gonsales very constantly upon his oath did promise
him again, and having taken the powder of him, asked him in

concerned (orig. concern).   **burdened** charged.   **to deliver it**
(orig. and to deliver it).   **do for my life** (orig. do it for my life).
eftsoons afterward.

what sort he was to use it. And he told him that if at supper he did cast it there upon her meat or into her broth, she should die that night following without either pain or torment, or any grievous accidents,[◊] but go away even as though she were asleep. That evening at suppertime Gonsales failed not to put the powder into his wife's potage, who, having taken it, as soon as supper was done, feeling herself very heavy and drowsy, went to her chamber and got her to bed—for she lay not with Gonsales but when he list to call her, which had been very seldom since he did fall into love with the strumpet—and within an hour after, the operation of the powder took such force in her body that she lay as though she had been dead and altogether senseless. Gonsales in like sort when he saw his time went to his bed, and lying all that night with a troubled mind, thinking what would become of Agatha and what success his enterprise would take, the morning came upon him before he could once close his eyes, which being come he rose, not doubting but that he should assuredly find his wife dead as Alonso had promised him. And as soon as he was up he went out of his house and stayed but an hour abroad, and then he returned home again and asked of his maid whether her mistress were up or no. The maid made him answer that she was yet asleep, and he, making as though he had marveled at her long lying in bed, demanded her how it happened that she was so sluggish that morning, contrary to her custom, which was to rise every morning by break of the day, and had her go and wake her for he would have her to give him something that lay under her keys.[◊] The wench, according to her master's commandment, went to her mistress' bedside, and having called her once or twice somewhat softly, when she saw she waked not, she laid her hand upon her, and giving her a shag,[◊] she said withal, "Mistress awake, my master calleth for you." But she lying still and not awakening for all that the maid took her by the arm and began to shake her good and hard, and she notwithstanding neither answering nor stirring hand or foot, the maid returned to her master and told him that for aught she could do she could not get her mistress to awake. Gonsales, hearing the maid to say so, was glad in his

accidents unfavorable symptoms.   lay under her keys that she had under lock and key.   shag shake.

mind. But feigning himself to be busied about somewhat else and that he regarded little her speech, he bid her go again and shake her till she did waken. The maid did so, and rolled and tumbled her in her bed, and all in vain. Wherefore coming again unto her master, she said unto him that undoubtedly she did believe that her mistress his wife was dead, for she had found her very cold, and rolled her up and down the bed, and that yet she stirred not.

"What? Dead?" quoth Gonsales, as if he had been all aghast and amazed, and rising therewithal, he went to her bed's side and called her, and shaked her, and wrung her by the fingers, and did all that might be, as he thought, to see whether she were alive. But she, not feeling anything that he did, lay still like a dead body, or rather like a stone.

Wherefore, when he saw his purpose had taken so good effect, to dissemble the matter he began to cry out and to lament and to detest his cruel destiny that had so soon bereaved him of so kind, so honest, and so faithful a wife. And having in the end discovered° her body, and finding no spot or mark whereby any token or sign of poisoning might be gathered, as one that would not seem to omit any office of a loving husband, he sent for the physician to look upon her, who, having used some such means as he thought meet° to make her come to herself, finally, seeing her to remain unmovable and without sense, concluded that some sudden accident had taken her in the night whereof she had died, and for dead he left her.

At which his resolution, though Gonsales were very glad, yet to the outward show declaring himself to be very sorry and full of woe and heaviness, he behaved himself in such cunning sort as he made all the world believe that he would not long live after her. And having called her friends and lamented with them her sudden death and his misfortune, in fine, he caused her funeral to be very sumptuously and honorably prepared, and buried her in a vault which served for a tomb to all his ancestors, in a church of a friary that stands without the city.

Alonso, that was very well acquainted with the place, and had himself a house not very far from that friary, went his way that same night unto his said house, and when he saw the time to

discovered undressed.   meet useful, appropriate.

serve for his purpose, he got him to the vault or tomb wherein Agatha was laid with one of these little lanterns that they call blind lanterns, because they turn them and hide their light when they list.[3] And because he was a young man of very good strength and had brought with him instruments of iron to open the tomb and lift up the stone that covered it, he got it open, and having under-propped it surely, he went into the vault and took the woman straightway in his arms, minding to bring her out and carry her away, so asleep as she was. But the force and virtue of the powder being finished and spent, as soon as he moved her she awakened out of her sleep, and seeing herself clad in that sort among rags and dead bones, she began to tremble and to cry:

"Alas where am I? Or who hath brought me hither, wretch that I am?"

"Marry, that hath your cruel and unfaithful husband," answered the scholar, "who, having poisoned you to marry a common strumpet, hath buried you here, whither I came to try if by my skill I could revive you and call back your soul, by those remedies which I had devised, unto your body again, which if I could not have done as I intended, I was resolved to have died here by you and to have laid my dead body here by yours to rest until the latter day,◊ hoping that my spirit should in the meanwhile have come and enjoyed yours, wherever it had been. But since the heavens have been so favorable unto me as in this extreme danger wherein you were to grant such virtue unto the remedies which I have used toward you, as the which I have been able to keep undissolved your gentle spirit with your fair body, I hope, my dear, that you will henceforth consider what the affection of your wicked husband hath been toward you, and how great good will, and by consideration thereof, discern and resolve which of us two hath deserved to be beloved of you."

Agatha, finding herself in that sort buried indeed, did easily believe the truth which the scholar told her, and to herself concluded that her husband had showed himself in her behalf a man of all other most cruel and disloyal. Wherefore, turning herself toward the scholar, she said unto him:

latter day the final period of history, the end of time.

"Alonso, I cannot deny but that my husband hath been to me not only unkind but cruel also, nor I cannot but confess that you have declared yourself to be most loving and affectioned toward me. And of force I must acknowledge myself beholding unto you, of no less than of my life, since, alas, I see myself here among dead bodies buried alive. But forasmuch, although my husband have broken his vow to me, I have not yet at any time failed my faith to him, I do require you that if you desire that I should esteem this kind and loving office of yours as it deserveth to be esteemed, or make account of this life which you have given me, you will have due regard and consideration of mine honesty, and that you will not by offering me any villainy—which nevertheless I cannot any way misdoubt° where I have always found so much and so great courtesy—make this your courteous and pitiful act to be less commendable and praiseworthy than it is. Which if you do bridle your unlawful and sensual appetite and desire, will remain the most virtuous and worthy of honor and fame that ever courteous gentleman hath done for a miserable woman since the world began."

Alonso failed not with affectual° and manifest arguments to persuade her that her husband had now no more right or title to her at all, and that although° he had, yet if she were wise, she should not commit herself unto his courtesy again, since by this mortal token he had given her a sufficient testimony of his rancor and evil will towards her whereby she might well enough be assured not to escape whensoever she should resolve to put herself again into his hands. And that therefore she was not to make any account of him, but to show herself thankful for so great a benefit as she had received, and to requite him so with her favor and courtesy as he might now in the end attain to gather the fruit of his long and constant good will and of his travail sustained for the safeguard of her life. And with those words bending himself towards her, he would have taken a kiss of her lips. But Agatha, thrusting him back, said to him again:

"If my husband⁴ have broken those bands wherewith I was knit unto him by matrimony through his wicked and lewd demeanor, yet have not I for my part dissolved them, neither will I

misdoubt suspect.   affectual earnest.   although even if.

at any time so long as I shall live. As for committing myself unto
his courtesy or going any more into his hands, therein I think
it good to follow your advice; not that I would be unwilling to
live and dwell with him if I might hope to find him better disposed, but because I would be loathe to fall eftsoons° into the
like danger and grievous peril. And as for requiting you for this
your commendable travail in my behalf, I know not what better
recompence I am able to give you than to rest bound unto you
forever, and to acknowledge myself beholding unto your courtesy
for my life, which obligation, if it may satisfy you, I will be as
glad and content as I may be in this miserable state wherein I am.
But if your meaning perchance be that the loss of mine honesty
should be the reward and hire for your pains, I do beseech you
to depart hence out of this tomb, and to leave me here enclosed,
for I had rather die here thus buried quick through the cruelty of
my husband, than through any such compassion or pity to save
my life with the loss of mine honor and good name."

The scholar by those words perceived well enough the honest
disposition of Agatha, which he wondered at, considering that
the terror of death itself was not able once to move her from her
faithfulness and constancy of mind. And though it were grievous
unto him to find her so steadfast, yet, hoping that by time in the
end he might overcome her chaste and honest purpose, answered
that he could not but commend her for her disposition, though he
deserved a kinder recompense of his long and fervent love, and she
a more loving and faithful husband. But since she was so resolved,
he would frame himself to be content with what she would, and
not crave of her anything that she would not willingly grant him
to have. And therewith helping her out of the sepulchre, he led
her home unto his house and left her there with an old woman
that kept his house, to whom he recommended her and whose help
he was assured of to dispose the good will of Agatha towards him,
and the next morning returned into the city.

Gonsales, after a few days, seeming not to be able to live with-
out a wife to take care of his family,[5] wedded that honest dame
Aselgia and made her mistress of himself and all that he had.
This his new marriage so soon contrived caused the friends of

eftsoons afterward.

Agatha to marvel not a little, and to misdoubt that the sudden death of their kinswoman had not happened without some mystery. Nevertheless, having no token nor evidence or proof, they held their peace. But Gonsales, having his desired purpose and living with his new wife, it befell unto him, through God's just judgment with this his jolly dame, as it chanced to Agatha with him before. For Aselgia—that was never wont to feed with so spare a diet, as she that had never been contented before without great change, nor had not been used to that kind of straightness which Gonsales, growing jealous of her, began to keep her in, but had always lived at liberty and with such licentiousness as women of her profession are wont to do—became in short space to show herself so precise° unto him, and to hate and abhor him in such extreme sort that she could not abide to see or hear him spoken of. By occasion of which her demeanor towards him, Gonsales to his grief began at last to know and to discern what difference there is between the honest and careful love of an honest wife, and the dissembling of an arrant strumpet.[6] Wherefore one day among the rest, complaining of the little love which he perceived she bare him, and she answering him thwartly,° Gonsales falling into heat of choler said angrily unto her:

"Have I, thou naughty pack,° poisoned Agatha for thy sake, that was the kindest and the lovingest wife that ever man had, and is this the reward I have and the requital thou yieldest me, to show thyself every day more despiteful and crabbed than other?"

Aselgia, having heard him and noted well his words, took hold of them and straightway thought that she had found the way to rid herself of Gonsales, wherefore she revealed his speeches unto a ribald° of hers—such a one as supplied her want of that which Gonsales alone, nor ten such as he were able to satisfy her withal—and induced him to appeach° him for that fact, assuring herself that the law would punish him with no less than death, and thereby she to remain at liberty to do what she list again, as she had done before. This companion accused Gonsales, upon

precise strict and narrow in behavior, withholding her favors.
thwartly perversely, stubbornly.   pack worthless person, appearing usually with the adj. "naughty".   ribald a dissolute or licentious person; here her pimp.   appeach to inform against.

his own words, unto the friends of Agatha, who having had half a suspicion thereof before, went and accused him likewise before the judge or head magistrate of the city. Whereupon Gonsales and his woman were both apprehended and put to their examinations to search out the truth, which Gonsales, being half convicted by the confession of the gentle peat° his new wife, but chiefly grieved with the worm of his own conscience, and to avoid the torment of those terrors which he knew were prepared for him, confessed flatly, affirming that he had poisoned her with a poison which he had kept of long time before in his house, performing yet therein the promise which he had made unto the scholar. And upon his own confession, sentence was given against him that he should lose his head.

Alonso, when he understood that Gonsales was condemned to die, was very glad thereof, supposing that he being once dead, Agatha, who all this while for anything that the old woman could say or allege unto her in the behalf of Alonso, would never yield or consent to any one point wherein her honor might have been touched or spotted, should remain at his discretion and that she would no longer refuse to grant him her good will when she should see herself delivered of Gonsales. But the day being come wherein he was to be put to execution, she having had intelligence of all that had passed, and knowing that he was appointed to die that day, determined with herself that she would in that extremity deliver her disloyal husband and give him to understand how little she had deserved to be so entreated by him as she had been. Wherefore, having gotten out of Alonso his house, she hied her unto the city as fast as she could, and being before the justice or magistrate she said unto him: "Sir, Gonsales whom you have condemned and commanded to be put to death this day is wrongfully condemned, for it is not true that he hath poisoned his wife, but she is yet alive and I am she. Therefore I beseech you, give order that execution may be stayed, since that your sentence is grounded upon a false information and confession [that] is unjust, as you may plainly discern by me being here."

When the governor heard Agatha speak in this sort, whom he had thought to have been dead and buried, he was all amazed and

gentle peat   term of endearment for a light or spoiled girl, used ironically here.

half afraid to look upon her, doubting° that she was rather her
spirit or ghost or some other in her likeness than a lively° woman
indeed, for she was appareled in a very plain and black attire, and
was very wan and pale by reason of the affliction which she had
endured, first, for her own ill fortune, and then for the mischance
of her husband.

In this meanwhile, the sergeants and officers had brought Gonsales before the justice or magistrate to the end that he, according
to the custom of the city, should give them commandment to lead
him to the place of execution and there to fulfil his sentence upon
him. But as soon as Agatha perceived him, she ran unto him,
and taking him about the neck and kissing him, she said: "Alas,
my dear husband, whereunto do I see you brought through your
own folly and disordinate appetite which blinded your judgment?
Behold here your Agatha alive and not dead, who even in this
extremity is come to show herself that loving and faithful wife
unto you that she was ever."

The justice or governor seeing this strange accident,° caused
execution to be stayed, and signified the whole case unto the
lord of the country who at that time chanced to be at Seville,
who, wondering no less than the other at the matter, caused both
Gonsales and his wife to be brought before him, and demanded
of them how it had chanced that she having been buried for dead
was now found alive. Gonsales could say nothing but that for
the love he bare unto Aselgia he had poisoned his wife, and that
he knew not how she was revived again. But Agatha declared
how the scholar with his skill had delivered her from death and
restored her life unto her, but how or by what means she could
not tell.

The lord, having sent for Alonso and demanded him of the
truth, was certified by him how that instead of poison he had
given to Gonsales a powder to make her sleep, affirming likewise
that notwithstanding the long and earnest pursuit which he had
made to obtain her love, and the cruelty and injury which she
saw her husband had used toward her to put her in that danger
and peril of her life out of which he had delivered her, yet could

doubting suspecting.   **lively** living.   **strange accident** rare
event.

he never by any persuasion or entreaty win her to fulfil his desire or bring her to make breach of her faith and honesty. By which report the lord knew very well that in an honest woman the regard and respect of her honor and chastity doth far exceed any other passion, for any misery be it never so great. And commending highly the love and constancy of the woman toward her husband, and praising the policy of Alonso, he turned himself unto Gonsales and said unto him: "Full evil hast thou deserved to have so good and so virtuous a gentlewoman to thy wife, and in reason she ought now rather to be Alonso his wife than thine. Neither wert thou worthy of less than that punishment which the law hath condemned thee unto though she be yet alive, since thou as much as in thee lay hast done to bereave her of her life. But I am content that her virtue and goodness shall so much be available° unto thee that thou shalt have thy life spared unto thee for this time, not for thine own sake, because thou deservest it not, but for hers, and not to give her that sorrow and grief which I know she would feel if thou shouldest die in that sort. But I swear unto thee that if ever I may understand that thou dost use her henceforth otherwise than lovingly and kindly, I will make thee to thy grievous pain prove how severely I can punish such beastly and heinous facts, to the example of all others."

Gonsales, imputing his former offence to want of wit and judgment, made promise unto the lord that he would always do as he had commanded him. And accordingly having forsaken clean that baggage strumpet that he had wedded, he lived all the rest of his days in good love and peace with Agatha his wife, whose chaste and constant mind caused Alonso, where before he loved her for her exterior beauty, ever after to reverence her and in manner to worship her as a divine creature for the excellency of her virtue, resolving with himself that a more constant faith and honest disposition could not be found in any mortal woman.

available capable of producing a desired effect.

OF ARAMANTHUS
BORN A LEPER

The Argument of the Seventh History.

Aramanthus, son to Roderick King of Tolosia, being born a leper, was sent by his father to the Isle of Candy¹ for remedy, and by a tempest at the sea the ship was driven into Turkey where she was cast away and no man saved but the child, which was taken up by a poor fisherman and fostered as his own son, and afterwards serving the Turk in his wars showed himself so politic that the Turk by his only advice encroached much upon the Christians, and, in fine, by his mean the city of Tolosia was taken, his father put in prison, and how in the end he was known to be the son of Roderick.

I shall not need by any long circumstance to describe how many troubles, tumults, broils, brabbles,◊ murders, treasons, how kingdoms have been disturbed, how many countries laid waste, how many cities have been sacked, how many towns have been razed, and how many mischiefs have ever happened sithence the first creation of the world until this present day by that monstrous vice ambition. Considering that, every history maketh mention, every chronicle beareth record, and every age, time and season

brabbles noisy quarrels.

have seen with their eyes, and this our tale that followeth shall something make more evident.

There was sometime remaining° in the famous city of Tolosia a worthy king whose name was Roderick, who was likewise espoused to a most virtuous queen called Isabel, and truly a happy court it might be called which they held, as well for the love that was between the king and queen as for the virtue and clemency wherewith both the one and the other were accompanied.

There was remaining in the court the Duke of Caria who was the only brother of Roderick, king of Tolosia. This duke, being a great deal more vicious than his brother was virtuous, practiced no other thing but how he might come by the kingdom of Tolosia, knowing that there were no more between him and it but the king, who loved him more dearly by a great deal than he deserved. But it fell out the Queen Isabel was known to be with child, the duke, very loath that any other heirs should step in between him and home, devised to poison the queen, and so had thought to have done by as many as the king should have taken to a wife, if at any time they proved to be with child. But by the providence of God, this poison took no great effect in the queen, saving that when she was delivered of a son the child was found to be in a notable leprosy. And the king, having intelligence of an excellent physician—but especially for the curing of that disease—remaining in the Isle of Candy, prepared a ship presently to send the child which, by the extremity of a contrary wind, was driven into Turkey, and the ship cast away upon the main and all the men drowned excepting the child, which being in a cradle was carried to the shore as it lay, where a fisherman found it, with such sumptuous furnitures about it, with a very rich jewel hanging about the neck. He took it up in his arms, and carrying it home, with baths and homely ointments of his own devising, within a very little space the child was restored to perfect health, whom he called Aramanthus, and brought him up as his own son, the child knowing no other, indeed, but that the fisherman had been his father. And as Aramanthus grew in years, so he proved of a very comely personage, but of a most excellent and perfect

sometime remaining at one time living.

wit, although he had no other training up, but used to go to the sea with his father a-fishing.

Now it fell out that the Turk was levying a mighty army to set upon the Christians. The cause was this: he had two children, a son and a daughter; the daughter her name was Florella whose beauty was very excellent, and minding to match his daughter with some noble prince, he pretended that such countries, cities, towns, castles, forts, or whatsoever he could by conquest get from the Christians, to give them all for his daughter's dowry.

Aramanthus, hearing of this preparation to the wars, would needs become a soldier, whereat his father the fisherman was greatly displeased and began to preach unto his son the incommodities◊ of war and with how many miseries soldiers are besieged. Aramanthus, whose baseness of his bringing up could not conceal the nobility of his birth, would in no wise be persuaded, but go he would, and being pressed◊ for an ordinary soldier, when he came to the place of service showed himself so valiant, and in very short space became to be so expert, that the captain under whose ensign he served bore away the credit from all the rest, and in the end was himself preferred to charge,◊ which he governed with so great discretion and still conducted with such celerity and sleight◊ that who but Aramanthus and his company had the only name throughout the Turk's camp. And where there was any attempt to be given where valiancy should be shown, Aramanthus he must give the charge, and where any policy must be put in practice, Aramanthus he must lay the plat,◊ that, to be short, he grew into such credit with the Great Turk himself that Aramanthus only◊ gave him counsel in all his affairs, and therewithal had so good success that his practices still prevailed and came to happy end, that the Turk by his advice had done wonderful spoils◊ upon the Christians and had taken from them many cities, towns, and provinces.

And thus leaving them in the wars for a season, I will convey my tale again to Isabel, queen and wife to Roderick, who was

---

incommodities inconveniences.   **pressed** conscripted to serve in the military.   **preferred to charge** given a command.   **sleight** skill, cleverness.   **plat** plan, strategy.   **only** alone.   **done wonderful spoils** made great inroads, taken much booty.

now the second time known to be with child, whereat the Duke of Caria being wonderfully wrath, pretending to find a quick dispatch for all together, he secretly accused the queen of adultery to the king his brother, and with such allegations and false witnesses as he had provided, so informed the king that his tale was credited, and the rather for that the king, knowing his queen to be with child, did think himself too far spent in years to do such a deed. And yet the king was replenished with so great pity that he could not endure to hear of her death; he therefore by a messenger commanded her presently to depart the court, and in pain of her life never after to come in his presence. These news did wonderfully amaze the queen, who with many piteous intercessions desired to know her accusers, and that she might but speak for herself before his majesty and then, as he should find her, to use her according to her deserts. But all in vain, for the duke had so thoroughly incensed the king that he would neither abide to see nor hear her. The duke, understanding how matters had passed, came to the queen and seemed much to lament her case, persuading her to hold herself contented for a little season, not doubting but in time that he himself would so persuade with his brother that she should be heard to speak in her own defence; in the mean season, if it pleased her to use his house in the country, he would provide for her all manner of necessaries whatsoever she should want, and for her better comfort, if she had any assured friend whose company she desired that she might secretly send for them to hold her fellowship and to pass the time, and that he himself would many times visit her and daily inform her how matters did pass in her behalf with the king his brother.

The poor queen, thinking all had to proceed of good will which this traitor had proffered, gave him more than a thousand thanks, reposing herself and the innocence of her cause only in this Judas, who practiced nothing else but her death and the death of that she went withal.◇

The next day he provided a couple of ruffians, such as he knew were for his purpose, which should have secretly conveyed her to the duke's house, as she had thought. But, as the duke had willed them, as they rode over a forest when they came to the side of

that she went withal i.e. her child.

a wood, they took her from her horse, spoiled her of such things as were about her, and minded to have killed her and thrown her in some bush. But it fell out that there were certain banished men in the wood which lived in that desert in manner of outlaws, and hearing the piteous complaint of the queen, they came to her rescue. But the villains that would have slain her, perceiving them, fled and left the queen where these outlaws came unto her, unto whom from point to point she declared everything how it was happened unto her. The outlaws having great compassion when they knew her to be the queen, for that they had ever heard her to be nobly reported on, brought her with them to their cave where they ministered such relief to her distress as men might do that were in their estates.° The queen, thinking that God had preserved her life to some better purpose, contented herself for a season to remain amongst them where she learned to play the cook and to dress their meat such as they brought in or could provide for in the forest. And thus leaving the queen with these outlaws, I will return again to speak of Aramanthus, who was now devising to frame a plot how he might betray the city of Tolosia whereof his father was king as you have heard.

For the Turk, having intelligence of the pleasantness of this city and of the wonderful wealth and riches wherewith it did abound, and therewithal had learned that it was of such force and invincible strength that there was no manner of hope how it might be subdued, whereat the Turk was very sorrowful and sad.

But my young fisherman, Aramanthus, whose cunning never failed where courage could not help, caused the Turk with his whole army by sea to come before this city which is situate fast upon the seaside and there to come to an anchor, where Aramanthus himself, as a messenger appointed from the Turk, came to the King of Tolosia to whom he told this tale: that the Turk his master, having been in diverse parts of Christendom where he had made wars a long space and upon diverse considerations, minding to depart with his army into his own country for a season, and being upon the seas, one night as he was lying upon his bed, behold, a vision appeared unto him in a dream which showed him how grievously he had offended the God of the Christians in the

estates circumstances.

persecuting, spoiling and the murdering of them, as he had done in this journey, and for that he should know that the Christian God was the most high and almighty God indeed, whom with his tyranny he had so displeased, he should be crippled all of his limbs from that time forth till his dying day, which should very shortly follow. With this he awaked, and giving a piteous groan, such as was about him° coming unto him found him in a wonderful maze and so benumbed in all his parts that he was not able to stir hand nor foot. The next day, calling his counsellors and captains about him, not able of himself to come forth amongst them but as he was brought out of his cabin on men's backs, he declared unto them the whole circumstance of the premises, and being stricken with a wonderful remorse in conscience, he determined to sail back again, not minding to depart from out those parts of Christendom till he had made satisfaction of all such spoils and outrages as he had committed against the Christians, and himself with his whole army to become christened, and there to be instructed in the true and perfect faith. And as he continued this determination, behold, a contrary wind hath driven us on these parts, where hearing of the fame of this noble city of Tolosia, he hath sent me unto your grace, desiring nothing but your safe conduct for himself and certain of his chief lords and counsellors that be about him, that in this noble city they might be baptized and receive the Christian faith, promising hereafter not only to join in league and perfect amity with the Christians, but also to link with them in religion, himself, his countries, kingdoms and provinces.

This tale was not so smoothly told but there was great doubt and suspicion had in the matter. In the end, thinking they could receive no prejudice° by receiving of so small a number, gave safe conduct for the Turk himself, and for five hundred of his company such as it pleased himself to appoint.

The next day, the Turk was brought into the city on men's shoulders, with his appointed company, where he was worthily received by the king himself with the rest of his lords, and brought into a palace of purpose very richly furnished, where being laid

such as was about him those persons near him.   prejudice danger.

down upon a bed as though he had been able neither to stand nor sit, and giving the king with the rest of his company great thanks for his entertainment, he desired him with the duke his brother, according to the custom, to be his godfathers when he should be christened, to which request they both willingly agreed. The next day, the Turk himself was the first that received Christendom, and then all the rest of his noble men that were with him, the which being finished, many godly exhortations were preached unto them by learned men. The Turk seemed in very grateful manner to take this courtesy wherewith the king had used him, and thus taking his leave, himself with all his company departed again aboard the ships, the Turk himself being carried upon men's backs, making show as though he had been so feeble and weak that he had not been able to have moved or stirred any one joint without help, feigning that he would have departed with his company into Turkey.

The King of Tolosia, with all his people and citizens, seeing with what devotion the Turk with the rest of his company had received Christendom, began to think assuredly that only by the divine providence of God the Turk was so converted, and doubted nothing of the tale which Aramanthus before had told them, which turned in the end to their utter subversion. For the next day Aramanthus, coming again to the king, brought word of the death of the Turk, and with a piteous discourse, uttered with a number of feigned sighs, said that: "about twelve-o-clock of the night past the Turk deceased, and desired at the hour of his death that as in this worthy city he had received the true and Catholic faith, so likewise that he might be entombed and receive Christian burial in the cathedral church, to the which he had given by his will forty thousand franks; more to the common treasure of the city a hundred thousand franks; to the king himself as a precedent° of his good will, a rich jewel which himself did wear of great estimation; to the duke his brother, his own armor and furniture. Item, to the relief of the poor within the city, ten thousand franks; many other things," quoth Aramanthus, "he hath bequeathed that I have not spoken of, the which God willing shall be performed to the uttermost."

precedent indication.

The king seemed greatly to lament the death of the Turk, and began to conjecture assuredly that it was the will of God but to preserve his life till he had received Christendom, but the time of his burial was deferred for certain days till things might be provided and more ready for the pomp and solemnizing of his funeral. And wonderful cost was bestowed by Aramanthus, who had the only ordering of the matter, hoping in the end to receive the whole commodity, and also to be rewarded with a large and bountiful interest. The day of burial being at hand, Aramanthus desired the king that for so much as the Turk had finished his days in the midst of his army among his soldiers that he might likewise be buried like a noble captain and, according to the manner of the field, he might be brought to his grave with certain bands trailing their weapons as the custom of soldiers is to bury their dead. This request seemed to be very convenient◊ and therefore was the readier granted. But what should I stand with long circumstance to decipher all the ceremonies that were used in this treason. The day was come that this practice must be put in ure,◊ and an empty coffin solemnly brought to the city under show of great sorrow, when they were all filled with great joy and gladness to see what happy success was like to follow of that they had premeditated. And accordingly as Aramanthus had given order, five thousand of their choice men were appointed to march, the one half before, and the other half after the coffin, trailing their ensigns and weapons, and in this manner they entered the city where the king with his nobles and principals of the city were ready in mourning weeds to accompany the corse.

When Aramanthus saw his time, the alarum was given, and he himself was the first that laid hands of the king his father; the rest of his nobles were so enclosed that there could not one of them escape. Defense there was none to be made for the one side were in arms killing and murdering of as many as they could see stirring in the streets; the other side unprovided, glad to hide themselves for the safeguard of their lives. The rest of the fleet were likewise in a readiness, and running aland entered the city where there was no man to repulse them. And thus the famous city of Tolosia was taken by the Turks, even in a moment without

convenient reasonable.　　**put in ure** put into operation.

any manner of resistance. The churches and prisons were filled full of Christians where they were whipped, racked and tormented to the death unless they would forsake their faith. The king himself with his brother and all the lords were committed to prison, there to be fed with bread and water, and yet to be scantled° with such short allowance as it was not able to suffice nature, and so to be dieted unless they would forsake their faith.

Now the Turk, who only by the means of Aramanthus had conquered from the Christians so many cities and towns, for the love he bare unto him and in respect of his service, determined to make Aramanthus his son-in-law, and to give him his daughter Florella for his wife, and for her dowry all such parts as he had taken from the Christians by conquest; and understanding that the father of Aramanthus was but a poor fisherman, he pretended° likewise to make him a duke and to giving him living to maintain his estate. The Turk therefore with all possible speed hastened messengers with shipping to bring his daughter with the old fisherman, the supposed father of Aramanthus, to this city of Tolosia where he minded to perform that he had determined.

Now it fell out that the miserable Queen Isabel, whom you have heard was left with child, remaining with certain outlaws, was delivered of a daughter which she herself nursed in the cave where she had remained. And hearing that the Turk had taken the city of Tolosia, would needs go see what was become of the king her husband. Her daughter, which was not yet fully a year old, she committed to the outlaws to be fostered with such homely junkets as they could provide, who, seeing her determination, promised to dry-nurse the child so well as they could till she should make return. Thus preparing herself in a very simple attire, with a bundle of brooms on her head, she came to the city of Tolosia, where roaming up and down the streets to sell her brooms, she learned all that had happened to the king, and how he was ready to perish for want of food and sustenance. Wherefore, minding to give such succor as her ability would serve, she devised in the manner of a poor servant to get into the service of the Turk who was the jailor and had the custody of the king, where every night, as opportunity would serve, she conveyed to him through a grate

scantled restricted.   pretended intended.

such fragments as she spared out of her own belly, which were very short and therewithal much more homely, but something the better to amend his cheer,° she would lean herself close to the grate, and thrusting in her teat between the irons, the king learned again to suck, and thus she dieted him a long season. Neither wist the king what she was that bestowed on him so great grace and goodness, yet he blessed her more than a thousand time a day. And although there were many of his company that died for want of sustenance, yet he again with these banquets recovered himself, and began to wax strong, whereat the Turks began to suspect some partiality in the jailor and caused a privy watch to be kept. But Isabel, suspecting nothing, according to her accustomed manner at night when it was dark came to her nursery, where her order that she so long used was espied, and being apprehended by the watch, the next day she was presented to the Turk and in what manner they had found her. Whereat the Turk, wonderfully aggrieved, swore by Mahound° himself that she should presently be tortured with the greatest torments that might be devised. And in the midst of his fury, word was brought him that his daughter Florella with the fisherman that was father to Aramanthus were arrived and ready to present themselves before him, whereat the Turk wonderfully rejoiced, and calling Aramanthus, caused them to be brought in. Florella gave that reverence to the Turk which both appertained to the duty of a child, and also as belonged to his estate. Aramanthus likewise, although he were the greatest counsellor appurtenant° to the Turk, yet used that dutiful reverence to the fisherman his father as is to be required in a child. The Turk, embracing his daughter Florella, told her the cause that he had sent for her was to espouse her to Aramanthus, who, although the Destinies had denied to make noble by place of birth, yet through his virtues, valiance and worthy exploits, he had gained the title of true nobility in despite of Fortune's teeth. Florella, having heard of the fame and worthiness of Aramanthus, was the best pleased woman in the world.

And the Turk, turning him towards the fisherman, said: "And a thousand times happy art thou, old father, that hast lived to

amend his cheer augment his diet.   **Mahound** Mohammed.
appurtenant (orig. apertinent), belonging to.

see thyself so highly exalted in thy offspring."

The poor fisherman, kneeling down, said: "Most mighty and magnificent prince, not minding longer to conceal the thing which might redound so greatly to the contentation of such worthy personages, seeing then that Aramanthus, who only through his own valiancy hath aspired to so great dignity and honor, how greatly were I then to be blamed, and how worthily might I be condemned if I should take upon me to be the sire of him who by all likelihood is descended of royal and princely race. For better testimony behold this rich mantle and these other costly furnitures wherein I found Aramanthus wrapped, and by seeming saved by his cradle which brought him ashore from some ship that was wracked, where I found him by the seaside, as I said, wrapped in these sumptuous furnitures with this rich and precious jewel about his neck, being but an infant, by conjecture not above the age of a quarter of a year, where, taking him up in my arms, I brought him home to my house, called him by the name of Aramanthus, and thus fostered him up as my own child until the day that he came to serve your majesty in the wars."

The Queen Isabel, which stood by and heard this discourse, and seeing the furnitures and the jewels wherewith she had decked her child, assuring herself that Aramanthus was her son, could no longer stay her speech, but said: "And do I then behold my son with my unhappy eyes? Is he living here in presence whom I deemed to be dead? Oh most gracious gods, I yield you humble thanks, and would to God, my son, thy coming had been but half so happy as thy presence is joyful to me thy wretched mother."

"What news be these," quoth the Turk, "which I heard? I think the woman be out of her wits. But what art thou that wouldst challenge° Aramanthus for thy son, whose parents now I well perceive are no beggars like thyself."

"Yes surely," quoth the queen, "and much more miserable than those that go from door to door, and although his father sometime swayed the sword of government and sat in place and seat of princely throne."

"Dispatch then at once," quoth the Turk, "and tell me who is his father, and what is the misery wherewith he is perplexed,

challenge claim.

wherein if thou canst persuade me with a truth, assure thee that only for Aramanthus' sake, I am the man that will minister release."

"Behold then," quoth the queen, "King Roderick is his father whom thyself keepest here in prison in this miserable manner, and I whom thou seest here am his mother, the wife of the king, and sometime the queen of this wretched city of Tolosia, who being delivered of a son which by the pleasure of God was visited in my womb and born in an extreme leprosy, for help whereof he was sent by his father by shipping to the Isle of Candy, and till this present day there was never tidings heard, either of the ship or of any one man that was in her. And now behold I see with mine eyes the furnitures wherein I wrapped my child, and the jewel which I put about his neck with my own hands at his departure." The fisherman, verifying this tale to be true, said indeed that he found him in an extreme malady which he cured himself with medicines of his own providing.

Aramanthus, having heard how matters were sorted out, began to tear himself° saying: "Ah, most wicked and unnatural wretch, what Furies° have saved thee that thou wert not drowned with the rest, but that thou must be preserved as an instrument to work thy parents' wrack; come, come, you hellish hags and shew your force on him that hath worthily deserved it. But what hath Tantalus offended that he should continually be starved, or how hath Sisyphus that rolls the restless stone, or what trespass hath been committed by Prometheus, Ixion, Tityus, or Danaus' silly daughters drawing water at the well, that may be compared to that which I have done?[2] Is it possible then that I should escape unpunished? Or that the sacred gods will be unrevenged of my fact? No, no, I have deserved to be plagued and have merited more worthily to be tormented than any of these afore rehearsed." Florella, overhearing these desperate speeches, fell down in a swoon for grief to see her Aramanthus so disquieted. The Turk, after his daughter was come again to herself, sorrowed to see the heaviness of Aramanthus, caused the king his father with the Duke of Caria presently to be sent for out of prison.

tear himself curse, berate himself.   **Furies** in Greek mythology, winged women who were the avengers of crimes against kinship.

And taking Isabel on the one of his hands, and Aramanthus on the other, he said to the king: "Receive here, noble prince, a most loving and faithful wife and a most valiant and worthy son, and myself from an enemy, forever after this, to become thy most assured and trusty friend."

The king was wonderfully amazed to hear these speeches, [and] did think himself to be in some dream till in the end he heard the whole discourse how everything had happened, and being ravished with gladness, he said:

"O happy evil, which bringeth in the end so great a good, and welcome be that sorrow whereby is sprung a joy much more surmounting than ever was any heaviness." And with many like speeches he still embraced his son Aramanthus in his arms, and although he understood that it was the queen his wife which so lovingly had succored him when he was ready to have famished in the prison for want of meat, yet he could not find in his heart to bear her any countenance, considering what he had conceived against her by the information of his brother, as before you have heard; which being perceived by the duke, most humbly desiring forgiveness, he confessed to the king all his mischief from the beginning to the ending, whereof the king was both sorry and glad: sorry, for that he had so unnaturally dealt with so virtuous and courteous a wife, and glad for that he was so resolved and confirmed in her chastity which before he had in suspense.

And now the Turk, for the love that he bare to Aramanthus, and for the liking that he saw to be in his daughter towards him whom he himself had appointed to be her spouse, became indeed to be christened with all his retinue that was about him, and then restoring Roderick again to the Kingdom of Tolosia. By all consents the marriage between Aramanthus and Florella was concluded with great pomp and magnificence, and thus the Turk leaving this new married couple in the city of Tolosia,◊ departed with his army into Turkey.

The Queen Isabel, not forgetting the great goodness she had received by these outlaws which before had saved her life and with whom her daughter yet remained, so dealt with the king her husband that they were all together sent for, and very joyfully

Tolosia "and" deleted.

receiving his daughter, restored the outlaws again to their liberty, bestowing of them for recompense rooms° and offices of credit and estimation. Thus to conclude, everyone being well contented, they lived together in quietness with many long and happy days.

rooms positions.

OF PHYLOTUS AND EMELIA

The Argument of the Eighth History.

Phylotus, an old and ancient citizen of Rome, falleth in love with Emelia, a young and beautiful virgin the daughter of Alberto, who, knowing the wonderful wealth of Phylotus, would have forced his daughter to have married him, but in the end was prettily deceived by Phylerno, the brother of Emelia, who married with Phylotus in his sister's stead, and other pretty actions that fell out by the way.

It hath many times been had in question, and yet could never be decided, from whence this passion of extreme love doth proceed, whose fury is such where it once taketh possession, that, as they say, love is without law, so it maketh the patients° to be as utterly void of reason; but in my opinion the self same thing which is many times shadowed under the title of love may more properly be termed and called by the name of lust. But be it love, or be it lust, the difference is nothing so much as the humor that feeds it is wonderful strange and hath no manner of certainty in it excepting this: it is without partiality, for commonly when it driveth us to effect,° it is done without any manner of respect, for sometime it maketh us to linger after our friends, sometime

patients those sick with love.   effect to affect or to love someone.

to languish after our foes, yea, between whom there hath been had mortal hostility. The son hath been seen to fall in love with the wife of his father,[1] the father again in like manner with the wife of his son, the king hath been attached with the poor and needy beggar, the people again in liking with those of high degree. Yea, and though there have been many which have seen their own error and therewithal have confessed their abuse, yet they have not been able to restrain themselves from prosecuting their folly to the end. And albeit reason proffereth us sundry sufficient causes why we ought to refrain the appetite of our own desires, yet fancy° then is he that striketh such a stroke that reason's rules can naught at all prevail. And like as those whom love hath once entangled, the more they strive the further they be tied, so it is impossible that love should be constrained where affection breeds not liking nor fancy is not fed. But where these two hath once joined in election, all other affects° be so dim and blinded that every vice seemeth to us a virtue, whereof springeth this proverb: "In love there is no lack." So that indeed to say the truth, if there be any piety to be imputed to this raging love, it is in that it is not partial nor hath it any respect of persons, but be they friends, be they foes, be they rich, be they poor, be they young, be they old, be they wise, be they foolish, love is still indifferent and respecteth all alike; but if any man will think that in respect of beauty we esteem not all the rest, I am able to say it is not true, considering how many have forsaken the better liking and have chosen the worse,[2] so that for my part the more I consider of it the more I am amazed, and therefore will beat my brains no more about it, but leave it to the credit of such as have been lovers themselves, whose skill in the matter I prefer before mine own, and will come to my history of Phylotus, who, being an aged man, fell in love with a young maiden far unfitting to his years, and followeth in this sort.

In the gallant city of Naples, there was remaining° a young man called by the name of Alberto. This Alberto, being married not fully out a year, his wife was delivered of a son whom he named Phylerno, and upon diverse considerations, minding to

fancy the imagination whose images sometimes corrupt the reason.
affects affections, faculties.　remaining dwelling.

change his habitation, he prepared himself to go dwell at Rome, and first taking order for his son Phylerno, who for the tenderness of his age he left still in Naples at nurse, himself, his wife, with all the rest of his household came to Rome, where he had not very long remained, but his wife was likewise delivered of a daughter whom he called by the name Emelia, who, as she grew in years, she likewise proved to be very beautiful and fair. And amongst a great number of others, there was dwelling in Rome an ancient citizen whose name was Phylotus, a man very orderly in years and wonderfully abounding in goods; this Phylotus, having many times taken the view of Emelia, began to grow very sore in love with her, or rather I may say in his old years began to dote after this young maiden, for it cannot be properly called love in these old men whose dotage, if it were not more than outrageous, either their great discretion would repress it, either their many years would mortify it. But Phylotus in the end desired Emelia of her father in the way of marriage. Alberto, according to the custom of parents that desire to marry their daughters more for goods than for good will between the parties, more for lucre than for love, more for living than for learning, more for wealth than for wit, more for humor than for honesty, and so they may have great store of money, they never consider further of the man. Alberto in like manner knowing the wealth wherewith Phylotus was endued—who had never a child but one only daughter whose name was Brisilla—gave his full consent without any further consideration of the inequality of the years that was between Phylotus and his daughter. He never remembered what strifes, what jars, what debates, what discontentment, what counterfeiting, what dissembling, what lowering, what loathing, what never liking is ever had where there is such differences between the married, for perfect love can never be without equality, and better were a married couple to continue without living than without love. And what are the occasions that make so many women to stray from their husbands but when they be married to such as they cannot like of? But surely if women did thoroughly consider how dangerous it is for them to deal with these old youths, I think they would be better advised in meddling with them, for besides that they be unwieldy, loathsome, and sir reverence of you,° very unlovely for you to lie by, so they be commonly inspired with the spirit of jealousy, and then they will look to you so narrowly and mew° you up so closely that you will wish a thousand times the priest had been hanged that married you, but then too late.

But to return to our history: Alberto, respecting more the wealth of Phylotus than the liking of his daughter, gave his consent to take him for his son-in-law, and told Emelia how he had disposed of her. Emelia, seeing what an old baby her father had chosen to be her husband, most humbly desired him to give her leave to choose for herself, whereat her father, being very angry, began sharply to rate° her, saying, "and art thou then so much wedded to thine own will that thou scornest to be directed by me, thy loving father, or thinkest thou that thy wisdom doth so far surmount my wit that thou canst better provide for thyself than I which so carefully have hitherto brought thee up? Or doth the tender love or the chargeable cost which I have bestowed on thee deserve no better recompense than to despise those that I would have thee to like of?"

Emelia, falling down of her knees before her father said, "Most dear and loving father, most humbly I beseech you, for the affection which by nature you bear me, not to think me so graceless a child that I would go about to contrary you, or stubbornly would refuse whatsoever you would think convenient for my behoof. And although you shall find in me such duty as is meet for a daughter, and all obedience that is fit for a child, yet, sir, consider the heart which cannot be compelled neither by fear, neither by force, nor is not otherwise to be lured than only by fancy's free consent. And as you have bestowed on me this frail and transitory life, so my body shall be at your disposition as it shall please you to appoint it, and will conclude with this humble petition, desiring you not to bestow me of any that is not agreeable to my fancy and good liking."

"Well," quoth her father, "then see you frame your liking to like well of my liking. I have promised you to Phylotus in marriage, and Phylotus is he that shall be your husband. And look

sir reverence of you saving your reverence, if you will.   mew lock.   rate berate, scold.

you go not about to contend against that I have determined; if you do, never account me for father nor friend," and thus he departed.

Emelia, hearing this cruel conclusion of her father, was wonderfully abashed, and being by herself in her chamber, she began to consider of her father's words. And for fear to incur any further displeasure, she devised how she might frame herself to the liking of her lover, and with a young woman's mind, she first began to consider of his wealth, of his calling, of the reverence wherewith he was used in the city, and that likewise in being his wife she should also be had in estimation and be preferred before any other woman of meaner credit—and to desire superiority it is commonly every woman's sickness, and therefore this could not choose but please her very well. Then she remembered how commodious it were to marry one so wealthy as Phylotus, whereby she should not need to beat her brains about the practicing of housewifery, but should have servants at commandment to supply that turn, this likewise pleased her very well. But because she would well persuade herself, she began to conjecture how she should spend the time to her contentment, and therefore she began to think what a pleasure it was to be well furnished with sundry suits of apparel that in the morning when she should rise she might call for what she list to put on according as the time and the fashion did require and her fancy served her best. For thus Phylotus was well able to keep his wife, and this pleased her likewise very well. And then when she were up, she might break her fast with a cup of malmsey° or muscadine° next her heart.³° It was very good for ill airs in a morning, and this she thought was but an easy matter and likewise pleased her very well. When she had broken her fast, then she might stir about the house and look to this and see to that, and where she found anything amiss, not to touch it with her own fingers for marring the beauty of her hand, but to call for Cecily, Joan or Kate, and to chide them like sluts that they could not spy a fault but when

malmsey a strong, full-flavored white wine, originally from the region of Monemvasia in Greece.   muscadine a variation of muscatel, a rich sweet wine made of the muscat grape.   next her heart on an empty stomach.

they must be told, this likewise pleased her very well. Then to have provided for dinner some junkets that served best her appetite; her husband had good store of coin, and how could it be better spent than upon themselves to make their fare the better? This likewise pleased her very well. Now when she had dined, then she might go seek out her exemplars◊ and to peruse which work would do best in a ruff, which in a gorget,◊ which in a sleeve, which in a coif,◊ which in a caul,◊ which in a handkerchief, what lace would do best to edge it, what seam, what stitch, what cut, what gard, and to sit her down and to take it forth by little and little and thus with her needle to pass the afternoon with devising of things for her own wearing, this likewise pleased her passing well. Then to provide for supper some shift of diet and sundry sauces the better to help the stomach: oranges, lemons, olives, capers, salads of sundry sorts—alas, a crown◊ will go a great way in such trifles. This likewise pleased her very well. When she had supped, to use some exercise according to the season, if it were in summer, to go walk with her neighbors to take the air, or in her garden to take the verdure of sweet and pleasant flowers, this likewise pleased her very well. When she was come in and ready to go to her chamber, a cup of cold sack◊ to bedward is very good for digestion and no cost to speak of where such abundance doth remain, and this likewise pleased her very well.

But now, although she had devised to pass the daytime with such contentation, when she remembered at night she must go to bed to be lubber-leaped,◊ and with what cold courtesy she should be entertained by her gray-headed bedfellow, what frozen embracements he was able to bestow of her, all was marred and quite dashed out of remembrance, and all the commodities before spoken of that she should receive in the time of the day would not serve to countervail that one incommodity in the season of the night. Like as we say, one vice spills◊ a great number of virtues. Thus Emelia was now to seek and could in nowise frame

exemplars a book of patterns. **gorget** an article of dress covering the neck and breast; a wimple. **coif** small headdress of linen. **caul** netted cap or hairnet. **crown** silver coin bearing a crown, worth five shillings. **sack** generally a Spanish white wine, but often sherry. **lubber-leaped** made love to by a clumsy lout. **spills** distroys, squanders.

herself to love Phylotus. But when she had flattered herself with
a thousand delights that she should receive in the daytime by his
wealth, when she remembered bedtime she was as new to begin
as before. Wherefore she remained in great perplexity, thinking
her hap to be over hard and the comfort very bare where the
best choice had such assurance of doubtful end. For to marry
after her father's mind she knew would breed her loathed life,
and to gainsay what he had determined would likewise lose her
father's liking, that she wist not for her life whereon to resolve.
And thus from day to day as she continued in this doubt, there
happened to hit into° her company a young Roman gentleman
whose name was Flanius, who suddenly fell in love with Emelia.
And taking the time whilst his opportunity served, he let Emelia
to understand of the great love he bare her. Emelia, according
to the custom of women, made the matter very coy at the first,
although in her heart she were right glad, considering her case how
it stood. Flanius was so much the more importunate upon her
and with such nice terms as wooers be accustomed, he so courted
and followed Emelia that she, perceiving his fervent affection,
told him a very short circumstance° how her father had disposed
her to one that she could not like of, and therefore, if he would
first promise to take her as his wife, and that he could find such
means to convey her from her father's house in secret sort—for
otherwise she was sure her father would be a let to hinder their
purpose—she was contented to hearken to his speech and yield to
his demand. Flanius, the gladdest man in the world to hear these
joyful news, swore unto her that all should be accomplished, and
that with as much speed as herself would desire.

There was no more to conclude of then but how she might be
conveyed from out her father's house. Flanius devised that late
in an evening, or in the nighttime when everyone were quiet in
their beds, if she could find the means to get forth of doors, then
he would be ready to receive her. But that could not be, for both
her father and mother never failed to be at home in the evenings,
and at nights she was lodged in her father's chamber that it was
impossible for her to get forth, so that there was no remedy but

hit into fall in with.   very short circumstance very soon
thereafter.

that the feat must be wrought in some afternoon when both her
father and mother used to be abroad about their business. And
then she knew not how to come forth alone, because she had not
been accustomed so to do, and to follow a stranger it would breed
the greater suspicion.

But Flanius, to avoid all these surmises, devised the next
evening to convey her in at some back window of her father's
house a suit of man's apparel, wherein the next day in the afternoon, her father and mother being abroad, she should shift
herself,[◊] and so come her ways unknown of any to such a place
where he himself would be ready awaiting for her and so convey
her home to his own house. This device Emelia liked passing
well, and according as it was appointed, the next evening Flanius conveyed this suit of apparel in at the window where Emelia
was ready to receive it, and laying it up in safety till the next
day in the afternoon, her father and her mother being both forth
of doors, she quickly shifted herself into this man's apparel, and
thus forth of doors she goes to her appointed place where Flanius
was staying, who according to promise conveyed her home to his
own house.

This matter was not so closely[◊] handled by Emelia but she was
espied by one of her father's servants, who being on the backside,[◊]
through a window saw her how she was stripping of herself, and
marked how she put on the man's apparel, whereat the young
fellow had great marvel and stood still beholding to see what
would fall out in the end. But when he saw her go forth adoors,
he hastened after into the street. But Emelia was so suddenly
gone that for his life he wist not which ways to seek after her,
wherefore in a wonderful haste he came to his master, whom he
found in the city in the company of Phylotus, saying, "Oh sir, I
have very evil news to tell you."

"What is the matter," quoth his master, "is anything amiss at
home?"

"Yea, sir," quoth the servant, "your daughter Emelia is even
now departed into the city in the habit of a man. But which ways
she went I could not for my life devise, for after she got once forth

shift herself change clothes.   **closely** secretly.   **backside** at
the rear of the house.

of the place where she shifted her, I could never more set eye of her."

"Is Emelia gone?" quoth her lover, Phylotus, "Oh God what evil news be these that I hear?" And without any further stay, both the father and the lover got them out at the doors together and about the streets they run like a couple of madmen.

Now it fell out that Phylerno, the son of Alberto and brother to Emelia, whom you have heard before, was left at Naples being an infant, and had remained there till this time at school, and at this very instant was come from Naples to Rome to visit his father and mother, of whom he had no manner of knowledge otherwise than by their names. And it fortuned that Alberto and Phylotus happened to meet with Phylerno in the streets, who was so like his sister Emelia that both Alberto and Phylotus assured themselves that it could be no other but she. Wherefore, Alberto coming to him, said:

"Stay, stay, most shameless and ungracious girl. Dost thou think that by thy disguising of thyself in this manner thou canst escape unknown to me, who am thy father? Ah, vile strumpet that thou art, what punishment is sufficient for the filthiness of thy fact?"◊

And with this he seemed as though he would have flown◊ upon her in the street to have beat her. But Phylotus thrust between them and desired his neighbor to stay himself. And then embracing Phylerno in his arms, he said:

"Ah, Emelia, my sweet and loving wench, how canst thou so unkindly forsake thy Phylotus whose tender love towards thee is such that as I will not let to make thee sovereign of myself, so thou shalt be dame and mistress of all that ever I have, assuring thee that thou shall never want for gold, gems, jewels, such as be fit and convenient for thy degree."

Phylerno, seeing a couple of old doting fools thus clustering about him, not knowing what they were, had thought at the first they had been out of their wits, but in the end by their words, perceiving a further circumstance in the matter, he devised something for his own disport to feed them a little with their own folly, said:

the filthiness of thy fact the sinfulness of your deeds.　　**flown** (orig. fline), rushed.

"Pardon me, I beseech you, this my grievous offence wherein I know I have too far strayed from the limits and bounds of modesty, protesting hereafter so to govern myself that there shall be no sufficient cause whereby to accuse me of such unmaidenlike parts,◇ and will ever remain with such duty and obedience as I trust shall not deserve but to be liked during life."

Phylotus, having heard this pitiful reconciliation made by his Emelia, very gently entreated her father in her behalf.

"Well," quoth her father, "seeing you will needs have me to forgive this her lewdness◇ at your request I am contented to pardon her." And then speaking to Phylerno, he said:

"How say you, housewife, is your stomach yet come down?◇ Are you contented to take Phylotus for your husband?"

"Yea, my good father," quoth Phylerno, "and that with all my heart."

"Oh happy news," quoth Phylotus, and herewithal he began to set his cap on the one side, and to turn up his mustachios, and fell to wiping of his mouth as though he would have fallen a-kissing of her by and by in the streets. But remembering himself where he was, he brought Alberto with Phylerno into a friend's house that was of his familiar acquaintance, and there the marriage between them was thoroughly concluded◇ and all parties seeming to give their full consents. Phylotus desired his father-in-law that he might have the custody of Emelia, swearing by his old honesty that he would not otherwise use her than his own daughter Brisilla until the day of his nuptials and then to use her as his wife, to which request Alberto seemed very willingly to give consent. But then, because Phylotus would not carry his beloved through the streets in man's apparel, he desired his◇ father-in-law to go home and send some suit of her own apparel wherewith to shift her before he would carry her to his own house. Alberto, seeing matters so thoroughly concluded, took his leave of them both and going his ways home he caused all his daughter's apparel to be looked◇ together, and to be sent to the place where

parts behavior, manners.   lewdness ignorance; indecency.   is your stomach yet come down (opposite of "to have a high stomach," to be proud and stubborn), are you no longer proud and stubborn.   concluded agreed upon.   his (orig. "her").   looked gathered, placed.

Phylotus was remaining with Phylerno, who taking forth such as should serve the turn for the present, Phylerno, so well as he could, arrayed himself in one of his sister's suits of apparel, and thus departed with Phylotus to his own house, where Phylotus calling his daughter Brisilla, he said unto her, "behold here the party whom I have chosen to be your mother, charging you of my blessing that you honor, reverence and obey her and with all diligence that you be attendant upon her and ready at an inch to provide her of anything that she shall either want or call for. And you my dear and loving Emelia, I do here ordain and appoint you to be mistress of this house and of all that is in it, desiring you to accept of this my daughter to do you service in the day-time, and in the night to vouchsafe her for your bedfellow until our day of marriage be prefixed,◊ and then myself will supply the room. Phylerno, seeing the excellent beauty of Brisilla, was nothing sorry to have such a bedfellow, but thought every hour a day till night was come, which being approached, to bed they went, where Phylerno did not think it his readiest way to give any sudden attempt, but therefore he brake into this discourse following:

"My Brisilla, were it not but that we be found partial in the causes of our friends, but especially where the causes do touch our parents, our judgments be so blinded by affection that we can neither see, nor well confess a manifest truth. But if matters might be considered on, without respect of persons, with indifference and according to the truth and equity of the cause, I durst then put myself in your arbitrement,◊ my Brisilla, and to abide your sentence, whereto I doubt not but you would confess the prejudice I sustain. It is much intolerable and almost impossible for a young maiden to endure, and the rather, if you would measure my condition by your own estate, who being as you see a young maiden like yourself, and should be thus constrained by my friends to the marrying of your father, whom I do confess to be worthy of a better wife than myself. But considering the inequality of our years, I cannot for my life frame myself to love him, and yet I am forced against my will to marry him, and am

prefixed determined.   arbitrement judgment, control.

appointed to be your mother that am more meet to be your companion and playfellow. But that affiance° which I have conceived in your good nature hath made me thus boldly to speak unto you, desiring but to hear your opinion with indifferency whether you think I have good cause to complain or nay; and then peradventure I will say further unto you in a matter that doth concern your own behoof."

Brisilla, hearing this pitiful complaint, very sorrowful in her behalf, said: "Would to God I were as well able to minister relief unto your distress according to your own contentment as I am heartily sorry to consider your grief, and do well perceive the just occasion you have to complain."

"Ah, my Brisilla," said Phylerno, "I am as heartily sorry in your behalf, and peradventure do understand something which yourself do not yet know of which will grieve you very sore. But first, Brisilla, let me ask you this question: do you know my father, or nay?"

"No, sure," quoth Brisilla, "I have no manner of knowledge of him, neither did I know whether you had any father alive or nay, but now by your own report, and as strange as it was to me to hear the words which my father used to me this day when he brought you home, for that I never understood before that he went about a wife."

Phylerno was very glad to hear these news because it served so much the better for his purpose, and thereof said as followeth:

"This tale that I mind to tell you, my Brisilla, will seem more strange than all the rest, and yet assure yourself it is nothing so strange as true, and therefore give ear to that I mind to say. Do you not think it very strange, indeed, that the one of us should be made both mother and daughter to the other, and that our fathers which be now so decrepit and old should be so overhaled° with the fury of their fond and unbridled affections that to serve their own appetites they force not° with what clogs of care they cumber° us that be their loving daughters, but have concluded between themselves a cross marriage°—and so indeed it may well

affiance affinity.   **overhaled** overcome.   **force not** do not care.   **cumber** encumber.   **cross marriage** an exchange of daughters in marriage.

be termed that will fall out so overthwart° to our behoofs,° who being now in our young and tender years. And should both of us be made the darlings of two old men that seek to prefer their own lusts before their children's love, and measure their fiery flames of youth by the dead coals of age, as though they were able with their cold and rare° embracements to delay the forces of the flesh, whose flames doth exceed in these our green and tender years and as much possible for us to continue in liking as flowers are seen to agree with frost? But in plain terms, my Brisilla, and to decipher a very truth, it is contracted between our aged parents that your father, as you see, should first take me to his wife, which wedding being once performed, then my father in like manner should challenge° you, according as it is concluded between them."

"Alas," quoth Brisilla, "these news be strange indeed, and it should seem by your words so fully resolved on that there is no hope of redress to be had in the matter."

"None in the world," quoth Phylerno "but this between ourselves, the one of us to comfort the other."

"A cold comfort," quoth Brisilla, "we shall find in that. But oh pitiless parents that will prefer your own pleasures with your children's pain, your own liking with your children's loathing, your own gain with your children's grief, your own sport with your children's spoil, your own delight with your children's despite. O how much more happy had it been that we had never been born."

"Alas my Brisilla," quoth Phylerno, "torment not yourself with such extreme anguish, for if that would have served for redress, the matter had been remedied, and that long sithence. But I would to God, my Brisilla, that I were a man for your only sake, and having so good leisure as thus being together by ourselves, we would so handle the matter that our fathers should seek new wives."

"Alas," quoth Brisilla, "such wishes are but waste, and impossible it is that any such thing should happen."

"Impossible?" quoth Phylerno, "nay surely Brisilla there is nothing impossible but I have known as great matters as these

overthwart contrary.   behoofs interests.   rare infrequent.
challenge lay claim to.

have been wrought. Do we not read that the Goddess Venus transformed an ivory image to a lively and perfect woman at the only request of Pygmalion? Diana likewise converted Acteon to a hart, Narcissus for his pride was turned to a flower, Arachne to a spider, with a great number of others have been transformed, some into beasts, some into fowls, and some into fishes.[4] But amongst the rest of the miracles that have been wrought by the goddess, this story falleth out most meet and fitting to our purpose:

"There was sometime remaining in the country of Phestos a married couple, the husband called by the name of Lictus, the wife Telethusa, who, being with child, was willed by her husband so soon as she should be delivered, if it were not a lad, that the child should presently be slain. His wife being delivered at her appointed time brought forth a girl, and yet notwithstanding her husband's commandment, brought up the child making her husband believe it was a boy, and called it by the name of Iphis, and thus as it grew in years, was appareled like a lad, and being after by his father assured to a wife called by the name of Ianthe, a young maiden and the daughter of one Telest dwelling in Dictis. Telethusa, the mother of Iphis, fearing her deceit would be known, deferred of the marriage day so long as she could, sometimes feigning tokens of ill success, sometimes feigning sickness, sometimes one thing, sometimes another. But when all her shifts were driven to an end and the marriage day at hand, Telethusa coming to the temple of the goddess Isis, with her hair scattered about her ears, where before the altar of Isis she made her humble supplications and the gentle goddess having compassion transformed Iphis to a man.[5]

"Lo here, Brisilla, as great a matter brought to pass as any we have spoke of yet, and if the gods be of as great force and might in these days as ever they were in times past, we want but the same zeal and faith to demand it, and sure in my opinion if either of us made our request to the gods, who commonly be still assistant to help distressed wights, they would never refuse to grant our reasonable requests, and I will adventure on it myself, and that without any further circumstance."

And herewithal he seemed with many piteous sighs, throwing up his hands to the heavens, to mumble forth many words in secret as though he had been in some great contemplation, and suddenly without any manner of stirring either of hand or foot did lie still as it had been a thing immovable, whereat Brisilla began for to muse and in the end spake to him, but Phylerno made no manner of answer but seemed as though he had been in some trance, wherewith Brisilla began to call and with her arm to shake him, and Phylerno giving a piteous sigh, as though he had been awaked suddenly out of some dream, said:

"O blessed Goddess Venus, I yield thee humble thanks that hast not despised to grant my request." And then speaking to Brisilla, he said: "And now, my Brisilla be of good comfort, for the same goddess which has not disdained to hear my supplication will likewise be assistant to further our farther pretenses, as hereafter at our better leisure we shall consider of. In the meantime receive thy loving friend that today was appointed to be thy father's wife, but now consecrated by the goddess to be thy loving husband, and herewithal embracing Brisilla in his arms, she perceived indeed that Emelia was perfectly metamorphosed, which contented her very well, thinking herself a thrice happy woman to light of such a bedfellow. Thus both of them, the one pleased very well with the other, they passed the time till Phylotus had prepared and made all things ready for his marriage day. And then calling his friends and neighbors about him, to the church they go together, where Alberto gave Phylerno his son in the stead of his daughter Emelia to Phylotus for his wife. When all the rest of the marriage rites that are to be done in the church were performed, they passed forth the day with feasting and great mirth until it was night, when the company began to break up and everyone to take his leave, and Phylotus with his bride° were brought into their chamber, where Phylerno desiring the company to avoid,° and making fast the door he said to Phylotus:

"There resteth yet a matter to be decided between you and me, and seeing we be here together by ourselves, and that time and place doth fall out so fit, I hold it for the best that it be presently determined."

"What is the matter then?" quoth Phylotus. "Speak boldly

bride (A. birde, an amusing error, corrected in later editions).
avoid leave.

my Emelia, and if there be anything that hangs in dispense° between us, I trust it shall easily be brought to a good agreement."

"I pray God it may," quoth Phylerno, "and to reveal the matter in brief and short circumstance, it is this: you are now my
husband and I your lawful wife, and for that I do know the difference in our years, yourself being so old and I very young, it must
needs fall out there will be as great diversity in our conditions, for
age is commonly given to be froward, testy and overthwart, youth
again to be frolic, pleasant, and merry, and so likewise in all our
other conditions we shall be found so contrary and disagreeing
that it will be impossible for us to like the one of the other's
doings, for when I shall seem to follow my own humor, then it
will fall out to your discontentment, and you again to follow that
diet which your age doth constrain will be most loathsome unto
me. Then you being my husband will think to command me and
I must be obedient to your will, but I being your wife will think
scorn° to be controlled and will dispose of myself according to my
own liking. And then what brawls and brabbles° will fall out, it
were too much to be rehearsed, and thus we shall live neither of
us both in quiet nor neither of us both contented, and therefore
for the avoiding of these inconveniences, I have devised this way,
that being thus together by ourselves, we will try by the ears
which of us shall be master and have authority to command. If
the victory happen on your side, I am contented forever after to
frame myself to your ordinance and will as it shall please you
to appoint; if otherwise the conquest happen on my side, I will
triumph like a victor and will look to bear such a sway that I
will not be contraried in anything whatsoever it shall please me
to command."

Phylotus, knowing not what to make of these speeches, and
thinking the time very long till he had taken his first fruits, said:
"Come, my Emelia, let us go to bed, where I doubt not but we
shall so well agree that these matters will easily be taken up,
without any controversy such as you have spoken of."

"Never while I live," quoth Phylerno, "before I know whereon
to resolve, and whether you shall rest at my commandment, or I
at yours."

dispense remains to be settled, disposed of.   scorn resent.
brabbles noisy quarrels.

"Why," quoth Phylotus, "do you speak in earnest, or would you look to command me that am your husband to whom you ought to use all duty and obedience?"

"Then were I in good case," quoth Phylerno, "that should be tied to use duty or obedience to a man of your years, that would not let to prescribe° us rules of your own dotage to be observed in stead of domestical discipline."

"Then I perceive," quoth Phylotus, "we shall have something ado with you hereafter that will use me with these terms the very first night. But see you make no more to do, but come on your ways to bed."

"And I perceive," quoth Phylerno, "the longer that I bear with you, the more fool I shall find you," and with this, up with his fist and gave Phylotus a sure wherret° on the ear. Phylotus in a great rage flies again to Phylerno; there was between them souse for souse,° and bore for bore, that it was hard to judge who should have the victory. In the end Phylerno gets Phylotus fast by the grey beard, and by plain force pulls him down on the floor and so bepommels him about the face that he was like to have been strangled with his own blood which gushed out of his nose and mouth. Wherefore holding up his hands he cried:

"Oh Emelia, I yield myself vanquished and overcome. For God's sake hold thy hands and I will never more contend with thee during life."

Phylerno staying himself said, "Art thou contented then to yield me the conquest, and hereafter this according as thou hast said, never more to strive with me, never to gainsay anything whatsoever it shall please me to command?"

"Never while I live," quoth Phylotus, "and therefore for God's sake let me arise, and challenge° to yourself what superiority you please, which for me shall never be denied so long as I shall live."

"Well," quoth Phylerno, "but before I will let you arise, I will have you promise to confirm these conditions, which follow on this manner. First, that at my pleasure I may go abroad with my friends to make merry so often as I list, whither I list, and with whom I list. And neither at my going forth to be demanded

not let to prescribe not refrain from prescribing.   **wherret** blow, slap.   **souse for souse** blow for blow.   **challenge** claim.

whither I will, nor at my return to be asked where I have been. I will further have you condescend to this, that forasmuch as I have learned that it is not only very untoothsome,° but likewise very unwholesome for youth and age to lie soaking together in one bed, I will therefore make no bedfellow of you but at my own pleasure, and in manner as followeth, that is to say, this first year I shall be contented to bestow one night in a month to do you pleasure if I may see you worthy of it or that you be able to deserve it; but the first year being once expired, four times a year may very well suffice, that is, one night a quarter as it shall please myself to appoint. There be many other matters which I shall not now stand to repeat, but these before rehearsed be the principal things wherein I will not be controlled, but mean to follow mine own liking. How say you, Phylotus, can you be contented to frame yourself herein to follow my direction?"

"Alas," quoth Phylotus, "I see no other shift, I must perforce endeavor myself patiently to abide whatsoever it shall please you to command, and do yield myself as recreant° and overcome, and wholly do put myself in your favor and mercy, ready to receive whatsoever it shall please you to award unto me."

Phylerno, letting him now arise, said, "Prepare yourself then to go to your bed, and anon at mine own leisure, I will come unto you, and depart again at mine own pleasure when I shall see time."

Phylotus, comforting himself with these sweet speeches did think it yet to be some part of amends that she had promised to come and visit him, went quietly to his bed, there to abide the good hour till Emelia did come.

Phylerno, having prepared one of these mercenary women whereof there are great store in Rome to be had, conveyed her to the bed of Phylotus, giving her instructions how to use herself, and went himself to his best beloved Brisilla, whom he had made privy to his whole device, and in this manner it was agreed between them, they had thought to have dieted Phylotus once a month with some cast stuff° such as they could hire best cheap in the town.

untoothsome unpalatable.   recreant coward; vanquished.
cast stuff cast off woman.

But it fell out that Flanius, whom you have heard before had stolen away Emelia, being at the church the same day that Phylotus was married and saw Alberto give his daughter Emelia to Phylotus for his wife, had thought assuredly that himself had been deceived by some devil or spirit that had taken upon him the likeness of Emelia. And therefore hasting himself home with all possible speed, came to Emelia, and blessing himself he said:

"I charge thee in the name of the living God that thou tell me what thou art, and that thou presently depart to the place from whence thou camest. And I conjure thee in the name of the Holy Trinity, by our Blessed Lady the Virgin Mary, by angels and archangels, patriarchs and prophets, by the apostles and four evangelists, Matthew, Mark, Luke and John, by all the holy martyrs and confessors, and the rest of the rabble° and blessed rout of heaven, that thou quietly depart without any manner of prejudice, either to man, women, or child, either to any manner of beast that is upon the face of the earth, the fowls of the air, or the fishes in the sea, and without any manner of tempest, storm, whirlwind, thunder or lightning, and that thou take no manner of shape that may seem either terrible or fearful unto me."[6]

Emelia, hearing these words, marveling much what they meant, with a smiling countenance came towards Flanius saying, "why how now, Signore Flanius, what, do you think me to be some devil or any hag of hell that you fall to conjuring and blessing of yourself?"

"I charge thee come no nearer," quoth Flanius, "stand back, for these enticements can no longer abuse me when I have seen with mine own eyes my beloved Emelia married in the church and given by Alberto her father to Phylotus for his wife. What should I think of thee but to be some fiend, or sent unto me by some enchantment or witchcraft, and therefore I will no longer neither of thy company, neither of thy conference."

And herewithal taking Emelia by the shoulders he thrust her forth of doors, and shutting the door after her he got him to his chamber where he fell to his prayers, thinking assuredly that Emelia had been some spirit.[7]

rabble crowd, mob, usually disorderly and of low degree, here used ironically.

But Emelia, after she had a three or four days made what means° she could to Flanius and saw it was in vain, was driven to go to her father, before whom falling upon her knees she desired him most humbly to forgive her.

Alberto, taking her up in his arms, said that he knew nothing wherein she had offended him, but her suit might easily be granted.

"Dear father," quoth Emilia, "I know I have offended and so far as my fact deserveth rather to be punished than pitied, the remembrance whereof is so loathsome unto me that I fear to call you by the name of father, having showed myself so unworthy a daughter."

These words she pronounced with such sorrow that the tears streamed down her cheeks, wherewith Alberto, moved with natural affection, said:

"Dear child, I know no such offence that ought to be so grievously taken, but speak boldly; whatsoever it be, I freely forgive it."

Emelia, very much comforted with these speeches, began to discourse how she first disguised herself in page's apparel, and what grief it was to her conscience that she should so far stray from the duty and obedience of a child, and to become a fugitive in a man's apparel. But her father not suffering her further to proceed in her tale, said:

"Alas, dear daughter, if this be the matter, it is long ago sith I have both forgiven and forgotten these causes and therefore let these things never trouble you. But tell me now how do you like of your bedfellow, how agree you with him, or he with you, I would be glad to know."

"Alas, dear father," quoth Emelia "that is the matter that I come to you; he hath turned me away and will no longer take me for his wife, and what is the cause that hath moved him unto it, I protest before God I know not for my life."

"Hath he turned thee away?" quoth Alberto. "Myself will quickly find a remedy for that matter," and without any more to do, would not tarry so much as while his gown was a-brushing, but out of doors he goes towards Phylotus, whom by chance he

means here complaints, protestations.

met withal in the streets, and in a great chafe begins to challenge him for abusing of his daughter, swearing that he would make all Rome to speak of his abuse if he meant to proceed in that he had begun.

Phylotus, wondering to see the man in such an agony, began to wish that he had never seen him nor his daughter neither, and, that "if anybody had cause to complain, it is I," quoth Phylotus, "that have married such a wife that is more like to a devil than a woman, and I perceive now is maintained in her mischief by you that are her father, who ought rather to rebuke her than to take her part and to encourage her in her lewdness."

"What encouragement is this you speak of?" quoth Alberto. "I know not what you mean by these words. But assure yourself of this, that as I will not maintain my child in anything that is evil, so I will not see her take a manifest wrong."

"Do you think this to be good then," quoth Phylotus, "that your daughter should bestow such handsel° on her husband as she has already bestowed upon me?" And then pointing to his face, he said: "See here your daughter's handiwork; how think you, is this requisite to be borne withal, that you stand so much in your daughter's defence?"

Alberto, seeing his face all swollen and the skin scratched off, perceived that Phylotus was at a fray and had good cause to complain. And wondering that his daughter was so suddenly become a shrew, said: "If this be my daughter's handiwork I can neither bear withal, neither will I allow it in her so to use her husband. And therefore I pray you, let me hear the matter debated between you, and I doubt not but to take such order as there shall no more any such rule happen between you."

"I am contented you shall debate what you will," quoth Phylotus, "so it may be done with quietness, but I will never more contend with her for the mastery while I live; she hath already won it, I am contented she shall wear it."

"I pray you then," quoth Alberto "that you will go home to your own house, and I will go fetch my daughter and will come

handsel usually a groom's gift to the bride, but also from the bride to the groom; also generally a good luck gift presented at the beginning of an enterprise, here, ironically, a beating on the wedding night.

unto you straightway, and I doubt not but to take such order between you as shall fall out to both your likings."

"I pray God you may," quoth Phylotus, "and I will go home and there will stay your coming."

Alberto likewise went to his own house, and calling Emelia, said never a word unto her, but willed her to follow him, and coming to the house of Phylotus, whom he found within tarrying his coming. And by fortune at the same instant, Phylerno and Brisilla both were gone into the town to buy certain things that they had need of. And Alberto, beginning first to rebuke his daughter that would seem in such manner to abuse her husband, and with a long discourse he preached unto her with what duty and obedience women ought to use their husbands withal, and not to take upon them like masters to correct and chastise them. Emelia denied not only the fact, but also she denied Phylotus to be her husband.

"What have we here to do?" quoth her father. "How canst thou, shameless quean,◇ deny that which within these four days was performed in the face of the whole world?"

Emelia, standing stiff to her tackling,◇ would in no wise confess that ever she was married.

Then her father began to charge her with her own words which he had used to her before, how she had disguised herself in man's apparel and so stole away forth of doors, the which Emelia never denied. "Why then," quoth her father, "did not I meet thee in the streets, and at the request of thy husband here present did forgive thee thy fault, to whom I then delivered thee, and with whom thou hast ever sithence remained?"

Emelia made flat denial of any of all these sayings to be true. Alberto, in a great fury, would have taken witness of Phylotus in the matter, but Phylotus fearing another banquet at night when he should go to bed, durst not in any wise seem to contrary Emelia. In the end, after great fending and proving had in the matter, Emelia from point to point discoursed to her father how she first fell into the liking of Flanius, and by his practice so

shameless quean a brazen or ill-behaved woman.   **standing stiff to her tackling** rigging; holding stoutly to her position.

conveyed herself away in his page's apparel and had with him remained all this while, till now he had turned her away.

Her father would in nowise allow this tale to be true, but Flanius, being well known to be a courteous gentleman, Alberto devised to send for him, who presently at his gentle entreaty came to the house of Phylotus, where he spared not to confess a truth that only for the love that he bare to Emelia he devised to steal her away, and there came one unto him in the likeness of Emelia, and in the same apparel that he had provided for her, whom he very charily° kept until such time as he saw with his own eyes that Emelia was married in the church to Phylotus. And then assuring himself that he had been deceived by some spirit that had taken upon [him] the similitude and likeness of Emelia, he presently came home and turned her away, and what was become of her he could never learn.

Alberto, much amazed to hear this tale, said: "Signore Flanius, do you know your Emelia again if you see her?" And then pointing to his daughter he said: "Is not this the same Emelia that you speak of, which you have turned away?"

"I know not," quoth Flanius, "the one from the other, but sure I saw with mine eyes two Emelias so like that the one of them of force must needs be the devil."

"There is no question," quoth Phylotus, "but that is my wife; if there be ever a devil of them both, I know it is she. Out alas that ever I was born, what shall I now do? I know I have married a devil."

And by fortune as Alberto chanced to look forth of the window, he espied Phylerno and Brisilla in the street coming homewards. "Peace," quoth Alberto, "here cometh the other Emelia; we shall now try which of them is the devil, I think, before we depart."

By this Phylerno was come in, and hearing how matters had been debated and were fallen out, again knowing Alberto to be his father, and what prejudice his sister Emelia was like to sustain if she should be forsaken by her friend and lover Flanius, confessed the whole matter, humbly desiring his father to forgive him.

When he had awhile wondered at the circumstance, and the truth of everything laid open and come to light, all parties were

charily cautiously.

well pleased and contented, saving Phylotus, for when he remembered first the loss of his love, Emelia, then how Phylerno had beaten him, what a bedfellow he had provided him while he himself went and lay with his daughter, these things put all together made him in such a chafe° that he was like to run out of his wits. But when he had raged a good while and saw how little help it did prevail° him, he was contented in the end that his daughter Brisilla should marry with Phylerno, and Flanius very joyfully received again his Emelia—when he knew she was no devil—and both the marriages consummated in one day. And so I pray God give them joy and every old dotard so good success as had Phylotus.

chafe state of anger, agitation.   **prevail** avail.

The Conclusion

Gentle Reader, now thou hast perused these histories to the end,
I doubt not but thou wilt deem of them as they worthily deserve
and think such vanities more fitter to be presented on a stage—as
some of them have been—than to be published in print—as till
now they have never been.[1] But to excuse myself of the folly that
here might be imputed unto me, that myself being the first that
have put them to the print, should likewise be the first that should
condemn them as vain, for mine own excuse herein I answer, that
in the writing of them I have used the same manner that many
of our young gentlemen useth nowadays in the wearing of their
apparel, which is rather to follow a fashion that is new—be it
never so foolish—than to be tied to a more decent custom that
is clean out of use. Sometimes wearing their hair frizzled so long
that makes them look like a water spaniel, sometimes so short
like a new shorn sheep; their beards sometimes cut round like
a Philip's dollar, sometimes square like the King's Head in Fish
Street;[2] sometimes so near the skin that a man might judge by
his face the gentleman had had very pilled° luck. Their caps and
hats sometimes so big as will hold more wit than three of them
have in their heads; sometimes so little that it will hold no wit at
all. Their ruffs sometimes so huge as shall hang about their necks
like a cartwheel; sometimes a little falling band that makes them
look like one of the Queen's silk women.[3] Their cloaks sometimes
so long as it shall trip on their heels; sometimes so short as will

pilled close-cropped, threadbare, poor.

not hang over their elbows. Their jerkins◇ sometimes with high
collars buttoned close under their chin, sometimes with no collars
at all about their necks like a wench in a red waistcoat that were
washing of a buck;◇ sometimes with long saucy sleeves that will
be in every dish before his master, sometimes without sleeves
like Scogin's man that used to run of sleeveless◇ errands.⁴ Their
doublets sometime faggot-waisted◇ about the navel, sometimes
cow-bellied◇ below the flanks that the gentleman must undo a
button when he goes to piss.

In their hose so many fashions as I cannot describe, sometimes
garragaskins◇ breeched like a bear, sometimes close to the dock◇
like the devil in a play, wanting but a tail, sometimes round like to
Saint Thomas' onions,⁵ sometimes petite ruffs of two inches long
with a close stocking clean above the nock of his tail, sometimes
disguising themselves after the use of Spain, sometimes after the
Italian manner, and many times they imitate the French fashion
so near that all their hair is ready to fall off their heads.⁶

Now I am sure if any of them were asked why he used such
variety in his apparel, he would answer, because he would follow
the fashion. Let this then suffice likewise for mine excuse, that
myself, seeing trifles of no account to be now best in season, and
such vanities more desired than matters of better purpose, and
the greatest part of our writers still busied with the like, so I have
put forth this book because I would follow the fashion.

And now friendly reader, because I have entered thus far to
speak of fashions, I will conclude with a tale that maketh something for my purpose. I have read it so long ago that I cannot
tell you where—nor the matter is not great though I do not tell
you when.⁷ But in England, as I think, and, as it should seem,
near about London there was sometimes dwelling a gentleman,
though not of very great wealth yet of a very honest life and
of good report amongst his neighbors, whose name was Master

jerkins short coats of leather.   washing of a buck a washing tub
or vat, buck-washing, thus a woman in a red undergarment carrying
out this task.   sleeveless difficult, impossible.   faggot-waisted
drawn in, like a bundle of faggots, narrow.   cow-bellied large and
full like slops.   garragaskins (usually spelled galligaskins), wide
hose or breeches, narrow at the waist, full at the knee.   dock fleshy
part of the tail.

Persinus. This gentleman had a daughter whose name was Mildred, about the age of eighteen years, of a singular beauty, very well trained up by her own mother, who was likewise living and with whom she now remained. It fortuned that a devil of hell called Balthazar, no inferior devil but a master devil, a principal officer and commander in hell—and trust me, if there were ever a devil that was an honest man, Balthazar was he—saving that being now an ancient devil and well spent in years, he began to wax wanton and to dote in the love of Mistress Mildred, but yet not like our greatest part of lovers nowadays that still practice their loves unlawfully, more for lust than for loyalty. But Balthazar, contrariwise, bare his love honestly, lawfully, yea, and in the way of marriage, the which to bring to pass he took such continual care and travail in his mind that he now confessed the fire of hell to be but a trifle in respect of the scorching flames of love. Sometimes conjecturing in his mind what bashfulness is found to be in young damsels in these days, but especially when a man comes to proffer them love, they are so shamefast that with a good will they would never hear of marriage till they were thirty years old at the least, and many of them, if it were not for men, I think could be well contented to lead apes in hell.[8] Otherwhiles he remembered the greedy desire that is generally in parents, who never consent to the marrying of their fair daughters without some great jointure.◊ Now the devil had no lands, and therefore to find the best remedy he could, they say the devil is able to put upon him all manner of shapes. So he took upon him the presence and personage of so gallant a young gentleman as fitted so well the fancy of Mistress Mildred that without any long circumstance she was contented to accept him for her husband, the which being perceived by her father and mother, not minding to contrary their daughter's liking, gave their free consents. There was no more to do but to appoint for their marrying day, the which being once expired, the devil sitting by his best beloved, uttered these words, or such like as followeth:

"My good Mildred, my dear and loving wife, I must confess myself not a little beholding unto you that neither examining my pedigree from whence I came, neither what I am, neither yet how

jointure dowry.

I am able to keep you, would notwithstanding vouchsafe to take me for your husband. I must think your courtesy proceeded of love, and do account myself so much the more beholding to you, and now to give you some trial that you have not made your choice of a rascal or a knave of no reputation, I am contented to give you one demand whatsoever you think best to require of me. And therefore, my dear, ask what you list, your desire shall be satisfied—always provided that hereafter you never trouble me with any further requests."

The young wife, wonderfully well contented with these loving speeches of her courteous husband, desired of him a little pause and respite. And now coming to her mother, to whom she unfolded the whole contents of the premises, sitting them down together to consider of the matter, after a great number of consultations and as many imaginations had between them, in the end they concluded that her request should be for a suit of apparel of a gallant fashion but even then newly come up. And coming to her husband with this demand, they had their wish presently accomplished and this suit of apparel laid by them so well made and fitted as possibly could be desired. Thus all parts° were well pleased, they continued in good liking for the space of one month, at which time another new fashion was then come up, as well in the attiring of their heads as also in the making of the gowns, kirtles° and stomachers.° Mistress Mildred, being now quite out of conceit° for that she had never a gown to put on her back but of a stale cut and the fashion at the least of a month old, who would blame the gentlewoman though she took it very grievously? Alas, her mind was so far out of quiet that her meat almost did her no manner of good. Which sudden alteration being perceived by her husband, he began to entreat her to show him the cause of her conceived grief, the which when she had revealed, the good honest devil her husband said:

"Well, my dear wife, although when I satisfied your last demand my conditions were that you should never trouble me with any further requests, yet once again to recomfort you, ask of me

parts parties, sides in the matter.   kirtles outer skirts or petticoats.   stomachers ornamental coverings worn under the lacings of the bodices.   conceit reason, good humor.

what you will. I will grant your desire, but to cut you of all hope that hereafter this I will never be troubled again with new fashions, assure yourself that this is the last request that ever I mind to grant you."

Mistress Mildred, giving him twenty kisses for his kindness, went again to her mother with these joyful news, and concluding as before, they brought the devil an inventory of new fashions, beginning with caps, cauls,◊ coifs,◊ ruffs, partlets,◊ sleeves, gowns, kirtles, petticoats, and there was no stitch, no cut, no lace, no guard,◊ nor no fashion that was then in use but in this inventory it was to be found. And as before, this bill was no sooner presented, but all things were in readiness so well fitted and fashioned as if the most cunning workmen in England had been at the making. But what should I say? Before another month was expired, there was a new invention, for then came up new fashions in their caps, in their hats, in their cauls, new fashioned shadows, then came up periwigs, frizzling, and curling, then came up doublets, bombasting◊ and bolstering,◊ new fashions in their gowns, kirtles and petticoats, then they began to wear crimson, carnation, green and yellow stockings; to be short, there was such alteration in women's apparel from the top to the toe in a month that Mistress Mildred thought herself now again to be clean out of fashion, the remembrance whereof brought her likewise to be quite out of countenance. But when she remembered how she was prohibited from making any further demands, it did so gall her at the heart that now she began to frown, lump and lower◊ at her husband, which when he perceived, he said unto her:

"Why how now, my good Mildred, I fear me thy head is troubled again with new fashions from whence cometh these sudden fits. What is the matter that breedeth such alteration in thy manners, tell me I pray thee, what is it that doth offend thee?"

The poor gentlewoman, not able to speak one word for weeping, at the last bursting out into these terms: "If," quoth she, "I had made my choice of a husband worthy of myself, I should

cauls netted caps.   coifs a close-fitting cap, covering the back and sides of the head as well.   partlets collars or handkerchiefs. guard an ornamental border or trimming.   bombasting stuffing, padding.   bolstering padding.   lump and lower look sulky, frown and scowl.

never have given him cause thus to wonder at me, nor myself
have had occasion to complain for such a trifle, for that I might
have done as other women do, and have followed every fashion
and every new device without either grudging or restraint of my
desire. I should not then have been enjoined to such a kind of
silence, but I might have made my husband privy to my wants. I
should not then have been kept like Joan of the country in attire
of the old fashion devised a month ago."

While Mistress Mildred was proceeding in these speeches or
such other like, the devil her husband was struck in such a dump°
that, not able any longer to endure her talk, he not only avoided
himself from her presence, but also devised with speed to fly the
country. And coming to Dover, thinking to cross the seas, finding
no shipping ready he altered his course and got him into Scotland, never staying till he came to Edinburgh where the king kept
his court, and now forgetting all humanity which he had learned
before in England he began again afresh to play the devil, and so
possessed the King of Scots himself with such strange and unacquainted passions that by the conjecture of physicians and other
learned men that were then assembled together to judge the king's
diseases, they all concluded that it must needs be some fiend of
Hell that so disturbed their prince,[9] whereupon proclamations
were presently sent forth that whosoever could give him relief
should have a thousand crowns by the year so long as he did live.
The desire of these crowns caused many to attempt the matter,
but the fury of the devil was such that no man could prevail.

Now it fortuned that Persinus, the father of Mistress Mildred,
at this present to be at Edinburgh, who by constraint of some
extremity was now compelled to practice physic wherein he had
some pretty sight,° but therewithal so good success that who
but Persinus the English physician had all the name through the
whole realm of Scotland. The fame of this physician came to the
hearing of the king, who, sending for Persinus, began to debate
with him of the strangeness of his fits, proffering large sums of
money if he could find a remedy, to whom Persinus answered
that it passed far his skill. The king notwithstanding would not
give over, but entreated Persinus to take in hand the cure, which

dump reverie, state of depression.   **pretty sight** understanding.

when he still denied, did think it rather proceeded of stubbornness than for want of experience, wherefore he began to threaten him, swearing that if he would not accomplish his request it should cost him his life.

Persinus, seeing himself so hardly bestead,◇ was contented to try some part of his cunning; and the next day when the king was in his fit, he was brought in to see the manner how it held him, whom the devil perceiving to come in at the door, speaking to Persinus he said in this manner:

"My father Persinus, I am glad I see you here, but what wind hath driven you hither to this place?"

"Why what art thou," quoth Persinus, "that callest me thy father?"

"Marry," quoth the devil, "I am Balthazar that was once married to your daughter, indeed a devil of hell, though you never knew it before, whom your daughter wearied so much with her new fashions as I had rather be in hell, than married to such a wife."

"And art thou then Balthazar?" quoth Persinus. "Why then I pray thee, good son, depart the King of Scots, for he hath threatened me for thy cause to take away my life."

"Marry," quoth Balthazar, "even so I would have it, it were some part of acquittance◇ for your daughter's kindness towards me."

Persinus, seeing the disposition of the devil, thought it not good to deal any further with him at that present, but afterward when the king was come to himself, he requested of him but respite for one month, and against the day that he should then take him in hand again, he devised with the king that all the ordinance in the town might be shot off, all the bells in the town might be rung, and that all the trumpets, drums, and all manner of other instruments might altogether sound about the court and lodging of the king.

These things being accordingly prepared and the day come that was assigned, Persinus being with the king at the beginning of his fit, according as it was appointed the ordinance was shot off, the bells began to ring, musicians played on every side, at which

so hardly bestead   so eagerly pressed.   acquittance   repayment.

sudden noise the devil began to wonder, and calling to Persinus he said:

"Why, how now father, what meaneth all this noise?"

"Why," quoth Persinus, "dost thou not know the meaning? Then I perceive devils do not know all. But because thou must be acquainted with it, I will tell thee aforehand. The last time I talked with thee thou toldest me thou hadst married my daughter, and thy tokens were so true that I am sure thou didst not lie, for which cause knowing where thy biding° is, I have sent for her to the town, and this noise that thou hearest is her welcome to the court."

"And is my wife then come hither to seek me out?" quoth the devil. "Then I shall be sure to be troubled with new fashions; nay, then, farewell Scotland, for I had rather go to Hell," and thus leaving the king he departed his way.

Now to conclude, if a silly woman were able to weary the devil that troubled him with new fashions but once in a month, I think God Himself will be wearied with the outrages of men that are busied with new fangles at the least once in a day; I can no more, but wish that gentlemen leaving such superficial follies would rather endeavor themselves in other exercises that might be much more beneficial to their country and a great deal better to their own reputation, and thus an end.

biding abode.

Textual Notes and Commentary

Notes to the Prefatory Epistles and Poems

1 Riche names here the fashionable dances of the age. Many of them required considerable skill and agility in the execution. They were cultivated primarily at court and imitated in the large country houses. One of the more important contemporary sources on the dance is the long poem entitled "Orchestra" by Sir John Davies, but there is a lack of precise information from the period about actual performance details. The Queen was an excellent dancer and is featured in a famous painting executing a leap while dancing the volta.

2 The half ironic whimsy of "yours in the way of honesty" captured the fancy of contemporaries; the phrase became the object of parody and imitation. Riche signs off by wishing the ladies the fulfilment of all their secret desires, then pronounces his own honesty—which is also to say, chastity. Cranfill (pp. liv–lviii) has traced the line even in letters written by spies of the era. Thomas Nashe called attention to it, as did Gabriel Harvey.

3 In the *Alarm to England* (1578), Riche promises to deal in a subsequent work with a more agreeable and entertaining subject. Because this promise is first mentioned in the *Farewell*, rather than in *Don Simonides*, which was also published in 1581, we might conclude that of the two, the *Farewell* was written first. But Riche clarifies that it was not the *Farewell* that he had in mind as the more entertaining book, but a work on military matters. He may have put this project aside in order to write fiction. His intentions behind the title *Farewell to Military Profession* are literary: a farewell to the writing of military books, insofar as Riche did not leave the military life as a profession.

4 Riche names here some of the principal locations in the Dutch wars, no doubt scenes of action he meant to describe in the projected book mentioned in the preceding note. The names were in the news throughout the early 1570s, and it is not easy to determine which actions Riche himself might have participated in as an eye-witness. We know that Thomas Churchyard relied on Riche's notes on the Dutch campaigns while preparing *A True Discourse Historical of the Succeeding Governors in the Netherlands and the Civil Wars There* (1607). Riche may have been among the 500 soldiers forced to return to England in 1574 when the English under Colonel Chester were driven from their stronghold in Maaslandsluice (Maeslandsluis). Riche gives a close account in the *Alarm* of the siege of Zieriksee in June, 1576, and of Brielle, or Bryel Island. The Gouldsluce or Goudasluice was a key stronghold for preventing the entry of the Spanish cavalry, although Valdez finally succeeded in May, 1574, and slaughtered many of the English. The classic history of the Dutch wars remains *The Rise of the Dutch Republic* by J.L. Motley.

5 Because James Fitzmaurice Fitzgerald was known to have landed in Ireland on July 16, 1579, we must presume the *Farewell* was completed before that time. Fitzmaurice had arrived with his three ships in order to recapture Ireland from the English with the help of the papacy. Riche no doubt had to abandon his writing for some time while performing his duties in the quelling of the rebellion.

6 The proposal was put forward by B.M. Ward in *The Seventeenth Earl of Oxford* (London, 1928), pp. 192ff., that the French fop of the portrait could be no other than Lord Oxford, and that Riche had been encouraged to make the slur by his patron, Sir Christopher Hatton, one of Oxford's political opponents. Oxford had championed the Queen's marriage to the Duc D'Alençon—a match the implications of which horrified many of the English; Hatton had been in the vanguard of the opposition.

7 Riche raised this issue regularly in his satires, in the *Alarm* in 1578, and again in *Opinion Deified* in 1613, and in later books, arguing that the illegal exportation of domestic products such as corn, leather, hides, butter, cheese, bacon, beef, beer, tin, cloth and wool was impoverishing the nation.

8 Here is another touchstone topic for Riche, namely the low level of financial support for the military and its campaigns. For him it was a moral issue that money was spent at home on luxuries while the poor soldiers lived in misery in the defense of their country.

9 Sir Christopher Hatton was the Vice Chamberlain; Riche may have served him as an informer while in Ireland. He dedicated several books to Hatton, undoubtedly as to a patron from whom he expected financial remuneration. Hatton was a liberal patron to as many as two dozen authors during the period (Cranfill, p. 240).

10 Holdenby, built for Sir Christopher, was one of the most remarkable country estates of its age.

11 This was one of the most sumptuous houses then in England that was not directly in royal hands. By 1605, however, James I had managed to procure it, and it was there that Charles I was held just before his execution in 1647.

12 The house was not completed before 1583.

13 Holdenby was noted not only for its many chimneys, but for the fact that they all worked, which meant that there were fires in many rooms for the comfort of guests. Many houses had merely decorative chimneys on the roof—a common architectural affectation of that age.

14 Hatton was also noted for his generous relief of the poor.

15 For signs and portents 1580 had been a banner year: floods in January; an earthquake on April 6; apparitions in Cornwall around May 18; and a comet on Oct. 10 (Cranfill, p. 241). Pamphlets and broadsides that recounted these events and speculated on their meanings were numerous.

16 History could bear Riche out in this appraisal: the previous four centuries had been marked by English armies going north periodically to suppress the Scots. Nevertheless, the assertion could not remain in the edition of 1606, after James VI of Scotland became the King of England.

17 Judith is the heroine of the Old Testament apocryphal book bearing her name. She was a brave widow among the Israelites who made her way, in time of war, to the camp of Nebuchadnezzar and into the tent of Holofernes his general, where she managed to cut off his head and then make her escape with the trophy. Queen Elizabeth is here compared to Judith as a champion of Protestantism who, in fighting the Catholics, made the "ravening wolves" at her doors fear that she would slaughter them—a curious conflation of images.

18 Here Riche uses "writ" for "write," a habit that, as Cranfill points out (p. 243), leads to potential confusion in subsequent passages where he uses "quite" for "quit" and "spitfull" for "spitefull."

19 Riche hints that he was unable to take his "discourses" or stories to London in person, and thus could not supervise the printing of them, or check for errors.

20 The term "forged" has been interpreted in the introduction as meaning parts beaten together into new narrative shapes as by a smith, rather than as meaning either counterfeited or stolen.

21 Riche does not stress the authority or even the credibility of his narratives, though he repeatedly casts them as histories later. They are passed over here as harmless recreations, and he asserts the conventional view that he had never meant them for print, but only for the amusement of close friends.

22 L.B., as discussed in the introduction, is, beyond much doubt, Lodowick Bryskett, fellow sojourner in Ireland, who, knowing Italian, and having translated a long treatise by Giraldi Cinthio, is the perfect candidate for the original translator of these three stories from the *Hecatommithi*.

23 Cranfill (pp. 243–44) has made a considerable effort to identify W.I. Gentleman. He has produced four possible candidates and has confirmed their potential associations with Riche: Captain William Jenkins, a soldier in Ireland; William Jones, a fellow critic of the excesses of the Anglican clergy in Dublin; William Jones, the translator of Lipsius and Nennio; W.I., the author of *The Whipping of the Satyre* (1601).

24 Momus was the god of fault-finding among the ancient Greeks whose task it was to criticize the other Olympian gods. Here he is seen as the leader of the tribe of railers and critics.

25 After considerable research in collaboration with other scholars, Cranfill (pp. 244–45) was able to reconstruct the composite portrait of a Baptist Starre originating in Cambridge who was variously a poet, a constable, an outlaw, and a tax evader in Surrey, a cooper in London, a debtor to Riche's cousin Lea, and a friend to Riche.

26 Zoilus of Amphipolis was a 4th century B.C. critic of Homer whose writings were so severe and pedantic that he was allegedly thrown from the Scironian rocks. A critic subdued and tame can avoid such a fate.

Sappho Duke of Mantona

1 Riche no doubt found the name Sappho in Painter and thought it appropriate for a male character, perhaps, as Cranfill suggests, because of the terminal "o." Likewise, the name Mantona comes from a misprint in Painter's story of "Rhomeo and Julietta" for the city of Mantua, spelled "Mantuona." There is little reason to think that Riche intended by his choice, however, the city of Mantua.

2 Cranfill (p. 246) points out that the names of the major characters, Claudius, Sappho, Aurelianus and Phylene were drawn from
different stories in Painter's *Palace*.

3 Riche here indulges in a euphuistic antithesis that is not entirely
clear. The helm is to war what the plumes appear to be to court,
but the significance of their blowing away is open to interpretation;
the image suggests wavering policy, sudden changes of position,
opportunism in the conducting of one's career.

4 By 1581 rushes were rarely used to cover floors, but the practice was
of sufficiently recent memory that they could still figure metonymi-
cally for the floor of a castle.

5 This is the first of many instances of the word Riche spells "trauaill,"
which means variously travel and travail. Only the context clarifies
his intent.

6 The original reads Duchess of Messilina, but elsewhere Messilina is
her given name, and not her place of origin.

7 Chalking, usually behind a door, was the traditional method whereby
inn keepers recorded what had been consumed and the amounts
owed.

8 The sense of the sentence appears to be that he had carefully
planned his strategy, and that now everything was working out
according to his expectations.

9 As in the case of Mantona, the spelling for Caire has been kept
insofar as there is no textual proof that Riche meant Cairo, although
this was a possible Elizabethan spelling for that city.

10 This appears to be the earliest use of the phrase "hucksters handling" according to the *NED* (Cranfill, p. 251), and means something (or someone) left "in a position in which it is likely to be
roughly used."

11 The description of the duties of a sexton has a particularly English
tone: ringing the bells and setting the clock. Sextons also kept the
church tidy and in repair, and may also have dug the graves in the
churchyard.

12 The reference is to Narcissus who, for refusing love, was made to
stare upon his own image in the water, and who then fell into despair
attempting to embrace it.

13 This is the first of several poems in the *Farewell*, and is the best of
them according to Collier. Riche had talent as a versifier, but was
not an original poet. The six-line stanza rhymed ababcc had been
used by Spenser in *The Shepherdes Calendar*, and Riche used it not
only in *Don Simonides*, but in "An Epitaph upon the Death of Sir
William Drury." Many of Riche's superfluous commas marking the

caesura have been removed because they often divided nouns and verbs, or verbs and their objects—a practice confusing to modern readers.

14 Cranfill (p. 259) notes that all four early editions use the word "desolved," although in Painter, Riche's source, one finds "the effect of hir resolued minde." That reading has been adopted.

15 Cayoe was altered to Caire in the C text. Some doubt remains, however, that the A and B compositors were in error. First, it is a compound departure, involving two letters; second, Riche mentions no Turks in Caire when Sappho sets out for the city.

16 The figuratively ironic phrase "an almond for a parrot" (spelled parrat) was a proverbial formula for rebuking an impertinent or silly remark. Shakespeare uses it in *Troilus and Cressida* V.ii.194–96.

17 All editions agree in their use of the word "guiltless," although the sense of the sentence calls rather for the opposite.

Of Apolonius and Silla

1 The normal spelling is Apollonius, as in Apollonius of Tyre or the name of the philosopher. Riche could have derived the name from either source. Silla's name, no doubt, comes from Cinthio's *Hecatommithi* (I.x), as well as Silvio, the name for her brother.

2 It is curious that Riche should have chosen Pontus, the name of a region on the Black Sea, for the name of a male character. Speculation is free as to how conscious or unconscious he was of the nature of the choice.

3 It is instructive to hear Riche censure himself for the prolixity of his first story, and to hear him promise henceforth to tell his tales as quickly as the matter would allow. This shows either a clear sense of an impatient readership, or a sense of a new narrative form based on conciseness, rapid intrigue, and an uninterrupted movement of events. That was a novel view of fiction in the age of the chivalric romance.

4 Constantinople was lost to the Ottoman Turks under Mohammed II in 1453.

5 It was a common practice to take small birds with bird-lime—a glutinous substance smeared on twigs and bushes. Shakespeare alludes to the practice in a figurative sense in *Henry VI, Pt. III*, V.vi.13–14.

6 Cranfill (p. 269) notes that Silla's lament, not included in Riche's version of the story, actually existed as a "deplorable four-page poem," the complaint of Nicole, in Riche's principal source, Belle-

forest's *Histoires tragiques*. Riche, no doubt, appreciated the degree to which such a long rhetorical set piece would compromise the momentum of his plot. He asserts that with so tender and sympathetic an audience as he knew his to be, such an appeal to pathos would be unnecessary.

7 A compound image that alludes both to the story of Joshua, for whom the sun stood still while he completed his conquest in Gibeon (Joshua 10:12–14), and to Phaethon, son of Helios, who was destroyed by Zeus because he was unable to control the horses of the chariot of the sun while driving them in his father's place across the sky.

8 This is a representative example of the way in which Riche breaks into his narratives to tease and taunt his female readers—here by warning them of the sleights and subtleties of men, who can go so far as to deceive women even regarding the identity of the fathers of their own children.

Of Nicander and Lucilla

1 Alfonso, duke of Ferrara (1476–1534), is remembered today principally for having married Lucrezia Borgia in 1502.

2 This story was originally by Geraldi Cinthio, and because Don Hercules, which is to say Duke Ercole II, was Cinthio's patron, the author ensures that the duke receives favorable if not outright flattering treatment in the story. Ercole II (1508–1559) was the son of Alfonso and Lucrezia.

3 The description of the entry of love through the eyes, which could lead to the polarization of the imagination through the continual presence of the image, and the threat of death due to excessive desire, was understood during the Renaissance in literal and physiological terms. Don Hercules' generosity in releasing the girl from his grasp is the greater insofar as he must combat within himself this urgent and potentially fatal desire.

4 Riche's style is unclear here due to a surfeit of "thats." In "as she that considered," "that" may refer back to "mishap" so that the sentence could be paraphrased: "the contrast between their estates was great, which she considered a great misfortune; and in consideration of this misfortune, she realized that she could not permit herself to love him."

5 In this lament Riche employs only in the first stanza the ababcc pattern he used for Silla's lament, then alters it to abcbdd. Again, caesura commas have been omitted where they divide elements into

patterns not normally separated. Lucilla answers in abcb quatrains in trimeter with third lines in tetrameter.

6 Cressid began her career in English in Chaucer's *Troilus and Criseyde*, in which she betrays her lover Troilus to seek safety in the Greek camp where she meets Diomede. Her name became synonymous with inconstancy.

7 The first and second editions read "this." The reading offered here is adopted from the C text.

8 Cranfill (p. 280) conjectures that "no whit nor more nobly born" is a textual corruption, given that there is nothing resembling it in the original. That is to presume that Riche did not invent the "no whit nor more" formula merely to underscore his point.

9 Here is further evidence of Cinthio's intention to praise his patron, Duke Ercole, by making him the generous princely protagonist of the story.

10 Spelled "dsoe" in the original.

11 One of the by-products of humanist learning was a repertory of stories reduced to illustrative phrases which could then be mentioned, almost compulsively by certain stylists, in order to grace the text, support arguments involving conduct, and thereby add to the copiousness of the style.

Of Fineo and Fiamma

1 The statement concerning the distances between cities does not appear in Giraldi's original and must have been added as a point of explanation either by Bryskett or by Riche, the former being the more likely, given his first-hand knowledge of the region.

2 Piracy had become widespread in the Mediterranean during the period, especially after Tunis had been annexed by the Ottoman Turks in 1575.

3 This information on the sumptuous villas along the shore near Genoa was also added to Cinthio's story, presumably by Bryskett, because he knew the region and wished to make clear the circumstances to an English readership.

4 This passage is not easily deciphered in the A text, the unique copy of the first edition, and could only be reconstructed through a consultation of the B text. Cranfill notes, however, insofar as Collier got it right in his edition of 1846 without benefit of the B text, that much of the deterioration of the A copy must have taken place since that time.

5 That the lovers were to be buried alive rather than burned as in the Italian original is one of the more significant variations in the

translation. There is no way to determine now whether the change was intentional or accidental. See Cranfill, p. 287.

Of Two Brethren and Their Wives

1 The original reads, "it is not less noisome for a man," which almost has possibilities as a kind of reinforcing double negative; but the sense is made clearer for a modern reader by dropping the superfluous "not."

2 Xanthippe, often spelled Xantippe, was the wife of Socrates; she was renowned for her shrewishness, as epitomized by her emptying the slop bucket over his head.

3 Cranfill (p. 290) records that the more common form of the proverb was "what the eye seeth not, the heart rueth not."

4 Later references clarify that Riche intended London as the setting of this story; with the exception of the short tale of Balthazar in the conclusion, this is the only English setting in the collection.

5 Usury then meant lending money at interest, and has since come to mean lending at a rate above that which is permitted by law. The practice was widely condemned in Elizabethan England, as it was generally by the Church, and the forty percent mentioned was a particularly exorbitant rate.

6 Sarah, the wife of Abraham (Genesis 16), gave her Egyptian maid to her husband as a wife because she was unable to bear him children. After Hagar gave birth, however, she became haughty, and Abraham allowed Sarah to banish both her and her son Ishmael. Later, Sarah gave birth, in her old age, to Isaac. The doctor reverses the logic of the story by imputing a fault to Dorothy's husband which he offers to make up to her as her lover; it is a perverse quotation of the Bible as a precedent for seduction.

7 Here, the doctor alters to his purposes the well-known proverb: "it is better to give than to receive."

8 Riche alludes to a complex medical condition known to physicians as *amor hereos* or lovesickness in which the patient, overcome by frustrated erotic desire, suffers from melancholy. There was considerable debate among medieval and Renaissance physicians whether lovers also suffered of an amatory fever. The *topos* persisted during the sixteenth century despite general medical doubt. According to Galen, Avicenna and their followers, the only sovereign cure for love melancholy was coitus with the beloved, or with a substitute. This view served the purposes of Dorothy's suitor. In so presuming, however, the doctor must display, or at least feign, ignorance of a growing corpus of medical treatises during the sixteenth century

that also recommended methodical, surgical and pharmaceutical cures for the disease.

9 Inasmuch as Henry V won the battle of Agincourt in 1415, Riche imagines the story as taking place over a century and a half earlier, and not in contemporary London. Did he think the events too preposterous to be credited to contemporary social life? Riche's reason for establishing this detail remains open to speculation.

10 Riche here plays upon a device found in Nicholas Udall's *Ralph Roister Doister* (1567) and in Thomas Wilson's *The Rule of Reason* (1553): the letter of insult so written that it could be turned to compliment merely through repunctuation. The narrator stretches our suspension of disbelief somewhat in presuming an omniscience sufficient to know just how Dorothy punctuated the letter when she read it to herself.

11 Bridewell was London's prison for women, a place much feared by prostitutes and other women offenders.

12 Cranfill (p. 297) has determined that Riche is here echoing Pettie's *Pygmalion's Friend*, rather than Gascoigne's *Don Bartholmew of Bathe*, which also speaks of "kits of Cressides kind." Greene uses the same formula in *Mamillia* and again in the *Carde of Fancie*. It reappears in Shakespeare's *Henry V*, II.i.80: "the lazar kite of Cressid's kind," speaking of Doll Tearsheet. The transmission of the phrase is indicative of the way in which verbal imaginations fed on former diction, and thus how easily such formulae could become common property and be passed on even in the works of the best authors. The reference is to Criseyde, whose faithlessness to Troilus in Chaucer's great narrative poem created this long-remembered motif.

13 This phrase may have been taken from the Clapham translation of Cornelius Agrippa's *A Treatise of the Nobility and Excellency of Womankind* (1542) (Cranfill, p. 299), indicating a direct or indirect reference to a book that may have served Riche in formulating some of his sentiments concerning women.

14 Cranfill (p. 299) traces this rhetorical device of converting neutral into pejorative connotations to Lyly's *Euphues: The Anatomy of Wit* (1578) which was, in turn, drawn from Barnaby Googe's "Egloga Septima." He finds the same formula used after the *Farewell* in Greene and Deloney, and in Shakespeare's *Much Ado About Nothing*, III.i.59–67. In fact, the device goes back at least as far as Lucretius's *De rerum natura*, IV.1160–69.

15 A long loose coat made of coarse material, usually worn by travellers or members of the working classes.

Of Gonsales and his Virtuous Wife Agatha

1 The protagonist's name was Consalvo in the original. Gonsales perhaps sounded more Spanish to Riche's ear.

2 The *Celestina* of Fernando de Rojas was a tragicomedy written in play form (though not for the stage) first in 16, and then in 21 acts, telling the story of Calisto and Melibea in which Celestina the bawd plays a prominent part. The work was known to the Elizabethans; allusions to it figured in several works of the period, including an interlude by John Rastell written as early as 1530.

3 This lantern had a sliding cover for concealing the light, and was hence associated with stealthiness or dishonest activities.

4 The name Alonso appears here in parentheses. It is either a slip for Gonsales, or is intended for emphasis in naming the person she was addressing. It has been suppressed to avoid confusion.

5 This is the only mention that Gonsales had a family. After lusting after Aselgia and poisoning his wife, the motivation to marry for the sake of his family seems strangely out of character.

6 This line in the story is the most likely to have inspired the title for the play *How a Man May Choose a Good Wife from a Bad*.

Of Aramanthus Born a Leper

1 The island of Crete.

2 These were commonplace names from Greek legend and mythology denoting torment, repetitive labors, grief—persons proverbially known for their trespasses against the gods. The sequence fixed itself in the English imagination, for it is echoed by Gascoigne and several others. Cranfill (p. 320) cites a close parallel in *The Forrest of Fancy* (1579). Prometheus, for stealing the fire of the gods, was fixed to a stone where a bird of prey came daily to pluck out his liver. Tantalus was placed in a stream in hell, yet was unable to drink. Sisyphus, a trickster king in life, in death was forced to roll his stone in Hades. Ixion, for falling in love with Hera (Juno) was endlessly tormented on a turning wheel in the underworld. Tityus, for offending Leto, was bound in hell where two vultures pecked at his liver. Danaus's fifty daughters were married against their wills, and the forty-nine who murdered their husbands were condemned to spend the afterlife attempting to fill jars with holes in the bottoms. The sequence no doubt originates in the *Metamorphoses* of Ovid, probably through the influential translation by Arthur Golding (1567), ll. 553ff.

Of Phylotus and Emelia

1 This combination of cross-loves evokes the story of Antiochus and
   Stratonice. Antiochus was the son of King Seleucus, who fell in love
   with his stepmother. The prince, despairing, became ill for love and
   was detected by the physician Erasistratus because his pulse raced
   each time Stratonice appeared. The doctor saved the prince's life
   by arranging a transfer of Stratonice from father to son. The story
   was preserved in the *Factorum et dictorum memorabilium libri* of
   Valerius Maximus, and was elaborated by Plutarch in the *Life of
   Demetrius* in his *Lives of the Noble Grecians and Romans*. The
   basic story and the medical techniques for diagnosis enjoyed popularity in both fictive and scientific writing. The motif appears in
   numerous short stories and plays, including *The Two Noble Kinsmen* by Shakespeare and Fletcher.

2 It was a commonplace proof of the folly and deceptiveness of love
   that handsome persons could cherish the physically unattractive.
   Jacques Ferrand, the French physician, in his *Of Lovesickness or
   Erotic Melancholy* (1623) attributes the phenomenon to the corruption of the lover's imagination. For critics of the Petrarchan cult,
   the flights of poetic imagery in praise of the lady were attributed
   to phantasms that corrupted the mental faculties.

3 Cranfill (p. 323) points out in a passage from Florio's *First Fruits*
   (1578), sig. D3, that these were the more expensive wines available
   in England, and that hence Emelia is showing her elegant tastes.

4 Riche here lists many of the current examples of transformation
   brought about through strong amorous passion, again, no doubt, using Ovid's *Metamorphoses* for his commonplace book. Pygmalion,
   King of Cyprus, fell in love with a statue (made by himself in
   Ovid's version of the story) which, through his prayers to Venus,
   was brought to life and was given to him in marriage. Acteon, for
   seeing the goddess Artemis (Diana) bathing, was turned to a stag
   and torn to pieces by his own hunting dogs. These are merely examples of Venus's power to alter the forms of life, that is, of her
   powers not only to reward but in this case to punish—if it was indeed Venus and not rather Diana herself who exacted the change.
   Narcissus, for scorning the love of Echo, was compelled by Venus
   to fall in love with himself and to despair in trying to caress his
   own image in the water. Arachne humiliated the gods by weaving
   their love stories into her tapestries. Athena, rather than Venus,
   destroyed her work and turned her to a spider after frustrating her
   attempts to hang herself.

5 The story of Iphis, born a girl but changed to a man by Isis, served Phylerno as a precedent and an argument for the possibility of what he promised to do. It comes from the *Metamorphoses* of Ovid, IX.665ff. The story was repeated by physicians during the Renaissance who were concerned with the question of sex changes. André Dulaurens mentions several contemporary cases in his *Controverses anatomiques* VII. ch. 8 in *Les Oeuvres*, pp. 224r–25r. Examples offered by the physicians were indifferently taken from case studies and from the poets, such as Aulus Gellius, *Attic Nights*, IX. ch. 4.

6 Cranfill (pp. 329–30) offers an abundance of examples of contemporary texts of the rites of exorcism from the *Rituale Romanum* to *The First Prayer Book of King Edward VI*: they demonstrate that Riche was repeating the general hierarchy of beings traditionally invoked for such purposes.

7 This superstitious fear on the part of Flanius would have had far greater credibility in 1581 than now, even though scholars and skeptics doubted the many stories then current concerning lamia, incubi and succubi. Medical philosophers, inquisitioners, theologians and fabulists were variously interested in these wondrous tales of demon lovers, of couplings with silent partners who, when forced to break the spell by speaking, return to their demonic states, or of dead girls returning to their lovers by night.

Conclusion

1 One wonders if Riche is being rhetorical here insofar as little survives today to suggest that any of these stories he rebuilds had been the subject of former plays. This is perhaps merely wishful thinking that they might someday receive dramatized treatment. Of interest too is his sense of the inferior status of the stage, in treating it as a venue more appropriate for such "vanities" than the medium of print. Here we could have wished that Riche had left us a few notes of his own, especially about former plays based on materials employed in his stories.

2 Philip's dollar was the Spanish piece of eight from the reign of Philip II. The portrait of Henry VIII with a square beard must have been featured on the painted sign of The King's Head in New Fish Street.

3 There was a growing taste for silk in Elizabethan England that, because of its costliness, caused many to recommend the cultivation of mulberry bushes in England in order to promote domestic production. Several publications urging sericulture appeared, including Thomas Moffet's *The Silkwormes and their Flies*, London, 1599 (Ed. Victor Houliston, Binghamton, N.Y., 1989). Because this

story is about new fashions, it is appropriate that Riche should mention the falling band, a linen strap fastened to the shirt by pins, or tied in front by strings—an affectation that appeared around 1580.

4 The allusion is to *The Jests of Scogin*. Men on important errands wore sleeves in their caps for safe conduct. Without the sleeve, missions were far more difficult to accomplish, and hence the proverbial phrase "sleeveless errand," which also denoted a silly, trivial, or unimportant task, such as going to market for some minor purchase, or the kinds of jesting errands Scogin performed. See Shakespeare's *Troilus and Cressida*, V.iv.5–9.

5 The onions of St. Thomas were large, round breeches resembling the shape of onions, usually referred to as St. Omer's onions.

6 Riche is alluding to the Elizabethan imitations of continental styles that led to the wide variety of dress visible in the streets of London. That in following the French styles one might also lose one's hair seems to be a reference to syphilis, the menacing new disease that, among its many disagreeable results, produced baldness; the disease was known to the English as the French pox.

7 Speculation is open as to which source Riche employed for his story, whether the Italian original, or more likely Jean Louveau's translation of *Le piacevoli notti* by Straparola, whose version of the story was derived from Machiavelli's *Belphegor*. Riche's refusal to disclose time or place suggests that when he noted the story down for future reference in his notebooks, he simply failed to enter dates and sources.

8 That it is the destiny of old maids to lead apes into hell as a punishment for refusing or for failing to attract a husband was proverbial. The phrase turns up in Shakespeare's *Much Ado About Nothing*, II.i.43–44.

9 The joke at the expense of King James of Scotland would have been appreciated by most of the English before the death of Elizabeth in 1603, especially because James himself had a scholar's interest in witchcraft and demon possession. Circumstances altered when he became James I of England, and took umbrage to any slurs, even the most playful and innocent, that were directed against the Scots. This section had to be reworked for the edition of 1606, quite probably by Riche himself. See the Introduction.